PSYCHOTHERAPY OF THE PSYCHOSES

Psychotherapy of the Psychoses

EDITED BY *Arthur Burton*

BASIC BOOKS, INC.

NEW YORK

PERMISSIONS

The editor and contributors extend grateful thanks to the following publishers and individuals for permission to quote from the indicated materials:

Bulletin of the Menninger Clinic: Karl Menninger *et al.*, "The Unitary Concept of Mental Illness," Vol. 22, 1958.

The University of Chicago Press: Lewis B. Hill, *Psychotherapeutic Intervention in Schizophrenia*, 1955; George H. Mead, *Mind, Self and Society*, 1934.

Hans Huber Publishers: Gisela Pankow, *Dynamische Strukturierung in der Psychose*, 1957.

International Universities Press, Inc.: J. Arlow, "Discussion of Dr. Fromm-Reichmann's Paper," in E. B. Brody and F. C. Redlich (eds.), *Psychotherapy with Schizophrenics*, 1952.

Alfred A. Knopf, Inc.: V. Frankl, *The Doctor and the Soul*, 1955.

Philosophical Library, Inc.: Jean-Paul Sartre, *Existential Psychoanalysis*, 1953.

Psychiatry: Edith Weigert, "Problems of Communication Between Doctor and Patient in Psychotherapy," Vol. 21, pp. 241-248, 1958.

The Psychoanalytic Quarterly: W. L. Pious, "Obsessive Compulsive Symptoms in an Incipient Schizophrenic," Vol. XIX, No. 3, 1950.

Yale University Press: P. Tillich, *The Courage to Be*, 1952.

CONTRIBUTORS

SILVANO ARIETI, M.D., is a faculty member of the William Alanson White Institute and is in private practice in New York City.

DONALD L. BURNHAM, M.D., is Director of Research, Chestnut Lodge Research Institute, Rockville, Maryland, and Teaching Analyst at the Washington Psychoanalytic Institute, Washington, D.C.

ARTHUR BURTON, PH.D., is Chief Clinical Psychologist, Agnews State Hospital, San Jose, California, and a practicing psychotherapist.

IGOR A. CARUSO, PH.D., is Founder and Director of the Vienna Working Circle for Depth-Psychology.

EDMUND FRUEHMANN, M.D., is with the Vienna Working Circle for Depth-Psychology.

DON D. JACKSON, M.D., is Head, Department of Psychiatry, Palo Alto Medical Clinic, California, and Director of the Mental Research Institute of the Palo Alto Medical Research Foundation.

GISELA PANKOW received her M.SC. from the University of Berlin in 1939, her M.D. from the University of Tübingen in 1949, her doctorate of science from the University of Paris in 1953, and her degree as a psychiatrist and neurologist in 1954. She is a practicing psycho-analyst in Paris, and lectures at the Medical Faculty of Bonn.

JOHN WEIR PERRY, M.D., is Assistant Clinical Professor of Psychiatry at the University of California School of Medicine, San Francisco, and a practicing psychoanalyst.

WILLIAM L. PIOUS, M.D., is Associate Clinical Professor, Department of Psychiatry, Yale University, New Haven, Connecticut, and a practicing psychoanalyst.

HAROLD F. SEARLES, M.D., is Senior Psychiatrist, Chestnut Lodge Sanitarium, Rockville, Maryland, and Training Analyst, Washington Psychoanalytic Institute, Washington, D.C.

MARGUERITE A. SECHEHAYE, is a Swiss psychoanalyst who lives in Geneva.

JOHN SHLIEN, PH.D., is Assistant Professor, Counseling Center, University of Chicago, Chicago, Illinois.

HELM STIERLIN, M.D., PH.D., is Staff Psychiatrist, Chestnut Lodge Sanitarium, Rockville, Maryland, and member of the faculty, Washington School of Psychiatry, Washington, D.C.

EDITH WEIGERT, M.D., is a Training Analyst, Washington Psychoanalytic Institute, Washington, D.C., and a practicing psychoanalyst.

OTTO ALLEN WILL, M.D., is Director of Psychotherapy, Chestnut Lodge Sanitarium, Rockville, Maryland; Associate Clinical Professor of Psychiatry, University of Maryland School of Medicine; and a Training Analyst, Washington Psychoanalytic Institute, Washington, D.C.

PREFACE

The excellent Introduction written for this volume by Marguerite Sechehaye has made my prefatory task a simple one. She has brilliantly traced the genetic influences which have made a volume devoted to the psychotherapy of the psychoses possible. It would seem that on this basis we can expect more contributions of this order in the future and, if this work helps provide the impetus, I will have been well satisfied.

It has been my conviction for many years that the boundaries between the neuroses and the psychoses were entirely artificial and of our own making. We have suffered in this regard from the impetus of the founders of psychiatry who, in the immense task before them, could not readily bring order to the psychoses as they did to the neuroses. The psychotics had in a sense to subsidize the neurotics so that we could get on with the business of treatment. Such artificial barriers have removed from us the most existentially insightful and rewarding of patients. Those who have spent long years in therapy with a schizophrenic person will know precisely what I mean here. It was because I genuinely felt that all of psychotherapy had something to learn from the psychotherapy of schizophrenia that I started this book. Now, after reading the fine contributions represented here, I am more than ever confirmed in it.

We have reached the point in our understanding of psychotic patients where we can see them as *persons* and where we can relate to them as such in psychotherapy regardless of what they are called. We refuse any more to be shackled by Kraepelinian diagnosis, and recognize in each patient a humanity and uniqueness which must be touched before growth can occur. These considerations override the abstract and thinking formulations we know as diagnosis.

In the schizophrenic is to be found all of the technical problems we know of in psychotherapy—but more so. Everything has an intensity and dimension which startles the psychotherapist—more is asked of him in "giving" or "receiving" than he is prepared for. But if he can encounter the patient in all of his needs and suffering, then he is rewarded both by personal gratification and by the deepest insights into the recesses of humanity.

More particularly, this volume is a way of bringing to our audience current dynamic conceptions of the psychoses and their psychotherapy. Probably nowhere in the field of psychotherapy do our conceptions change so radically with the experience of few cases as they do in the treatment of the psychoses. It thus seemed timely to collate and summarize the current status of the psychotherapeutic work with psychotics.

In this volume I attempted to sample the wide theoretical points of view extant in such psychotherapy—and so we have the influence of Freud, Jung, Rogers, Adler, Binswanger, Fromm-Reichmann, and others represented in the case presentations. Each provides its own justification and integrity and offers a balance and challenge for the reader. And I have not confined myself to this Continent alone. I have in fact drawn upon psychotherapists in Europe who are distinguished for their contributions to the psychoses and their work falls into its proper niche here.

As before, Don Jackson, M.D., was most helpful in the planning of this work and I am indeed grateful to him. John Shlien, Ph.D., was also a resource person in many ways as was Norman Elrod, Ph.D. My wife, Edith Burton, assisted with the huge task of getting the manuscript out and the many details which this entailed.

ARTHUR BURTON

August 1960

CONTENTS

PSYCHOTHERAPY OF THE PSYCHOSES

Introduction*

Marguerite A. Sechehaye

FOR ONE WHO HAS LIVED through the era of mistrust and doubt about the possibility of creating a psychotherapy for the mentally ill, the appearance of this important work of Dr. Burton's is very reassuring. This volume, whose title reveals the substantial changes which have taken place in recent years in clinical psychiatry, is composed of works by authors of various inclinations from different countries. The eclecticism of the work is still more marked when one knows that the authors are all either psychiatrists, psychoanalysts, or both, and that the theme is not only the psychotherapy of schizophrenia but also of psychoses in general. The extension of psychotherapeutic techniques to patients other than schizophrenics—patients who were believed inaccessible to treatment—shows the amount of progress effected by modern psychiatry and proves the growing interest in this area which was almost untouched ten years ago.

To what do we owe this prodigious evolution of the psychotherapeutic movement which, at first established only with neuroses, has progressively spread to wider and wider groups of endogenous psychoses? Two great currents seem to be at the origin of this diffusion of psychotherapeutic methods: the important observations of child analysts on the one hand, and on the other the findings of researchers who first attempted to find a psychotherapy adapted to the insane. These two currents, at first isolated and restricted within their own areas, influenced each other, little by little, and reciprocally enriched their respective ex-

* Translated from the French by Patricia A. Sherman.

periences. Today it is interesting to see these two great tendencies bisecting each other to form a vast theoretical and technical synthesis of the movement for a psychotherapy of the psychoses.

Under the influence of child psychoanalysis, it has been recognized that repeated early frustrations and persistent maternal deprivation are at the bottom of the future organization of a psychosis. It is easy to understand how important these disturbances in the child's earliest relations with his mother are for the elaboration of the personality when it is realized that she represents the model upon which he will establish his subsequent object relations. An early failure in these relations or a disturbance of the initial *"vécu"* *—with the rigid defenses that such failure entails in a child—constitute a predetermining factor for the psychosis.

As further observations were collected, however, the importance of frustrations and the pathogenic role of the mother were somewhat displaced in favor of the reactions of the child to these frustrations. Thus the present viewpoint of child analysts is more subtle and takes into account the terrain upon which traumas inscribe themselves—that is to say, the original libidinal and intellectual equipment, the more or less great force of needs, and the subject's capacity to tolerate frustrations.

A parallel development has taken place among the psychoanalysts who have tried to treat schizophrenics, the "lunatics" par excellence. Study of the literature shows us that the first researchers, and in particular the school of the *Bürghölzli*, with Bleuler and Jung, were above all fascinated by the manifest content of the psychosis and applied themselves primarily to the interpretation of the rich symbolic material of their patients. But in face of the fact that even the soundest of their Freudian interpretations proved ineffective against the psychotic process, they directed their efforts toward problems which were more especially theoretical. Without giving the history of the psychotherapy of the psychoses, it should be pointed out that in the last fifty years there have been some psychoanalysts in different countries who have interested themselves in the psychoses and have tried varied and often original approaches with their patients. There are landmarks to indicate the stages of the psychotherapeutic movement: the important works of Federn, Sullivan, the Menningers, and finally Fromm-Reichmann and Rosen. With these authors the manifest content of the psychosis loses its priv-

* *Translator's note:* The literal (and, as far as I can tell, the only) translation of this word is "lived." Probably *livingness* would most aptly convey the original sense.

ileged place to yield to the psychodynamic structure of the psychosis and to the basic disturbances sustained by the patient's personality.

On the other hand, we should not forget the importance of the works of the masters of phenomenology and existentialism, such as those of Jaspers, Gruhle, Minkowski, and Binswanger. They laid emphasis upon the *vécu*, the dramatic and profoundly human meaning of the psychosis. They have worked out a veritable ontology of the psychotic fate and have authoritatively described, within their respective frameworks, the primary delirious experiences of the schizophrenic and the existial attitudes that the patients develop to the disintegration of their ego. Each author, each school, thus contributes its stone to the building of a psychodynamic structure of psychosis and to a psychotherapy of mental patients which, it goes without saying, will differ in form and technique in accordance with the theoretical position of the authors.

There is a growing tendency, however, to give the leading role in the formation of the adult's disturbances to the child's earliest experiences with his environment. At first psychoanalysts attributed personality disintegration to complexes and traumas, then they left this oversimplified viewpoint behind and arrived at a more subtle conception of the problem, giving a dominant place to the defense mechanisms which the patient organizes against primary anxiety. For my part, since 1938 I have thought that there are a number of factors at the origin of psychotic troubles, of which actions and counterreactions form the psychopathologic structure. In the first place it seemed that frustrations become pathogenic not only because of the seriousness of their objective character but also as a function of the *type of frustration,* of their *repetition,* and of the *tolerance threshold* of the subject, a threshold which is often very low. Secondly, the immediate circle of the future psychotic is frequently perturbed, inadequate, ambiguous, or frankly bad—the mother is schizoid, cold, "immature," or a "double personality," the father nonexistent, or dominating and castrating. It follows that the child will receive a number of small frustrations which, although unperceived by the family circle, are nonetheless injurious. His essential needs will not be satisfied, or at most satisfied very inadequately. Sometimes, on the contrary, the child will be "stifled" by the bestowal of too much affection while being severely deprived at the level of his ego needs. In either case the child responds to these various deprivations by an intolerable anxiety which necessitates his elaborating a defense system to shelter him from the imposed suffering. His ego is thus troubled at its foundations and will thenceforth remain vulnerable and inadaptable. If the basic stages of the psychoaffective development are badly integrated, the scaffolding of the personality will be thrown off balance.

It is therefore not at all surprising that at adulthood, and often as early as adolescence, the future psychotic collapses in the face of the responsibilities of life and falls into schizophrenic catastrophe or some compensating delusional activity. The psychosis, in this structural and genetic perspective, appears like an existential defeat in the face of demands for new modes of organization to which the fragile ego proves itself incapable of adapting. That is why an insignificant event can sometimes be such a decisive factor in the outbreak of psychosis—it finds some resonance in the psyche of the subject.

As I have shown elsewhere, the schizophrenic undergoes a massive regression to the pregenital stages of development and organizes around himself a wall of rigid defenses which at first appear to be invincible. These defenses stand against the mortal anxiety which invades him when the ego is submerged by the overflowing of the dissociated libidinal and aggressive pulsations and against the anxiety aroused by the exacerbation of unsatisfied needs. These defenses, however, also operate against any assuaging of these same needs, since the mother, who has become a cruel superego, had refused their satisfaction. It is these defenses, coupled with the tremendous feeling of guilt, which actually make up the patient's derangement and determine its impenetrability, driving him into autism and hardening him into dehumanized forms of life. Instinctive-affective regression involves the regression of all perceptual and cognitive psychic activity. From this arise the primitive forms of the patient's thought, his highly symbolic language, his projections, his participation in presymbolic magic—in short, his delusional and phantasmagorical activity.

At present there is unanimous agreement between child analysts and psychotherapists of the psychotic that early frustrations and disturbances in primary relations play a leading role in the formation of the psychotic character. But this unanimity goes even further in revealing that apparently irreversible disturbances disappear if the child or the psychotic experiences a "good object," that is to say, a "good mother." Has not Spitz very convincingly demonstrated that the backwardness and anaclitic depression of hospitalized babies are direct functions of the duration of the separation from the mother? And that, if the mother returns soon enough, a child fallen into total apathy will immediately recover a taste for life?

I have made the same experiment—and since then many psycho-therapists have renewed it with schizophrenics—to discover that, if one can succeed in creating contact with the psychotic by becoming the "good object" for him, there occurs—as with Spitz and his babies—a dynamic transformation of the disintegrated personality: the patient is literally reborn to life, to reality, and to himself. The whole problem with psychotics, then, is one of finding a relationship whose form is suitable for them—a relationship which is often anaclitic and in which the patient feels himself to be understood at the level of his regression. Only then can he receive, in a form which is specific to him, the grati-fication of his essential needs. This object relation, feared and desired at the same time, is lived by the patient in an extraordinarily intense manner; the psychotic, returned to the oral stage, seeks a total fusion with the therapist-mother. It is through this fusion that the schizophrenic is able to have the entirely new and profoundly beneficial experience of seeing for the first time his essential needs in appropriate form. The psychotic, having found love in a form which, because it is the most archaic is also the most intense, recuperates the strength to live and to regain touch with reality. Made secure by the presence of his psycho-therapist and the permanent gift which the psychotherapist makes of his person, the patient goes on from this point to rebuild his ego and fulfill his destiny as a man among other men.

From all that precedes, it can be seen that the understanding of psychotherapists has considerably shifted away from those ideas of force, resistance, action and reaction inherited from the physical sciences, and that their interest now centers upon the important concepts of needs, anxiety, and gratification. Today the analyst is conscious of putting into psychotherapy with schizophrenics not only his knowledge and technical skills but also, and above all, his most devotional qualities. The analyst looks for the man behind the patient, the existential being who suffers and aspires to respond and be responded to.

It seems, indeed, that the general movement of modern psychother-apy marches more and more toward true "humanism," for the insane are no longer considered incomprehensible, unapproachable, "foreign," but are looked upon as human beings who suffer and live out the drama of their psychoses. This understanding of the mentally sick in a human perspective profoundly involves the therapist. Psychotherapy, then, be-comes an extraordinary adventure, an existential wager—that of bring-ing a man out of the world of chaos and madness into the vibrant and ordered world of reality.

This approach to psychotics has also influenced classical psychoanalysis. New and hitherto little-known aspects of neurotics have been revealed. It has been recognized that for them, too, there could exist such severe frustrations that analysis in its orthodox procedure is unable to make amends. The analyst must then depart from his absolute neutrality and from his role of the reflecting mirror to favor the patient with his presence, his availability, and even his person. It is now understood that if certain patients show themselves incapable of benefiting from a classical analysis, it is because they expected from their therapist something other than accurate interpretations—human sympathy and warmth. This wound can heal itself only by a gift from the therapist, by his taking them under his wing and becoming the substitute "good mother."

Another advantage gained from experience of the psychotic structures is that it is possible to take an infinitely more subtle view of clinical psychoanalysis and to distinguish, under a pseudoneurotic structure, borderline cases and cases of "ego distortion." The classical analytic technique is also very poorly tolerated by the latter. Its frustrations only reinforce such patients' defense mechanisms and sometimes even precipitate them into a psychosis that they had previously succeeded in avoiding.

Consequently the psychotherapy of psychotics has enormously enriched the realm of orthodox analysis so that there are no longer two separate clans, the classical psychoanalysts who treat only pure neuroses and the psychotherapists devoted only to the therapy of psychoses. Nowadays the Freudian theories of transference, resistance, introjection, and identification are used as much for psychotics as for neurotics. Of course these theories are applied to the psychotherapy of psychotics by a different procedure which takes into account the psychopathologic structure of the patient and his level of regression. In the same way, the fundamental concepts of need, frustration, and of rewarding attitudes are no longer reserved for the sole benefit of schizophrenics, but are extended to certain particularly serious neuroses. However, as Eissler and Bouvet have so clearly shown, these variations of the analytic technique should always be discriminating, prudent, and transitory. In analysis it is the profound, authentically human attitude of the analyst which counts much more than the symbolic gratifications which must be reserved for the most severe psychotics.

Thus, with the patient as with the therapist, it is the human factor which prevails and, because it is the very nature of man which is involved, it is natural that the present tendency of analytic psychotherapy is to put the accent on the idea of the *object relations* of the patient-therapist couple and on the phenomena of transference and counter-transference. It seems that the more psychotherapeutic techniques reach scientific levels, the greater becomes the value of personal involvement. In this respect the psychotherapeutic movement follows the same evolution as the other modern sciences—the experts seek anxiously in the heart of atomic physics a philosophy of man, without which they can no longer live.

In conclusion, Dr. Burton's volume, in presenting a collection of observations and experiments with the psychotherapy of psychotics, is a vivid demonstration of the prodigious soaring of the modern analytic movement. This predominance of human over mechanical conceptions of madness is a deep source of rejoicing. It testifies to the supremacy of the spirit and of love in this modern world where it sometimes seems the robot with a heart of steel is becoming the master of the universe. It is the most dehumanized of beings who, being alienated from others and from himself and so most estranged from the human condition, has made us recover a new humanism. This is a profound lesson in humility and is of the deepest philosophical significance to the conscience of mankind.

CHAPTER I

Process, Psychotherapy, and Schizophrenia

Otto Allen Will

W HEN IT WAS SUGGESTED that I write about some aspects of my experience as a psychotherapist of schizophrenic people I discovered that I might lose myself (and any audience) in the mass of detail that accumulates during the years of such therapeutic ventures, or that I might so abstract and generalize my observations that the results would not seem relevant to any known human (patient or otherwise) or applicable in a practical sense to life in the consulting room. This chapter is not the place for presentation of great detail or elaboration of theory and will be used by me to outline certain features of human behavior which are in themselves no complete account of schizophrenia or its treatment, but may be useful in furthering some comprehension of both subjects. My primary concern at this time is to formulate greatly condensed but hopefully clear statements about the following:

A concept of the behavior patterns gathered somewhat loosely under the rubric "schizophrenia."

A characteristic of the process which I refer to as "misconceptions and unclarities regarding the identity of the self," as reflected in the formation of the self-concept, interferences to its development, threats to the unstable self in adolescence, efforts directed to its reformulations, and the failure of these—leading to regression, loss of the sense of self, and panic.

Selected integrants of the psychotherapeutic procedure particularly applicable to the schizophrenic process and problems of identity.

Excerpts from work with a patient which may serve to bind the abstract to that which is (supposedly) more concrete.

At the onset it is of importance to me to specify that which I shall *not* attempt to do:

I shall not claim that I "know" just what schizophrenia is, or precisely what its origins are.

I shall not insist that individual psychotherapy, as we now know it, is the only useful therapeutic approach (recognizing its difficulties, expense in money and time, and limitation of facilities).

I shall not deal with group or multiple therapy or with characteristics of the therapeutic social milieu, noting only that each of these approaches, although characterized as psychological, is concerned with the totality of the organism's behavior.[1]

I do not propose that the fragments of therapeutic intervention upon which I shall comment are necessarily examples of "what to do," or of particular skill in human relationships; they are intended as evidence of the interpersonal aspects of the disorder and one form of its treatment.

[1] It is useful to note that the schizophrenic person—who has been described as narcissistic, incapable of developing relationships with other humans, and resistant, if not impervious, to environmental influence—has responded favorably (and otherwise) to varieties of human experience, an observation not in keeping with his alleged invulnerability to others and inability to undergo change. In some hospital settings the patient "deteriorates," which is to say that he develops remarkably low morale in situations likely to diminish quickly the hopefulness in any one of us. Faced by lack of understanding compounded by his own difficulties in communication, and by general condemnation as "hopeless," "insane," and inexplicably "different," he understandably withdraws. In some group therapy situations he betters, and even after long hospitalization he may abandon "chronicity" upon the finding of a friend, once again accepting the threat of loss that accompanies the daring to love. He may do well (or otherwise) with therapists of different theoretical convictions and contrasting personalities. In all instances he does respond to some extent. I do not think that a patient "stands still" in a situation; he betters or worsens, grows or regresses, but is not uninfluenced. In the often obscure and poorly differentiated self of his patient each advocate of theory or therapeutic technique may discover that which he requires or wishes—"proof" of hope or hopelessness and a vision of both acceptable and forbidden aspects of himself.

There is as yet no technique which in itself is curative. Despite the usefulness of theory and technique each patient is essentially unique, as is each therapist, and the results gained with one therapist will differ from those with another; the "failure" or "success" of a patient with one therapist would not be exactly duplicated by his work with another. A psychiatric technique becomes therapeutic only through its expression by a human agent in an interpersonal situation.

In speaking as a therapist I am not identified adequately by the terms *psychiatrist* and *psychoanalyst*, as we so entitled are not cast from a single mold, but differ in our life experiences and retain much of our individual views despite shared aspects of our training. The therapeutic process is furthered through the recognition of two aspects of living: (1) the common qualities of men (including patients)—those patterns of behavior whereby past experience can be extended to a greater comprehension of the present, predictions made and foresight developed, and technical operations refined, tested, and demonstrated for use by others; and (2) the unique qualities of men, contributing to the elusive and ever altering complexity of the interpersonal field and resisting control by any mechanistic, reductionistic theory, or any therapy designed to "discover all" about human motivation.

The social field in which I play the role of therapist is influenced by my personality[2] and by my views of myself, my fellows, and my profession. Because certain of these notions are relevant to a comprehension of my attitude regarding patients and therapy, and influence (as well as being influenced by) my clinical work, I shall summarize them at this point, recognizing that some distortion may occur through their necessary condensation.

I do not think of people as "schizophrenics" (or as "diabetics" or "tuberculars," for that matter). I suggest that the human is to some extent the ruler of his own destiny and is able to make certain choices (unconscious or otherwise) about the course of his living, once he is enabled to accept his identity. The individual need not lose his identity to a "sickness," and my use of the appellation "a schizophrenic" may indicate that I concur with such identity loss and declare either my greater

---

[2] By personality I refer to those major patterns of behavior which can be observed as recurrently characteristic of an individual participant in interpersonal situations. Such patterns tend to persist, and reflect experiences in earlier interpersonal fields. Other patterns, less obvious, perhaps dissociated, and infrequently revealed, also mark the personality, which is to say that I do not expect to have any profound acquaintance with "all" of what constitutes myself or anyone else, but to a considerable degree must operate in response to observations of the somewhat apparent.

I consider man's behavior, characterized as "mental illness" or otherwise, to be very largely a reflection of previous (and to some extent current) interpersonal experiences (modified in some instances by severe organic defect and physiological malfunction). The influence of the anticipated future on current behavior must also be included in the evaluation of a personality at any particular moment.

interest in disorder than person or my fear of the person in my turning to the more impersonal concept of disease.

I am not content currently with thinking of schizophrenia as a disease entity. As a physician (and a member of the American culture—in the general meaning of that term) I have grown accustomed to think in terms of dichotomies—of person and object, inner and outer, body and mind (or soul), biological and cultural, organic and emotional, good and evil, past and present, present and future—and emphasize boundaries and distinctions without recognition on occasion of the possible artificialities of separation, and of the intermingling of one concept with others. I may think of a disease which *infects* or *invades* a person, who thereupon sickens and manifests *signs, symptoms,* and evidences pathological alterations, justifying the giving of a treatment with the hope that the illness will be driven from him, leaving him *well*—to the pleasure of his friends and the regret of his foes. Such concepts regarding a barrier between person and environment have demonstrable utility, but may limit our comprehension of schizophrenic behavior. The undue emphasis on such a dichotomy can lead to man's becoming the object—being depersonalized and losing his identity—and even becoming an object to himself in states of alienation and "detachment from the world."

I think of schizophrenia as being a dynamic process rather than a clearly circumscribed entity. Each "case" has an existence of his own, views the world in his own way, and must be dealt with somewhat uniquely for his own greater realization.[3]

The schizophrenic person with whom I am concerned at the moment is (as well as I can determine) adequately equipped to carry out his functions as a human, if provided with suitable opportunities for development and learning. Studies of possible hereditary-constitutional defects and of physiological disorders are of considerable interest and merit our respectful attention, but have not as yet demonstrated any essential weakness that "explains" such an ill-defined reaction as the schizophrenic. The idea that some people may be more vulnerable to stress than others seems evident, but the study of schizophrenia requires a more particular definition of stress and vulnerability, and at present I must work without undue dependence upon that concept. Should I

---

[3] This is not to say that patients do not display common properties concerning which predictions can be made, or that clinical knowledge cannot be applied (with modifications) to a variety of circumstances.

strongly "believe" in such a conception it is likely that I would seek its support when faced by some stressful necessity in therapy, and in that preoccupation overlook even more than I do the insights to be gained from participant observation in the interpersonal field.

Whatever "defects" or "weaknesses" there may be, it is my impression that the person who eventually displays the schizophrenic reaction has been subjected early in his life to interpersonal experiences that would be destructive to any of us, and that he may benefit from participation in social events directed toward less fearful and more open exchanges with his fellows. I am supported in this view by the responsiveness—often guarded and slow—of the patient to corrective learning experience provided in a therapeutic situation marked by acceptance and some clarity of definition of its characteristics and limits.

I do not think of the schizophrenic reaction as a "disorder of the mind," or of mind itself as an entity, a substance, or a thing located in the brain. In such a statement I am not suggesting that human behavior is somehow unrelated to the central nervous system, to an organic substrate, or to physiological phenomena. I do suggest that mind may be thought of as a function of the interpersonal field—of the behavior of the organism in its entirety—and cannot be studied apart from the events in which the organism participates. In this sense mind is the expression of the functioning of the organism—a reflection of the symbolic representation of social experience. In brief, mind cannot be separated from action, which for the human is largely interpersonal, molded by his culture, and symbolic in nature.

Man is unique in this world (as far as I know) in his ability to use and his dependence upon symbols, as shown most clearly in his elaboration of language. The symbol, created by man, enables him to communicate with his kind and transmit his experience to future generations and may at times seem to have an existence of its own strikingly detached from the events which it originally represented. That is, the symbol which "stands for" some feature of behavior in turn serves to mold behavior.

This concept has therapeutic implications in that the behavior (verbal and otherwise) of patient and therapist in their field of interaction is symbolic, and to some extent the therapeutic task is concerned with the determination of the significances of symbols and their often obscure referents. The activity of the therapist will be to some extent an expression (frequently unclear) of his beliefs, personality, and theories and will be responsive to other movements in the field, no matter how impersonal, objective, and noninfluential he may seek to be. In other words, as we seek knowledge about our patient, the very act of seeking and knowing has symbolic import and becomes a factor in determining that which is known.

I do not speak of schizophrenia as an affliction of some *part* of the mind, which is in itself a process and exhibits a totality of operation, reflective of symbols of past and present experience with their projection into the future. Although we may speak of a structure of mental processes in an effort to delineate subtleties of behavior, we are not then required to think of such constructs as existing apart from one another.

Man is a cultural animal. By culture I refer to that which is man-made—implements, customs, beliefs, laws, concepts of social groups, artistic expressions, language, and so on—the apparatus he has created to deal with the problems with which he is faced. The culture has an existence apart from that of any individual, and in a sense molds man as it is molded by him, and extends beyond his life to influence (and be influenced by) coming generations.

There is a cultural as well as a biological heritage, whereby the human develops concepts of himself, of others, of his world, and of values that are not readily altered by later life experience. Such concepts seem so "natural" to us that we often are not aware that anything exists that could be altered, and if awareness does develop, the possibility of change is felt more often as a threat to virtue than as an opportunity for growth. Man's fundamental view of himself and his universe is determined largely by the language which he learns and the environment in which he learns it. The symbol, depicting his culture, assumes a reality of its own, being treated as if it were a tangible entity, the discrepancies between its current meaning and the symbolized event going unnoted, or being subject to rationalization, and thus escaping possibly useful modification.

I am not picturing man as being in inevitable and hopeless conflict with the culture which has been created to meet his needs. Through his culture man becomes human, but in it he may discover unfortunate limitations to his further growth. In such case undue reverence for the sanctity of that which he has created may be his most serious weakness. Put in another way, man may destroy himself if he fears excessively change in himself and his culture, and if he fails to see that in a sense he may control his destiny by daring to evaluate and modify the culture of which he is a part, and which is a part of him.

The family organization is a reflection, but not an exact replica, of the larger culture within which it exists. Life in the modern United States is marked by an astoundingly rapid growth of population, increasing industrialization, urbanization, centralization of industrial control, and individual mobility (both geographically and on the social and economic scale). The kinship system is more diffuse than in some times past; that is, the usual family no longer includes grandparents, aunts, uncles, and cousins in the immediate living situation, and these relatives usually do not exert direct or immediate control over the lives of children other than their own. In other words, the "nuclear" family—parents and children—is the common unit in the United States, with the result that there may be an intensified need of parents for children (and vice versa) and a somewhat unusual concentration in parental hands of the function of cultural transmission.

Each family is an expression of the local culture (the small town in New Mexico, the eastern seaboard metropolis, for example) as well as certain general characteristics of the United States and western European tradition. Modern society is so complex that its intricacies cannot be grasped by any of us, but certain fundamental aspects of it must be learned quickly by the young human for his growth and survival. It is the task of the family—primarily the parents (or their substitutes)—to introduce the child to his culture, to interpet it to him, and to provide him with language, ways of behaving, and other tools useful in coping with the social scene.

The first two or three years of the child's life are spent for the most part within his family. There he develops his primary attitudes toward people and begins to learn how to deal with and interpret his culture. His parents teach him what to expect of others and how to respond to them; what he may and may not learn, what values to adopt, what to believe, how to view the world in which he lives, and how to judge that in which he will live. But even in the same communities families are not alike, each having its own somewhat private culture within which may be concealed extraordinary distortions of the larger society. In such situations the child may gain warped views of himself and his surroundings that may grossly handicap him in his later dealings with people and interfere with his ability to learn and to participate in growth-promoting experiences. Unless such restrictive attitudes are identified and corrected the child's development may become increasingly deviant and he may accumulate such defects of experience and learning that his personality is finally known as disordered, maladjusted, or "mentally ill."

There is some usefulness in considering the family to be a social field in which the structure of the organization is dependent upon the interaction of the constituent members, alteration in the role or major patterns of behavior of one participant requiring accommodating adjustments on the part of the others in order to maintain the dynamic equilibrium. In some instances the family field may be remarkably resistant to change, acting to deter the growth or separation of any of its members and opposing the intrusion of ideas which are unfamiliar and may seem threatening to its integrity. Such fear of change is marked in families which privately maintain ways of belief and living that may be destructive and isolating to their members, but are highly valued by them for personal necessities seldom revealed or even clearly recognized. In this kind of family the patient and his illness may play a role of such importance that changes in the patient—such as his hospitalization, his betterment, his increased independence and proposed separation from home—may be resisted or accompanied by the development or exposure of emotional disorder, physical illness, or even death in the case of some other relative.

I cannot enlarge on these concepts here, but I hold them to be of considerable importance in the treatment of the schizophrenic person. The patient has some sense of his involvement in the family field, recognizing (although he might not formulate it thus) that the behavior which we call sick is not only an expression of that field but also a necessary component of it, and that changes in himself cannot be attained without field alteration. The patient may seem to resist change not only because his role in the group is valuable to him but also because he fears that his growth will be destructive to others upon whom he has grown dependent. In brief, he has come to believe that personal growth and self-determination are dangerous—to himself, to those close to him, and, in the therapeutic situation, to his therapist; he is caught in a conflict between the need to grow and to exist as a person in his own right and the fear that to do so will be fatal to someone.

The task of the therapist is to recognize the complexity and intensity of such involvements and to provide assistance to other members of the field so that growth of one may be accompanied by growth of others. In some instances the therapist may meet with his patient and certain relatives for discussion of such problems, arrange such meetings with some colleague, or suggest individual or group therapy for particular members of the family. We have much to learn about family dynamics, but I am now of the opinion that the patient cannot be treated satisfactorily as an isolate apart from his family. The patient and his disorder are an integral part of the family organization and, to a lesser extent, of the larger culture.

The human is characterized by the lack of a clearly defined organization of instincts and by a prolonged period of dependence. As a result he is remarkably responsive to environmental influences and has an extended time in which he must learn how to live with his fellows in his culture. His growth is concerned with the expression and refinement of his inherent capacities, the organization of experience into a dependable and enduring concept of himself, and the development of roles suitable to the society in which he lives and, to some extent, meaningful and satisfactory to himself.

The infant discovers and forms something of his own identity, begins to recognize others as distinct from him, organizes rough concepts of time and space, acquires the rudiments of language, and learns to need, accept, and respond to tenderness effectively. The child improves his use of language, distinguishes fantasy from what is defined for him as reality, and begins to learn from teachers outside of his family. The juvenile develops group skills (cooperation, compromise, and competition), adopts the social stereotypes, and corrects certain of his views of his family and himself. In preadolescence the growing need for intimacy finds fulfillment in friendship, communication about personal beliefs is increased, and various autistic and private ideas may be expressed with the alteration of unfortunate misconceptions. In adolescence the needs for intimacy and lustful satisfaction may be met in a common object, heterosexual interests are patterned, and self-identity is increased. At this time the young person must consider himself as separating from the family; he must do something about a career, marriage, sexuality, and the further establishment of his own system of values. In brief, it is required that he recognize himself as a person, in some ways unique and separate, and at the same time bound through the remainder of his life to his culture and to his fellows. Throughout these early years the human has become remarkably responsive to the views that others hold of him (shown in both his conformity and rebellion) and has developed so strong and persistent a need for relatedness to his kind that unless it is met in some way he will not survive.

The course of development so briefly sketched may be interfered with by a variety of factors. Unless there is a satisfactory matching of growth potential with experiential opportunity, development will not occur in the manner suggested above. The intrusion of excessive or prolonged anxiety, a disjunctive force in interpersonal experience, may so complicate human relationships that they will be experienced as more destructive than profitable, and behavioral distortions will appear in the effort to reduce anxiety and maintain some semblance of the needed contact with others.

Schizophrenia

From the point of view of this presentation schizophrenia is thought of as a reaction and a process. By *reaction* I suggest that the behavior observed has been developed in response to stimuli of an interpersonal nature and may be further comprehended by attending to the reciprocal quality of the action in the social field. *Process* refers to a progression, marked by more or less clearly identifiable steps from one point to another. There is a time in a person's life when he is not anxious (in the usual meaning of the word), not fully human (in the sense of acculturation and the development of personal abilities), and not schizophrenic; this is sometime early in infancy. There is another time (for some of us) when the person is extraordinarily anxious, has failed to gain useful experience in certain important areas of development, and is clinically schizophrenic; this time is more commonly in late adolescence[4] (or later if problems of self-identification can be deferred somehow). I am not speaking of earlier outcomes of disastrous early life experience, such as marasmus, autism, and childhood schizophrenia, although I am inclined to think that their roots are to be found in the social structure in which the disorders appear.

We are concerned with those events which occur between the assumed "health" of infancy and the "sickness" of later years, as well as with the often all too inadequate ways which we have devised for dealing with the disorder once it has unmistakably appeared. I am saying that what we call schizophrenia is the more obvious manifestation of a process inaugurated early in the life of the individual, reflective of gross difficulties in the originating culture (family or its substitute), and uncorrected to a sufficient extent by later life experiences. Although many instances may be cited of "sudden onset" with no evidence of preceding disturbance, my contact with a number of such subjects indicates that interpersonal difficulties have been present long before clinical illness was detected, and had been concealed within the family and community—sometimes deliberately (from shame or fear of public

---

[4] Adolescence refers to phenomena which are both chronological and social; hopefully these are synchronized, otherwise problems of adolescence may be dealt with in "adult" life.

exposure of family peculiarities) or because of lack of recognition (the pathological fitting so precisely into the social system that what "is" seems "natural," and any change would be looked upon as disturbance). I think that studies of family life will continue to enlighten us about the stresses which may form the basis of the schizophrenic reaction, and I suggest that the observer in social research will find it necessary to be to some extent a participant in the social field of his concern.

Although I cannot specify "causes" of schizophrenia, or even define it with satisfactory precision, I do work with a certain conception of the disorder, which is currently somewhat as follows: The schizophrenic process has its origins in early life with the exposure of the infant to intense, recurrent, or protracted anxiety in his contacts with the mothering person. Such experience begins prior to the infant's acquisition of a clear concept of himself or others, of language skills, or of the interpersonal techniques (such as rationalization) for reducing anxiety. In those early months the infant's anxiety may be dealt with by his withdrawal into a sort of somnolent detachment, by the beginnings of sublimation, and by dissociation, whereby important but troublesome, anxiety-laden aspects of the relationship are not readily sensed and come to exist (to use an inadequate locution) "outside" of the self. The relationship with the parent is required for survival and there begin to develop in the infant and child ways of behavior which enable him to maintain a needed relationship with a minimum of anxiety. The child's life is complicated further by the probability that the anxiety of the mothering one is in part an expression of a troubled family, and that the culture of the family is deviant from the general culture and will indoctrinate the child with unrealistic and distorted ideas regarding his society.[5] Often the family, which normally functions to develop the child's dependence and eventually to encourage his independence, needs the child excessively, resists his growth, and interferes with his self-determination.

The child who has his early environmental experiences as described above will be chronically anxious, fearful of his fellows, unable to communicate freely with others, constantly on guard to keep painful matters from awareness, handicapped in learning, increasingly isolated, and unsure about his own identity. Unless this course of events is corrected by fortunate circumstances, the youth's thinking retains its autistic quality,

---

[5] It is interesting to observe that many so-called delusions, although expressed in poetic or psychotic terms, are accurate symbolic representations of early family relationships as viewed by the patient in his childhood, and are not to be dismissed casually as "false beliefs."

dissociation is not relieved, and skills that should be acquired in the various development eras go by default or are not sufficiently refined to become fully serviceable, the learning defects in one era compounding the difficulties of learning in the next.

As the requirements for greater self-identification become more pressing and no longer avoidable the young person must declare himself in some way. The time comes when he must resolve his growing need for intimacy, recognize and take action about his sexuality, plan a career, consider marriage (even if only to reject it), recognize himself as distinct from his family, and dare to stand forth as a person with a somewhat clearly formulated philosophy regarding himself and his universe. All of these moves require not only self-declaration but also some degree of intimacy and collaboration with others. For the young person, separation (independence) is felt as a threat to himself and the family group, intimacy implies anxiety, and self-determination may only reveal a dreaded emptiness and a lack of self. The alternative to action is isolation, which is intolerable, the need for intimacy having grown along with the dread of the anxiety which has come to be associated with it. In the struggle concerned with the attempts to resolve the fear of unrelatedness and anxiety, complicated by learning lacks and ineptness in simple verbal communication, the entire organism is involved, as is shown by the appearance of physical symptoms, the emergence of dissociated symbols of experience in the dream and hallucination, and the display of increasingly complex and less satisfying behavior leading to feelings of personal disorganization and, in many instances, panic—the culmination of overwhelming anxiety, a sensing of the prospect of unrelatedness, and failure in the attempts to find a durable and rewarding identity or concept of the self.

After such a crisis, experience may be reorganized through further dissociation, in which case the precarious pretense of good health is maintained only through unremitting alertness to any event that might possibly disturb the dissociated system; the price paid for such caution is considerable restriction of developmental potential, but the payment is made, as no one who has known severe anxiety is enthusiastic about its return. In some instances disorder may be followed by a greater semblance to health, such gains coming, I think, from fortunate social contacts which have increased the patient's self-esteem and his hopefulness about others; the provision of such opportunities is a fundamental (although not easy to attain) attribute of any hospital or other therapeutic situation.

The acutely disturbed schizophrenic person finds that much that is in his awareness is no longer familiar to him; his thinking is disordered by the presence of vague, poorly organized symbols of previous anxiety-fraught interpersonal relationships. The referents and meaning of these symbols are unclear and cannot be communicated to others.[6] As communication fails isolation increases, and the sufferer finds himself caught in a nightmare, driven by a feeling of urgency to make sense of the incomprehensibles with which he is involved. He seeks a simple formula to make all clear, and if he is unfortunate he may elaborate the paranoid solution with its grandiosity, apportioning of blame, and chronic reformulation of the past and present to refine and protect a "system" that will reduce anxiety. The cost of such a caricaturing of human living is high—for the patient and anyone with any vestige of interest in him. When the ties of human relatedness are poorly developed and fragile, despair may enter the scene and the hebephrenic change ensues, in which case life is maintained, but formal relationships are abandoned along with hope, and the organism becomes its own object and the referent for poorly organized symbols of interpersonal affairs. Here anxiety may be held in check through the maintenance of disorganization, but let no one think that this is a state of "peaceful vegetation," or that any other of these clinical syndromes provides contentment. They do not. There are other outcomes of the state of panic, but these are not now our concern. Disorder has advanced a great way when panic appears, and is compounded by the hebephrenic and paranoid developments

---

[6] The theory of dissociation cannot be dealt with here, but the following remarks are relevant to the theory. To a large extent the content of our awareness is composed of somewhat refined referential processes which can be organized, more or less satisfactorily verbalized, and communicated (approximately) to others. Symbols of experience which have been associated with great anxiety, have never been clearly comprehended, or occurred prior to our learning to speak, are not ordinarily in our awareness; when they do appear—as in dreams, fatigue states, periods of prolonged isolation, drug intoxication, and so on—they seem foreign to our knowledge of ourselves, cannot be put into words adequately, and (to use rather peculiar locutions) we "dismiss" them, "put them out of our minds," "stop thinking about them," or "forget" them. The schizophrenic person cannot ignore such symbols; they stay with him, along with more conventional ideas that can be put into speech. The symbols which are now so troublesome represent events which may not have been clearly comprehended (as a frightened child's view of his parents quarreling), or which have been dissociated because of their connection with severe anxiety; some of these events took place when the child's knowledge of language was slight and his concepts of time, space, himself,

which, while not incurable, may require heroic measures (in terms of time, as well as therapeutic devotion and skill) for their resolution.

I could wish that the young person en route to the schizophrenic revelation might have the opportunity of forming a relationship with someone not repelled by his anxiety, hesitancy, hostility, and autism. I should recommend psychotherapy for such a person prior to his experience of extreme withdrawal and panic, but in doing this I should recognize that he might reject or see no need for the proffered help, and that in most instances no one recognizes or admits the need until it is manifest to everyone except, possibly, the closest relatives.

This has been a long and perhaps obvious commentary preliminary to remarks more precisely concerned with psychotherapy. I have attempted to outline something of the basis for my thinking about the schizophrenic process, recognizing that such formulations (as well as others more private or even unknown to me) influence my behavior as a therapist. The psychotherapy may also be looked upon as a process, and as a social field in which therapist and patient participate, refine and report their observations, and display the results of influential events in their past as well as present. This process is above all a human relationship in which the skill and understanding of the therapist is used to help the patient gain more understanding of himself and others, and greater facility in the use of more satisfying interpersonal skills.

Let us turn our attention now to excerpts from my experiences as the therapist of a young woman who was my patient for a number of years.

ONSET OF THE DISORDER

The following abbreviated account has been compiled from hospital records, reports of relatives, and hundreds of interviews with the pa-

---

others, and cause and effect were in an experiential mode strikingly different from that of the adult. Events which were attended by great anxiety, were not understood well, or occurred in a different mode of experience cannot be transmitted easily to others. The child does not view the world as does the usual adult, nor does the poet. The psychotic person is not a child, and is not always a poet, but he seems at times like both, and we who listen to him feel frustrated as we recognize how bound we are by our conventional, adult frame of reference. Although we may not always understand what our patient says and does, we should recognize the possibility that he is puzzled and frightened by becoming aware of concepts (often fragmentary and disorganized) from different eras of his living, and that he feels a great urgency to get rid of these or to organize them so that they make sense and can be communicated to others. Until he can arrange his thoughts more conventionally he will feel crazy, which he does not find amusing.

tient,[7] the data being accommodated, of necessity, to my own biased point of view.

Miss X was the oldest of two children, and was "always" known as bright, affectionate, and "good." In her first college year she lived at home, and one night surprised her parents by entering their room unexpectedly, awakening them, accusing them of wishing to harm her, and striking her mother. When she was asked to explain herself she shouted that she had been aroused from sleep by her father's voice telling her that she was no good, and that she believed that her mother wished to kill her by poisoning her food and that she had spread derogatory stories about her in the community. Her parents denied this, asked where she had gotten such wild ideas, and suggested that she pull herself together and behave in her more usual fashion. The girl's response was another violent attack on the mother, complicated by the father's efforts at conciliation and control, and ending with the daughter running from the house to that of a neighbor, where she arrived weeping, disarrayed, frightened, and markedly confused. She locked herself in the neighbor's bathroom, swallowed several barbiturate capsules, broke the window (cutting her arms superficially), and finally subsided on the floor in the corner, mute and stuporous. She was taken to a hospital. Her mild drug intoxication and wounds were treated, and she remained there withdrawn and silent for five days during which time she seemingly paid no attention to anyone and was fed by tube. On the fifth day she became disturbed, attacked her nurse, screamed, broke furniture, attempted to run out of the room, and acted as if she were terrified. Upon being restrained she fought briefly, but again became mute and withdrawn, lying on her back on her bed, or curled up on the floor beneath it. Two days later she was transferred to a psychiatric hospital, diagnosed as dementia praecox (schizophrenia), catatonic type.

Miss X remained in the mental hospital for eighteen months, during which time she was treated with insulin (sixty-five comas) and electroshock (fifty convulsions). For weeks at a time she was mute and unresponsive, her withdrawal being interrupted by transient episodes of assaultiveness and destructiveness. She showed some improvement during the shock therapy, for several seven-to-ten-day periods dressing conventionally, eating, talking somewhat guardedly, and preferring to stay by herself rather than to join in group activities. When questioned about her difficulties she became tense, said that there was nothing wrong

[7] A number of these interviews were recorded for study by the therapist, or by patient and therapist together.

with her, and asked to be discharged from the hospital. She would say nothing about the events that preceded hospitalization and refused to visit with her parents. The quiet periods were soon followed by disturbance, and shock treatment was discontinued after the first year. During the last six months in the hospital Miss X spent the greater portion of each day in a single room because of her assaultiveness and her apparent fear of others. She would wear no clothing other than an old dressing gown, resisted bathing, frequently burned herself with cigarettes, and was apparently hallucinating. Through these months the approaches of staff members were repeatedly rebuffed, and toward the end of her stay there was very little optimism about the prospects of her betterment. Miss X became increasingly isolated, and any ideas that she had about being unapproachable and hopeless were confirmed and matched by those of the personnel. It was in a state of discouragement, low morale, withdrawal, bitter resentment, and a feeling of personal destructiveness that this woman of twenty came to the hospital where we first met.

In starting work with a patient it is useful to speculate how the disorder began. When did Miss X become schizophrenic? Was it the moment of wakening from a dream to hear the hallucinatory voice of her father saying that she was no good? Or was it later when panic had given way to muteness and stupor? Her relatives said the beginnings were not earlier, because the home was a pleasant one; their oldest daughter was, despite her shyness, doing well in school, and was thought to be liked by her contemporaries and admired by her elders who appreciated her goodness. As the troubled parents put it: "We can't understand it. There wasn't anything wrong that we could see, and we're sure that she would have told us if she had been worried. She was such a good girl. How could this have happened?"

For a long while I did not learn much more than was contained in the statement "nothing was wrong." With time I pieced together the account which follows in a greatly condensed and outline form. I shall not discuss details of family relationships except to note that prior to the patient's birth her parents were unhappy in their marriage, but decided to stay together "for the sake of the child." During the first six months of the baby's life her mother was profoundly depressed and preoccupied with the fear that she might kill the infant. The girl became the favorite of her father, who found her companionship much more agreeable than that of his wife. Both parents were ambitious for their children, their own self-esteem being dependent to a considerable extent on the accomplishments of their daughters. The home was characterized by a chronic low-grade bickering between the parents, each of whom had private rooms in which they spent much of the evenings alone. The mother's periodic depressions were often so severe that she did not venture outside of the house for months at a time, and the father's nightly preoccupation with obsessional rituals regarding secret scholastic interests about which he only hinted kept him successfully shut away in his room or in the library. The father worked at his profession and was noted for his honesty and forthrightness. He was respected as a "man with his feet on the ground," and one who "knew the value of a dollar." The mother was referred to as "delicate" and there was some public sympathy for her hard work (keeping house) and the sacrifices (unspecified) that she made for her children. In the community the family was thought of as "refined," and Miss X's "upset" came as a "great shock to everyone."

There were certain features of this family which I think contributed to Miss X's difficulties. In outline, these are as follows:

1. To operate effectively a person must be able to formulate something of a model of his environment. In doing this he is enabled to define with some degree of clarity who he is and the roles played by him and his relatives, and to recognize and reconcile discrepancies between his view of the family and the community's opinion of it. Miss X was not clear about her role and those of her parents, since these were shifting and obscure. For example, she was her father's daughter, but he displayed more interest in her than in his wife. When this was noted he retreated in guilty confusion, declaring love for his wife while he isolated himself in his library. Her mother treated her like a child, like a rival for the father's love, and at times (when depressed) like a mother who should be protective and understanding. Miss X thought of her family as the source of security and authority, but also as unhappy, frightening, and unpredictable. People in the community spoke of it as "nice" and a "good home." She could not reconcile these views and thus often thought of herself as ungrateful or crazy.

2. An environment in which the human may flourish should have some clarity and dependability so that its patterns of movement can be observed, information available in it can be organized, generalizations made about it, the important clearly distinguished from the relatively unessential, and suitable inferences drawn. There was little such stability in Miss X's home. Behavior of considerable importance in the determination of action often was covert and not readily available for in-

clusion in organization and prediction. The parental relationship was complicated and partially concealed behind the conventional façade of what "a good home should be." Miss X could not make adequate generalizations about her family, families in general, or about many aspects of community life because of the presence of conflicting data, often obscure, fragmentary, or presented with so much anxiety that appropriate questions about them could not be asked. "We don't talk about such things" was a watchword, but the exact nature of the "things" was never made clear.

3. When adequate structuring or understanding of the early life environment has not been possible the response to unfamiliar situations is often inadequate. Miss X did not understand herself or her family well, and she dreaded new experience as if it were destined to be threatening and unpredictable. This attitude increasingly disadvantaged her as she grew older, but was referred to as her shyness and as an example of "womanliness."

4. Family life was marked by chronic anxiety. This anxiety encouraged dissociation and the development of elaborate defensive techniques such as obsessional preoccupations interfering with accurate observation and evaluation.

5. Miss X did not have dependable models for herself and continued to be remarkably unclear as to who she was.

6. It is useful for the human to have dependable and clear-cut feedback to his behavior. In this family feedback was often variable, obscure, and multiple. For example, Miss X was never quite sure what response to expect when she was "good" or "bad," and she frequently was not clear as to the meaning of the response. At times the verbal statement (such as "You know that I love you, honey") contrasted markedly with tone of voice, muscular tension, and facial expression (which might suggest "I hate you because I need you and can't deal with you and you hate me"). From all this Miss X might think that if she did not "know" that her mother loved her she must be stupid or insane. If she accepted the verbal cues as real, however, she was required to ignore or deny the validity of the nonverbal communication. She did not have enough data to make sense of the social field within which she lived, finding it necessary to overlook or distort portions of it to maintain any degree of peace. In such denying, ignoring, and distorting, she failed not only to gain a coherent view of the field but also to develop a consistent, clear-cut, predictable view of herself.

7. It was noticeable that Miss X was not well known to her parents

in the sense that knowledge of her was readily available to their awareness. They spoke of her as a stereotype of a "typical happy girl," not noticing her growing confusion, fear, and withdrawal. The family relationships were so marked by anxiety that observations of each other were often unclear, and some semblance of family unity was maintained only by gross distortion of events.

8. The "private" worlds of the father's obsessional preoccupations and mother's depressions were never made clear to the child, but she had some awareness of the distress with which they were concerned. No one spoke of these things, and they became great secrets the knowledge of which was taboo. The girl lived as if there were much that she should not know, and as if she should guard a secret the nature of which was unknown to her, at the same time that it was of great importance to her.

9. The relationship of the patient to her sister was distant. The younger girl was more outgoing and openly rebellious; she said that her sister was "odd" and "too good," and that her parents were difficult, to say the least. The parents were seemingly proud of the oldest daughter's scholastic ability. They said that she was "free to be anything," that they did not want to "influence her" and that they wanted nothing of her except that she be "happy." [8] At the same time they expressed regret that she was growing up, spoke of the "loss of our baby," wondered "what will happen to us when she goes away," and suggested that nowhere would she find the love that had been provided for her in the family. In this environment Miss X came to feel that change and growth were dangerous and that gaining her own identity and separating from the family would somehow be destructive to herself and others.

As we review Miss X's living prior to her becoming officially a patient we note that in the various stages of her development she manifested difficulties of adjustment which interfered with the subsequent learning of skills important to her growth and contributed to a deviation of personality not clearly identified as pathological until the obvious disturbance in her late adolescence. As an infant she was good, rather passive, and less troublesome than her sister. As a child she was shy, preferred staying at home to playing with other children, and was sent to a private school where she did well in a small class. She did

---

[8] Such comments suggesting that Miss X was "free to be anything" implied to her that being "anything" was somehow not definable. In this sense Miss X felt no clearly expressed guidance or opposition whereby the growth of self-identity could be fostered.

not enjoy group play, withdrew from competitive activities, and was known as a poor sport. She found compromise and cooperation difficult, working best alone or with adults (such as teachers) who found her to be unusually intelligent, conforming, and eager to please. She frequently manifested a promise of performance that was not realized and an ineptitude seemingly out of keeping with her ability that led people to speak of her as "lacking in self-confidence."

In her early adolescence Miss X confided a little about herself to a girl friend; when this girl moved away from town no one took her place. Miss X did not go out with boys, was lonely, began to gain weight, and thought of herself as unattractive and possibly afflicted by an endocrine disorder. She read a good deal, spent long hours alone at the movies, and fantasied about what she might do if she, or life, were "different." Although she did well in her studies and took some part in school activities, she was becoming increasingly preoccupied and withdrawn, finding that it was easier to imagine social action than to engage in it. She was troubled by sexual feelings, was ashamed of them, attempted to dismiss "bad" thoughts from her mind, and was busy for a time with sublimatory activities in which she devoted much energy to special study projects at school and to church work.

In her third high school year Miss X displayed an increase of obsessional behavior; she was careful of what she did and said, was precise in her arrangements of objects in her room, tried to think "the right way," and was concerned by the "idle thoughts" which "filled her mind" and interfered with her concentrating. Her grades at school declined, which was "explained" as evidence of her being "too conscientious" and "overworked." In her senior year she complained of fatigue, headache, vague chest pains, and was listless, dropping out of all social activities in order to rest. She was preoccupied with ideas of having some "strange disease," and feared that her body was altering so that she would be more bestial than human. She felt that something was the matter, but was unclear about the nature of the trouble. She blamed herself as inadequate and somehow evil, and also began to think of others as being "at fault," saying (mainly to herself) that "no one understands," and that it is "my fate" to be disliked. She made some attempts to tell others about her feelings, but did not express herself clearly. She was assured that she was physically healthy, had a "fine mind," could be popular if she "only tried," and was not properly appreciative of how successful and well liked she "really was." Such responses led Miss X to be more ashamed of the way she felt; her loneli-

ness and fright increased, and she doubted that she could talk with anyone. Nevertheless she graduated from high school and entered a
women's college in her home town. There she felt odd, different, estranged from others, and ill at ease in group discussions and with the
unfamiliar and often offensive (to her) ideas expressed by her associates. She spent much of her time in the library, and late at night
walked the streets alone, puzzled and apprehensive that "something terrible" was going to happen to her. She ate poorly, worried about consti-
pation and strange bodily sensations, and her sleep was marked by un-
recalled dreams which sometimes led her to waken in fright. Depression
increased with withdrawal and she speculated upon suicide. It was at
this time that Miss X woke in fright, felt that she was living in a nightmare, seemed to hear her father saying that she was "no good," and was
"impelled" to "do something" about the confusing and hateful situation in which she found herself.

In this brief account from which many details have been omitted
it is notable that Miss X was struggling with problems of adaptation for
years prior to the hallucinatory experience which led to her hospitalization. In early adolescence she did not find a friend with whom she
could communicate with any semblance of freedom, and misapprehen-
sions of herself and her culture did not undergo significant correction.
She began to despair of finding much satisfaction in contacts with
others and increasingly abandoned action for fantasy from which some
pleasure could be derived without the risk of rebuff. Sublimatory reformulations of experience and obsessional substitutions were helpful
in reducing anxiety and were enough in keeping with conventional
norms to be acceptable and escape labeling as pathological. The satisfactions from such activities were not adequate; social demands for
self-declaration increased, and mounting feelings of anxiety were met
by adjustive processes more openly in conflict with social standards;
there was an increase in the use of evasion, rationalization, transfer of
blame, negativism, hypochondriacal preoccupations, physical symptoms,
and withdrawal. As the feeling of relatedness decreased, she experienced
isolation and panic, in which symbols of earlier life events came into
awareness and she lost a sense of self. She was frightened, puzzled, and
took violent action as if to seek some resolution of great but poorly defined problems. The action revealed her distress and she felt exposed
and crazy, making a suicidal attempt before retiring to a state of muteness and stupor in which all action was for a time renounced. The panic
reflects, as I see it, a marked increase of anxiety, a breakdown of com-

munication with others, and a serious threat to the sense of relatedness.

Preceding the panic, many activities served to reduce anxiety and also to maintain some contact with others. Simpler, goal-directed behavior was increasingly replaced by less direct and more complicated action which yielded decreasing satisfaction and was eventually so distorted as to be unsuited to conventional requirements. Behavior was elaborated in efforts to maintain communication within tolerable limits of anxiety and to meet social requirements of increased intimacy and self-identification. As the person's inadequacy to deal with the tasks of adult living is revealed the long-standing threat of unrelatedness grows more clear, and the conflict between the need for intimacy (with the accompanying anxiety) and the fear of isolation (with the loss of a sense of self) leads (if unresolved) to panic.

In very general terms, therapy with Miss X was concerned with the following: (1) the maintenance of anxiety within tolerable limits; (2) the development of a relationship (with therapist and others) marked by clarity, dependability, predictability, and considerable security; (3) the formation of a relatively clear concept of self understandable to some degree in terms of past events, and in keeping with current observations of oneself and with reflected appraisals of the self; (4) the identification and modification of distortions of the interpersonal fields in which the patient functions; (5) the provision of opportunities for the partial correction of certain experiential and learning deficits; and (6) the alleviation of the necessity for extensive dissociation.

The First Interview

When I first met Miss X she displayed no great enthusiasm for me, psychiatrists in general (or anything psychiatric), having found little in her life so far that reassured her about the benefits of human contacts, professional or otherwise. When I entered her room she was crouched in a corner behind the head of the bed, and drew away as I introduced myself. I spoke quietly, said that I would stay for a while, and seated myself in a chair across the room from her. Miss X kept her back turned to me, and after about ten minutes of silence I said that I knew a little about her previous hospitalization, having read the record, but that I wanted to hear from her what her experiences had been. She suddenly turned toward me, spat on the floor, and told me to get out. I did not leave, but said that I should remain for about an hour, and should return for several such meetings each week on a regular schedule. Miss X then said that she was no good, and that no one could help her. I suggested that there might be a certain extravagance in such statements, and that all I could guarantee was that I should attempt to get some clarity about what had happened to her and what went on between us. For a moment she seemed to be more relaxed, but then became frightened, pointed at her head, and said, "I know what you'll do." "No," I said, "we'll do nothing but meet and talk together. There's no insulin or electric treatment here." [9]

"I don't believe you," was the reply, but her tenseness subsided a little.

Without going into further detail regarding this particular interview, I shall outline certain things which I wish to accomplish in my first meeting with a patient. I do not always realize these goals, but I keep them in mind and try to discover what may lead me to fail in their attainment.

1. I make some simple concise statement regarding what I know about the patient's difficulties.

2. I briefly identify myself, answering directly any questions directed to me, and suggest that since I am a therapist and the patient is supposedly someone with difficulties in living, there is professional reason for our meeting.

3. If possible, I obtain some account from the patient about his life and his concept of his problems.

4. I attempt to act in such a fashion that excessive anxiety is not roused in the patient, and do not "push" at any topic when I observe a marked increase of discomfort.

5. I am not restrictive beyond setting limits to behavior that might be hurtful to the patient, to me, or to others.

6. If there is evident some marked distortion in the patient's perception of the current field, I comment on this and suggest other possibilities of interpretation.

7. I outline my plan for seeing the patient, give him a schedule of my appointments with him, and indicate without undue pressure that I

---

[9] I do not make use of somatic procedures (insulin and electroshock) in the psychotherapy of schizophrenia. The difficulties encountered in treatment are to be dealt with by an investigation of, and an appropriate modification of, movements in the interpersonal field and not by maneuvers which, in my experience, jeopardize rather than improve the therapeutic relationship. Beyond the occasional use of mild sedatives I have not had experience with attempts to modify the course of therapy by chemical means (use of ataractic drugs, for example).

shall continue to see him, and that I shall not be driven away by fear of him or his behavior.

It was my opinion that Miss X would do well in intensive psychotherapy. This view was based on the following observations:

1. Her intelligence was superior and she had demonstrated ability as a student; she was obviously well equipped to deal with abstract symbol operations and their verbalization.

2. Although she had encountered difficulties in her living she had also had successes—as a member of her family, as a student, and as a participant in social activities. Self-esteem is not so fragile if there are some tangible, socially recognized and approved accomplishments in one's life.

3. Miss X had had some experience with a friend in early adolescence. Such a contact with intimacy, imperfect though it may have been, ties one to human relatedness, and is a useful background to the development of a therapeutic relationship.

4. Although Miss X was discouraged she had not yet succumbed to the demoralizing experience of prolonged hospitalization, and clearly hebephrenic or paranoid changes had not occurred.

5. Miss X showed organization of the ego despite her obvious great vulnerability to anxiety, and displayed a reactivity indicating that the despair which she often experienced had not been replaced by the apathy and detachment of chronic withdrawal.[10]

The Therapist

I don't know just what kind of a person is best suited for work with a schizophrenic patient. I have observed that various people with con-

[10] My therapeutic goals will be the same for the chronically ill as for the ambulatory patient, although the degree of their attainment may differ, depending upon the state of the patient's morale, and the behavior patterns which he has developed in the attempted resolution of his difficulties. If I should work with "limited" goals in mind, my attitude would be one that tends to devalue the patient as a "limited" person, in which case I might overlook much of his potential to the disadvantage of the treatment process. As a therapist my goal is to help the patient attain greater realization of himself. As something of a realist I know that we may not go as far as we might wish. If I define limitations too clearly, however, I may limit unnecessarily what can be done. I must also be aware of the limitations of my knowledge, which is to say that I cannot work with a despairing attitude, and that as I persist and learn more, more may be accomplished.

Note also that the factors given for my thinking that Miss X had a favorable prognosis may not be present in some patients who do well in intensive therapy. The real test is found in the patient's reactions with the therapist.

trasting personalities do well as therapists, which leads me to think that the schizophrenic person has considerable ability to form a relationship in which growth is possible providing that the therapist (or other) has patience as well as a fair degree of liking and respect for his fellow man. There are certain qualities which seem to me to be of importance in a therapist.

1. He should be able to participate in, as well as observe, the reciprocal action of the therapeutic field as there will be many times during which he cannot be the detached onlooker.

2. He often will be required to deal with rapidly shifting events, the mode of communication and action altering with little preliminary notice. He must also endure the discouragement and frustration arising during long periods in which no progress is evident and in which he may become the target of hostility and despair, and the participant in painful loneliness.

3. He should have some interest in, and facility with, nonverbal communication.

4. If the therapist has a great need to organize speech and behavior in logical, rational sequences, he will be disturbed by the frequency with which the treatment is marked by the illogical, by time distortions, by seeming inconsistencies, and a quality of the odd. In brief, he must feel some comfort with the primary process.

5. The unduly conventional therapist may find it necessary to "fit" his patient into a conventional mold, not permitting the patient to develop in a different, and possibly more suitable, fashion. Such conventionality may hinder therapy.

6. The therapist should be able to participate in a relationship marked at times by great intensity and structured so that mutual growth can occur, dependence can be experienced and independence fostered, appropriate limits set, and eventual separation made possible.

7. The therapist will experience strong feelings during the work, and must maintain a curiosity about his own behavior and motivations. At times he will find it useful to discuss the course of therapy and his participation in it with a colleague, and on occasion he may seek further clarity about his actions in the therapeutic sessions by talking about them with his patient. By this last I do not mean that I favor burdening the patient with my own reactions, but I do suggest that there may be times when patient and therapist may collaborate in seeking the explanation for a troublesome aspect of behavior exhibited by either of them.

8. Unless the therapist has had some personal experience of the distress of anxiety he may be insensitive to his patient. In any case he will experience at times considerable anxiety in his work, and this he must attempt to understand and endure, without seeking to eliminate it entirely.

9. The relationship with the schizophrenic person (and with many others not so entitled) is marked by recurrent approach and withdrawal. The patient, having developed the need for relationship, responds to its persistent and understanding offer with some acceptance and improved communication. Having experienced much anxiety with humans, he is wary of relationship and tends to withdraw from it, the mounting anxiety disturbing communication. In the moves toward closeness the person finds the needed relatedness and identification with another; in the withdrawal (often marked by negativism) he finds the separateness which favors his feeling of being distinct and self-identified. Such recurrent movements are components of growth and self-realization. They may be thought of as promise and disappointment, and as acceptance and rejection. The therapist must be able to tolerate these characteristics of the field without becoming unduly anxious or feeling rejected himself.

COURSE OF THERAPY

Miss X and I worked in therapy for four and a half years, the first eighteen months of which she lived in the hospital. During the first two years we met five to seven days each week, usually spending an hour together; but on some occasions the session was extended to two hours or longer. I frequently (usually each day) discussed the course of treatment with the nurses and others concerned with the patient's care, and the collaborative nature of this work deserves much greater attention than I am able to devote to it here. Although I had a regular schedule for my meetings with Miss X, I also saw her at unscheduled times at her request, or because she was disturbed, or because I thought that therapy would be advanced by so doing. In the last three years of treatment we met regularly three to four hours weekly.

In the first few months of therapy Miss X was frequently disturbed, and I made an effort to be consistent in my attitudes, to present a clear picture of myself, to avoid making verbal statements that conflicted with my nonverbal operations, and to set clear-cut and firm limits to any destructive behavior. During this period I usually met Miss X in her room because she was too frightened and unpredictably violent to come to my office. I emphasized tangible aspects of the situation available to observation by both of us, avoided "pushing" for information about obviously distressing subjects, and did not attempt to interpret the content of dreams and hallucinations, although I listened to her accounts of these as I did to any other communication—without excessive interest or surprise. One of my goals during this time was to identify a need of the patient, respond to it quickly when possible, help her recognize her own need and express it more clearly, and encourage her to accept the help of others in meeting her needs as well as to discover ways of more effectively meeting them herself.

During the first year Miss X's anxiety subsided somewhat. I was more acceptable to her; we were consistently identified as therapist and patient (although she was frequently anything but in agreement with many of my ideas); hallucinations appeared only at times of intense anxiety; and we were able to meet in my office.

After the reduction of the major disturbance Miss X spoke of me as a therapist, but made many observations about me that I did not attempt to interpret but observed as slowly forming a picture of me not entirely in keeping with the usual view of myself. I was described as some twenty years older than my actual age, harsh, cold, unsympathetic, controlling, and seductive, and she feared that my only concern with her would be to satisfy my own ambitions. With the experience of much anxiety and recurrent outbursts of rage Miss X noted that in her description of me she was telling me about her attitudes toward her father and men in general, and something of life in her home. We were able to discriminate realistic and accurate (sometimes painfully so) observations of me from those that were more exaggerated and to a greater extent influenced by her past.

With increasing clarification of her relationship to her father Miss X seemed more at ease, and for a couple of months she talked with relative freedom about many current and past events, but had very little to say of her mother. The sessions then became marked by increasing anxiety, the source of which we could not at first identify. Miss X became more suspicious of me and her anger increased, with the result that she would suddenly attack me.[11] I was now described as something

---

[11] In some instances the shifts in the field leading to an increase in anxiety and attack were not identified. On one occasion, after holding Miss X's arms and shouting angrily in response to her vituperations, she quieted and said: "I had to do something to break the wall of glass between us. I could see you, but you seemed to have no awareness of me. I couldn't reach you." In such

loathsome, filthy, disgusting, and essentially evil that would destroy the young woman. Any interpretations I made were met with denial, silence, or increases of anxiety, and I realized that I was being dealt with by Miss X in terms of experience that possibly had occurred early in life, had been dissociated, and could not be expressed readily in words. When her anxiety was very intense and her behavior unpredictable she would be admitted to the hospital for periods of one to three or four days. During this time of the recurrent intense anxiety accompanying the coming into awareness of symbols of very troublesome aspects of important interpersonal experiences, we slowly learned something of her relationship with her mother. I personally felt considerable anxiety while we worked on these problems, and was disturbed by the intensity of the patient's emotions, by my own anger and fear aroused in response to them, and by the vagueness and lack of organization that characterized the communication. At times I found myself strongly moved by feelings whose origins I could not at first discover; but later I noted that they were apparently in response to the multitude of nonverbal cues presented by the patient, not clearly observed in my awareness, but nonetheless reacted to by me in an empathic fashion.

With increased comprehension of Miss X's relationship to her mother, anxiety again was reduced. She visited her parents (which she had not wished to do for about two years), and the therapy continued in a more conventional manner. We sat in chairs about six feet apart, and I listened while she attempted to note and express verbally whatever "came to mind." Evidences of psychosis were no longer present and for the last two years we explored her current and past relationships (including the one between us), and she took part in activities which she had previously avoided. Her physical symptoms—fatigue, diarrhea, vomiting—were increased at intervals during the first three years of therapy, but subsided without our attempting to "explain" their possible connection to obscure referents.[12] She took pride in her obviously increasing attractiveness, gained tolerance of competitive situations, began to date with young men, and completed her college studies. We terminated our work together when she was well on the way to gaining increased satisfaction in her living, related to people without ex-

---

instances the loneliness and the need for human, physical contact were clear, and attack was seen not only as an expression of anxiety and anger but also as an effort to decrease isolation.

[12] The patient was referred to an internist for consultation during the exacerbation of physical symptoms.

cessive anxiety, had a reasonably accurate and confirmable view of herself (and of me), and was no longer so fearful of her self-identity.

In this case so briefly presented (and with others in my experience) the initial problem is to establish a working relationship characterized by some durability, a lessening of anxiety, and increasing clarity as to the identity of the participants. When this has been accomplished the various transference or parataxic distortions can be observed and eventually recognized. The more easily identified and less anxiety-ridden relationships are dealt with first—in this instance that of the father. Early life relationships characterized by great obscurity and anxiety can be dealt with adequately later in therapy after a considerable definition of the therapeutic field has been achieved and it has been proven to be dependable and somewhat secure.

An important and common aspect of the therapeutic relationship with the schizophrenic person is his need for and his fear of relatedness, accompanied by the feeling that his attainment of greater self-identity will be destructive to himself or someone close to him. In the therapeutic situation Miss X often expressed the feeling that "something dreadful is going to happen if I do something," but the nature of the "something" was unclear. She then said that she feared that I would die, or that she would kill me, or that somehow I would be destroyed by association with the evil that she felt to be so much a part of her, and she tried to terminate treatment. I persisted in meeting with her, making it clear that I appreciated her apprehension, but did not share it, and should be able to survive any "evil" in the relationship. As the security of our relationship increased Miss X expressed the fear that progress in therapy would be hurtful to someone in her family. Of this she said: "It's as if the price for my getting well is someone else dying." Her parents had been consulting regularly with a psychiatrist and it became clear to Miss X that I was not going to resist or suffer from changes in her, and that her parents were increasingly able to tolerate her growth. She then observed that she feared her own development and was anxious at her further self-identification, clinging, as it were, to the old ways of living, and mourning for the fading distortions of interpersonal relationships. Throughout the years of treatment we dealt repeatedly and in varying contexts with Miss X's need for relatedness, the anxiety aroused in her by relationship, and her fear of what seemed to be an alternative—isolation, loneliness, and self-destruction. In the work the anxiety of relationship was reduced, and she slowly learned that relatedness and self-identity are not incompatible—that there can be no true closeness to another unless there is also distance and the maintenance of a sense of self. All of her problems were not resolved and she would continue to be subject to anxiety; but she now knew a fair amount about herself in relationship to her past, her family, and her culture, and she was more free than she had been to let herself be known to others and to grow in the process.

The Dream

In the third year of our work Miss X told of a dream. I quote it here: because it describes some aspects of the developing therapeutic process as it existed after considerable understanding had been gained of her relationship with her father and mother. The comments about the dream were made by Miss X, and I shall not add any interpretation.

> I was walking along a road with my mother, and it seemed all right to be with her. That's strange. Anyway, we came to a sign that said "Don't walk here," but we went ahead anyhow, and I felt afraid. Then some policemen came and arrested us—for walking against the sign—and we didn't have any excuses. They took us to a sort of cave and left us there. The cave was dark, but I could see in it. There was a huge man there—a giant. Then I saw that mother was a snake—a real long one—but she was my mother also. And this is a strange thing—I was a kangaroo. Mother and I were afraid of the giant, but he was afraid of us too. It was a peculiar situation. Then I noted a little pygmy man watching all of us. The giant took a pair of scissors and tried to cut the snake, but the pygmy held the scissors and wouldn't let him cut it. Then the giant tried to stab the kangaroo with a big needle, but the pygmy stopped him again. Then the snake slid out of a window in the cave, and the kangaroo followed, and as the kangaroo pushed through the window I got squeezed out from inside it and was left in the cave. The giant wanted to touch me and look at me, but I held my coat tight around me and I tried to kid him and stall him even though I was afraid; but he persisted, and I wanted him close to me even though I said no.
>
> Then in walked a family of important people. I didn't know them. They were mourning someone dead. The giant seemed embarrassed, and he was quiet, as if in respect for the mourning. And then I saw that I didn't want him to ignore me and I asked him to come to bed with me and have intercourse. He said no, but I took off my clothes. The giant sat on the bed but he didn't have intercourse with me; he smiled at me, and I wasn't afraid. But I felt sort of futile, and then I woke up.

Of this dream Miss X said the following:

That was such a clear dream; it seemed complete. I felt frightened at times, but I got to feel safer as it went along. The giant was frightening, but actually his behavior was quite human. I knew this but found it hard to accept. The fact that I could see that the giant wasn't so terrible, and that he was afraid also, made it possible for the dream to continue; otherwise it might have been a nightmare and I would have had to wake up. The giant could have been any man that mother and I know; I guess he really was you [the therapist]. As long as mother was there in the form of a snake I couldn't see the benign part of the giant, but when the snake left I wasn't so afraid. Then the kangaroo left and I was just myself and began to feel that I could handle things. The dark cave, the giant, the snake, and the kangaroo—all seemed familiar and yet strange and odd. Even though it was pretty dark I could see all right. I think that the cave and the animals—the monsters—were like some of my life has seemed—dark, confusing, and frightening. You know I've felt that I was a beast, and that you—no one— would have anything to do with me when you found out how filthy I was. I don't feel so much that way now. I feel more human. In the dream the snake part of my mother went away, and then I was no longer inside of the kangaroo; the kangaroo was gone— the beast part—and I was myself.

The pygmy was sort of like you [the therapist]. You were both the giant and the pygmy. The pygmy stopped the giant's attacks on the animals—on mother and me—when we couldn't help ourselves. He didn't hate the giant; he was impartial. The pygmy did something definite and when I saw that he wouldn't let us get hurt I could do something definite also. You might say that the pygmy is the professional part of you—the analyst; the giant is you being a man—being angry, being like my father; it has been difficult to get a clear picture of just what you are like.

My father wasn't in the dream, unless he is sort of part of you. I'm not clear about that. I didn't see my sister either. When the snake and the kangaroo left, the pygmy was gone also, and the fantastic, weird part of the dream faded away. I suppose you could say that I didn't have to see me and my parents as beasts anymore. Anyway, it was a relief.

Next I think of the important people who were mourning for somebody. I remember that I was touched by the way the giant acted; it was very human of him to respect their feelings. These people were a family—mother, father, aunts, uncles, and children. They all wore black. Someone had died; it wasn't my father; this wasn't my family. I think that they were mourning some parts of me that are gone. I'm vague about this, but since I have been in therapy I feel at times that I'm losing parts of myself and I'm not sure who I am. I don't want to do all the things I did—I don't want to be so depressed or upset like I was—but it's frightening to feel different. Some of the ways in which I felt about myself and my parents have been changing, and I feel that in the dream I was all of the mourners sort of grieving about the changes. Maybe also the mourners represent my family and their not wanting me to leave them—to grow up. They want me to be independent, but they seem to be afraid of this also, and try to hold onto me. They don't do it so much anymore, and I'm not so afraid of being myself anyhow. As I said, I was impressed by the giant respecting the mourning. After all, that was sort of like you; you usually are respectful of my feelings; of course, sometimes you aren't very considerate. You're certainly not perfect.

It seemed to me that the giant wanted to hurt me and then he wanted to seduce me, but he was clumsy and sort of hesitant. When the family came in he wasn't so interested in me, but he didn't want to hurt my feelings by ignoring me, so he did show some interest. I wanted the giant to look at me, and I was afraid also. That was like my relation with you. You want to see what goes on in my mind and I think that you notice me as a woman; after all, you are a man. I felt sometimes that you were seductive like my father and that you were afraid of your feelings. In the dream I began to feel powerful and tried to get the giant to have sexual relations with me, but he didn't do this; he didn't let me take advantage of things. It has been good to know that you [the therapist] can be in control of things when they begin to get out of hand. Somebody has to set limits and I'm getting so I can do that myself. I'm not so afraid of being powerful now.

When mother and I disobeyed the sign in the first part of the dream it was like I was involved in a terrible rebellion. My going against the sign was like my old feeling that I had to destroy everything—including myself. Then I got imprisoned in a cave—like the hospital, and in some ways like my home. The giant was afraid of me, like you used to be afraid when I got so upset. I felt that you used to attack me and my mother—like the giant did—but the rational, psychiatrist part of you kept anyone from getting hurt.

It wasn't such an upsetting dream. I have felt so murderous and horrible for so long. I felt that I'd always have to be locked up, or that I'd be killed, and I hated everyone. But things are clearer now. I know more about you and me. That's why the dream could go on —my seeing that the giant [you] was actually human, and that I am human also. I guess that's worth learning.

"I suppose so," I said, and the session was ended.

CONCLUSION

In the course of my days I do not see a large number of patients, and not all of those whom I do see will be significantly bettered through my therapeutic efforts. I have not discovered in myself any unusual characteristics which particularly qualify me for this work. I am often baffled by the behavior of others (and sometimes by my own), and not infrequently experience anxiety, anger, and discouragement in the course of treatment. I do not think that intensive psychotherapy can be provided for every schizophrenic patient and, even if this were done, the results of such a human enterprise could not be guaranteed.

Despite these remarks I favor doing the type of therapy which I have so sketchily described in these pages. Although I have recounted some vicissitudes of the work, I enjoy doing it and find great pleasure in the growth of another person, as well as experiencing regret at the inevitable separation from those I have come to know well. In this work one will come to question concepts of hopelessness and "irreversible" change and find that the "sickest" patient has no experience that the "healthiest" of us has not known at some time to some extent. With each patient the therapist will grow and learn more of himself, which is an excellent outcome. He will also come to respect the remarkable adaptive capacities of the human (shown so clearly in the schizophrenic reaction), and the extraordinary complexity and influence of the culture and the social field on human development. He may then wonder how it is that we humans can be so destructive to our kind, and he may seek to discover with others what more can be done to learn about and modify the stresses which are hurtful to the young and contribute to those unhappy and disastrous distortions of human living seen in our schizophrenic patients. It is possible that as we dare to reduce our subservience to irrational aspects of our cultural mythology we shall not be so casual about the exposure of our children (and ourselves) to evil social influences incompatible with adequate human growth. If we do not free ourselves to some extent from undue respect for expensive customs and beliefs, we may discover that the fatal biological weakness of man lies in his resistance to useful change in that which he has created—his culture.

CHAPTER II

A Hypothesis About the Nature of Schizophrenic Behavior

William L. Pious

I AM GRATEFUL for this opportunity to revise my earlier considerations of schizophrenic behavior.[27, 28] * The extent, as well as the tentative nature, of the revision, in the light of more than ten years of experience and reflection, seem to me to point to problems of two sorts—those which are in the main inherent in the enigmatic nature of the subject matter, and those resulting from the limited usefulness and sometimes misleading connotations of available concepts and models.

Investigative approaches to schizophrenia are so disparate and so lacking in correlations as to lead one to wonder how they could possibly refer to the same subject matter. Many investigations define the subject partly in terms of the hoped-for findings. Most of them imply that schizophrenia is a specific condition capable of independent verification; this implication is often found side by side with an explicit statement that there are no methods of verification. The assumption of a specific condition seems to be present when the value of the results of an investigation of a group of schizophrenics is determined by their applicability to other groups of schizophrenics. The fact that equivalent results are often not achieved may, to be sure, raise some question about the nature of the investigation and its method, but it may equally well indicate that the expectation of equivalence is not warranted.

* Numbered references appear at the end of this chapter. Footnotes to the text appear with asterisks.

The basis for the use of the term "schizophrenia" in so many diverse contexts is to be found in the assumption of a consensus among investigators of equivalent training and experience that the behavior under investigation is schizophrenic. It is a fact that such a consensus can usually, but not always, be obtained. From this point of view the term is used to designate a group which includes all the manifold varieties of schizophrenic behavior (it is more convenient, although I consider it loose usage, to refer to the person, rather than to his behavior, as schizophrenic). However, the term "schizophrenia" has, today, at least two entirely different categories of meanings and it is not always clear from the context which is intended. One category, as mentioned, is empirical and is based on historical, descriptive, and observational data. The second is based on any one of a number of theoretical and hypothetical explanations of schizophrenia. The degree of consensus with regard to the first category is incomparably greater than any consensus concerning the many and diverse explanations implied in the second.[2]

There are limits to the scientific usefulness of consensus in the absence of some method of independent validation. These limits are of such a nature that the term "schizophrenic" may not be used to mean that all instances of schizophrenic behavior are basically equivalent. It is likely[2] that there may be many very different underlying factors from one instance to the next and from one group to the next. These considerations require that the term be used in its empirical meaning, avoiding any implication of one or another theory about schizophrenic behavior. The empirical meaning includes more than data of observation. It connotes that the behavior is classifiable and has no known somatic pathological determinant. It implies that the behavior has been differentiated from other subgroups of "abnormal" behavior such as manic, depressive, hysteric, obsessive-compulsive, paranoiac, etc. The group which includes all the subgroups may be compared with or contrasted with "normal" behavior. The subgroups are by definition to be compared or contrasted with each other. Since the empirical definition implies differentiation from other subgroups it is to be expected that with increasing knowledge and experience some cases which have been designated as hysteric or obsessive-compulsive or other may come to be designated as schizophrenic and vice versa.

The term "psychotic" is often used as if it were interchangeable with "schizophrenic." I prefer not to use the term "psychotic" in scientific discussion. It has many different meanings and shades of meaning, on many levels of discourse, which often cannot be disentangled. Its use does not necessarily exclude the presence of known and related somatic pathology. I hope to demonstrate that its connotations set an arbitrary limitation to the use of the term "schizophrenic" which leads, at the least, to awkwardness of description, to awkwardness of "diagnosis," to an arbitrary meaning for "recovery," and, often, to an arbitrary narrowing of research objectives.

Since the subject of schizophrenic behavior is a *terra incognita,* the use of concepts which have acquired specific and verifiable meanings in other contexts often introduces unwarranted connotations. I believe that new concepts are needed and that the current use of terms taken from many sciences, such as medicine, biology, psychology, psychoanalysis, and others, exercises much more of a deterrent effect than is realized on attempts to further understanding of schizophrenic behavior.

A much more thoroughgoing operational[4] consideration of the terminology in current use is surely required. For the present, my purpose is to make clear that I use the term "schizophrenic" in its empirical meaning and that the considerations to be presented are not intended as a sweeping explanation of or theory about schizophrenia. Some concepts will be offered and defined in terms of operations when feasible.

There are problems which remain implicit in the use of the empirical definition. There is by no means a consensus about all cases and there is very often disagreement as to whether or not any particular case is to be called schizophrenic. Furthermore, the term is used to designate a manifold variety of behavior, as diverse as catatonia and paranoid condition, and there is little consensus[2] about the basis for such inclusiveness. The hypothesis to be discussed attempts to isolate, from a somewhat novel viewpoint, what it is that is specifically "schizophrenic" about the spectrum of schizophrenic behavior. I hope that it will offer a basis for later consideration of a method related to psychoanalysis for the detailed investigation of the ways in which schizophrenic communication is organized.

OBSERVATIONS

My current views about schizophrenic behavior stem from my earlier work with a young man who had been diagnosed as having an obsessive-compulsive psychoneurosis.[28] The main features of these views have become clearer and have found some confirmation in my subsequent experience. I believe that the investigation of cases such as this one, where there is no manifest "psychotic" behavior to begin with, offers new insights into the special structure of schizophrenic behavior. I will, therefore, review some aspects of my earlier report:

> Initially, John, as I will call him, started in analysis and seemed to be progressing favorably. It soon became apparent that things were going wrong. He was becoming increasingly tense and aloof. He was self-depreciating and his thinking was stilted, superficial, and bizarre. He became haggard, his expression seemed frozen, and there were increasingly long periods of silence during which he was perplexed, blocked, and withdrawn. This first phase was brought to an end when he was requested to discontinue the use of the couch.
>
> For several months he generally sat on the floor, starting his sessions in the corner of the room farthest from me. He would sit with his back against the wall "for safety" and would remain close to the door. During the sessions he would alter his position in the room and later said that this was a way of indicating his rapport with me. When he felt "in touch" he would sit nearer to me. He often would make the gesture of drawing a line on the floor between him and me. He subsequently told me that this gesture was a way of indicating his fear of the subject matter as well as that there was some divergence between what I was saying and what he was thinking. *Why he had to communicate by gesture and movement was not explained.*
>
> He gradually began to appear warmer and less withdrawn. He would make momentary approaches to the couch and then began to sit on it and no longer sat on the floor. The second phase, which lasted for about a year, ended when he spontaneously resumed the recumbent position.
>
> The third and final phase continued for more than two years and was characterized by the fact that he dealt with his problem on an entirely different level of discourse and with a considerable diminution of the bizarre features of the first two phases.

Although the work with John was begun as a psychoanalysis, the changes in method that were required are so extensive that it would not be scientifically accurate to continue to call it psychoanalysis. While some may refer to it as "modified analysis" and others as "psychoanalytically oriented," a special designation would be preferable, since I believe it is homologous* to the psychoanalytic method rather than a

---

* The term *homologous* is used in its biological sense: "corresponding in type of structure and in origin, but not necessarily in function." (*American College Dictionary*) To avoid connotations that I consider undesirable I will refer to the work as an investigation conducted by an investigator.

modification of it. I would therefore urge caution in the use of the terminology of psychoanalysis since there is no a priori reason to assume that it may be applicable.

The work constituted an intense human experience extending over more than four years and my notes and recollections include an enormous amount of information concerning his life history and its complex and troubled development. In my earlier report [28] under the heading "Formulation," I abstracted a sampling of behavior which had recurred with some regularity in reaction to identifiable circumstances and which had appeared repeatedly in a sequence. My reason for having abstracted that particular sampling of behavior was that it was representative of what was specifically schizophrenic about his behavior.

The observations to be outlined fell into perspective toward the end of the third phase. By that time it was established that the obsessive-compulsive behavior—originally considered psychoneurotic—appeared episodically and was in fact one of a series of behavioral states which ranged from most archaic to least archaic in their organization. Observations of this sort have led me to consider it arbitrary to limit the term *schizophrenic* to those states which, although they belong to the entire sequence of states, seem so archaic as to be called "psychotic." I suggest that the full sequence of states up to and including "clinical remission" be called schizophrenic.

Each sequence of the behavioral states to be described was precipitated by a current experience, at times occurring within the working relationship and more often outside of it. These experiences were extremely diverse and their content was intimately related to John's history. Their effect was specific and stemmed from the fact that they all had in common a special form of deprivation. Typically, the experiences as they occurred in the working relationship took the following course. Something that was going on would impinge on a blind spot or problem of mine. The mobilization of my defenses would lead to some withdrawal on my part which would be reflected as some change in my attitude toward John.[38] I was generally unaware of the withdrawal for some time.* The effect of the withdrawal was to increase the psychological distance between us. It was this increase of the psychological dis-

* The problems mobilized in the work with John were not as severe as they can be on occasion, especially with chronic schizophrenics. Each investigator will find that there are some schizophrenics with whom he cannot work. Opportunities for consultation with a colleague are desirable and can help organize the observations. I am particularly grateful to Jan Frank, M.D., for his often invaluable advice in the course of my work with John.

tance that John experienced as a deprivation and that I will call psychological deprivation.

The behavioral states that were precipitated would appear in the following sequence (the names in quotes are taken from John's descriptions).

1. "Emptying." This phenomenon was abrupt and very transitory —so transitory that it frequently escaped direct observation. I quote from my report: "The abruptness and magnitude of the change during such an 'attack' were extraordinary. Chatting animatedly, he would suddenly stop, all expression would drain out of his face and his eyes would be dull and unfocused." The stopping and the draining of expressiveness seemed to be separate steps, although the entire duration must have been less than a second. Neither John nor I could define this state or give it psychological content. It would immediately be succeeded by other and much more colorful states.*

2. "Focusing." Whether the "emptying" was followed by an immediate restoration of the previous behavioral state or by a full sequence of behavioral states, with very variable durations, the transitions were accompanied by what John called "focusing." He would feel with more or less horror "that he was 'slipping' and would then focus on any detail and 'for the time it takes me to see things again, those little details become my whole life.'" I observed that his statement that he was "slipping" came after the "emptying" and a more accurate description would be that he had "slipped." His descriptions suggested that the "focusing" represented a continuing effort which was manifest in all the behavioral states. I observed that it would be temporarily reduced when he achieved a succeeding state. The behavioral states appeared in a regular sequence: (a) Perplexity, blocking, bizarre and apparently incoherent verbalization. (b) Episodes of estrangement.†

---

* In a recent article, Van Dusen[40] refers to a "hole" in the experience of chronic schizophrenics, which he describes as "selflessness, timelessness and spacelessness," . . . "it comes to be equated with death, insanity. . . ." This part of his description corresponds to the "emptying" that I am discussing. Van Dusen goes on to include a change in the quality of the "hole" to "a rather pleasant and warm place like a womb" as part of the nature of the "hole." I would suggest that this change in quality is more likely one of the first of the emerging behavioral states than part of the "hole" or a regression.

† "Dr. Paul Federn, in a personal communication, suggested that the term 'estrangement' be applied to these phenomena. He wrote, '. . . all cases of latent schizophrenia describe *some* features of what is ordinarily called depersonalization. . . . I think it necessary to differentiate deperson-

Although there were some manifestations of estrangement in all of the behavioral states accompanied by "focusing," there were also distinct episodes during which there were "disturbances of hearing, vision and equilibration . . . his surroundings seemed to move away from him, all dimensions rapidly increased, objects lost their interrelationships, and he became limited to isolated perceptions." (c) Ideas of reference and the development of paranoid thinking and delusions. (d) Agitation and intense preoccupation with self-tormenting thoughts which on some occasions had a delusional cast and at other times were more obsessive in nature. This state included many and varied rituals and some stereotyped behavior. (e) Obsessive-compulsive behavior which, like the state at the beginning of the investigation, was difficult to distinguish from an obsessive-compulsive psychoneurosis. The continued "focusing" might be useful for differentiation.

3. "The feeling of reality." When this behavioral state appeared in the third phase, there was a change which was manifested in all of John's relationships. His description was that he "could see things without 'focusing,' and felt that he belonged and was in touch with them."

John emphasized the fact that when he was "on the way up" after a deprivational experience, very minor deprivations would be enough to start the whole sequence over again. When, however, he had attained "a feeling of reality" or had achieved a relatively high level of organization, he could cope with relatively much more severe deprivations. No schizophrenic whom I have investigated would refer to being "on the way down"—it would invariably be "on the way up" or some equivalent statement.*

---

alization from estrangement or alienation and to use them for what are topically different phenomena. . . . Estrangement is always due to a loss of the libidinous component of cathexis of a mental ego boundary. . . . In *depersonalization* no ego boundary has lost its libido cathexis, but the coherence of the ego cathexis itself is interrupted . . . intentions, although correctly carried out, are not felt to belong to the ego.'

"The term 'estrangement' will be used throughout the text of this paper to designate the phenomena described, in terms of Federn's differential diagnostic criteria. He wrote about estrangement that 'depending on the part of the ego boundary deprived of its libido cathexis, . . . objects, . . . sensory impressions, . . . memories, thoughts, fantasies, and even emotions, may be perceived as strange, although another part of awareness may still be normally felt.' " [28]

* This statement is so condensed that it may give rise to inaccurate connotations. The schizophrenic's reports are very overdetermined. For example, John's statement that he was "slipping" referred to the fact that the

From early on John referred to his "mental image" of me. This "mental image" underwent all the vicissitudes of the sequences of behavioral states and seemed to have an increasing importance as the work went on. The clarity or degree of distortion of this "mental image" became a referent to the way things were going with him and to the way things were between us. After the "state of reality" appeared to be relatively well established, references to the "mental image" became fewer and finally dropped out. This was correlated with a dream that signaled the approaching termination of the work. The dream follows:

> I am walking with my mother and we come to a crossroad. I want to go straight ahead and she argues that we turn to the left. I begin to feel angry and guilty when I suddenly realize that my mother isn't really there and that the whole argument has been in my mind. Then I feel relieved and free to go ahead.

While the nature and content of the behaviorial states varies from one case to the next, the basic observations have been confirmed by my subsequent experience. These are: (1) the psychological deprivation, (2) the "emptying," (3) the "focusing," and (4) a sequence of behavioral states ranging from most archaic to least archaic in their quality. These observations make possible the formulation of a provisional hypothesis about the nature of schizophrenic behavior. Before considering the hypothesis, a number of terms which have been used in a special sense require definition.

DEFINITIONS

In describing John's behavior I have referred to "behavioral states," to "levels" of "organization," and to the extent or amount of "archaic" quality of each state. Primarily, what I have described is a recurrent series of changes in John's behavior which followed each other in sequence over a period of time and were precipitated by a psychological deprivation. Each change in the series had some duration, sometimes a matter of moments or days; at other times, weeks or months. The changes were sufficiently delineated that I call each a behavioral state.

Each behavioral state had its characteristic combination of gestures,

---

level to which he had progressed was not yet stabilized. It also includes a reference, by reversal, to the preceding "emptying." It would be more accurate to say that in those situations which I could investigate fully I could demonstrate that the "direction" was "on the way up."

movements, affects, intonations, and verbalization. In many, the way John moved about, whether he spoke or was silent, created the effect of pantomime or of charade. These characteristic combinations of behavior are referred to as "organized" because subsequent investigation would demonstrate that they were ways of communicating and, when translated, they would prove to be coherent and informative.

The level at which the behavioral state is organized refers primarily to its position within the sequence. By virtue of its position, the level can be characterized by the difficulty of translation—the degree of incomprehensibility. The "lower" the level (earlier in the sequence) the more incomprehensible the behavior. Each level is also characterized by the extent of the idiosyncratic nature of the verbal and other behavior. The term "archaic" includes not only the incomprehensibility and the quantity of idiosyncratic usage but also the degree of my sense of the "uncanniness" of the behavior.[13] Since the sense of the "uncanny" varies among investigators, the other factors serve as a way of verifying the impression.

These definitions are limited to schizophrenic behavior as it is observed within the working relationship. The behavior of a schizophrenic during a session often does not appear different from his behavior in the hospital ward and indeed may not differ from his behavior when he is alone. Such considerations suggest that the limited definitions may be tentatively extended and used as more general definitions of schizophrenic behavior. It would then be viewed in general as organized for the purpose of communication, with himself or with others. On the basis of this more generalized definition, catatonic, hebephrenic, paranoid, and other distinctive classes of chronic schizophrenic behavior may be thought of as "levels," each within its undetermined sequence.

Proposed Concepts and Hypothesis

In order to achieve some generality, a few concepts are proposed to replace some of John's idiosyncratic but colorful terms. The event he named "emptying" is undoubtedly given a different name by each schizophrenic and has been referred to by Van Dusen[40] as a central "hole." I suggest the term "nadir" * to convey that the position is below that of any imaginable state—figuratively a momentary death. In an earlier paper[27] I used the designation "pathogenic process," but the connotations of the term "pathogenic" now seem undesirable to me. *Progres-*

* I am using *nadir* with the definition "the lowest point." (*American College Dictionary*.)

sion strikes me as a useful name for the full sequence of behavioral states. It is better than the term "restitution," which is used in psychoanalysis with a somewhat different meaning. It has the advantage of being antithetic to the term "regression" which is often and, I am convinced, incorrectly applied to schizophrenic behavior. Progressive effort suggests itself in place of the term "focusing." John's reference to the "mental image" (of me) seems sufficiently apt and neutral to be retained for the present. I have defined the precipitating circumstances as psychological deprivation. This suggests a connection with such current ideas as sensory deprivation, sleep deprivation, etc., and I have a hunch that there may very well be such a connection.[17, 23]

John's description of the fact that less psychological deprivation was needed to start the progression over again when he was "on the way up" than when he had achieved a higher level suggests something in the nature of a variable threshold against the effects of psychological deprivation. Temporal variability makes observation and evaluation extremely difficult. The duration of any particular behavioral state ranged from a few minutes to several months. It is my impression that there were also times when changes occurred with extreme rapidity. This is one of the bewildering aspects of schizophrenic behavior and one that makes attempts at prediction precarious. There is reason to think that the capacity for progressive effort may vary from time to time and from case to case. I am sure that there are many factors involved in this, but I have been able to study only a few of them.

As a hypothesis, I suggest that a psychological deprivation, the nature of which is complex and very individually determined, reaches the equivalent of a threshold * quantity, at which point the nadir occurs.

---

* I am aware that my use of the term "threshold," like my use of the term "deprivation," introduces connotations of a quantitative kind, although my method of estimating is a subjective one. Both terms may also oversimplify the situation to which they refer. However, they avoid the use of other terms which carry connotations that I find undesirable. I am using them because of my hunch that there are connections with other usage of these terms. In this sense my use of them would constitute what Bridgman[4] refers to as a program for investigation.

In some ways, what I am describing as a threshold is very much akin to Federn's discussion[10] of weaknesses of the ego boundaries. The delineation of the levels of organization may also correspond to his concept of altered ego boundaries.

The notion of a threshold has interesting implications in connection with current theoretical considerations of the relative autonomy of the ego, more specifically in the ego's relation to the environment.[17, 18, 19, 30, 33, 34] My considerations of schizophrenic behavior suggest that there is a threshold

The latter occupies a zero position in terms of the immediately ensuing progression. The time required for a complete progression varies from a matter of moments to an indefinitely protracted period. What may appear descriptively as a regression to increasingly archaic levels of organization is not an actual regression. It is the effect of repeated psychological deprivations each resulting in a nadir event, followed by a progression. In time there is a decrease in the capacity for the progressive effort so that the progressions are halted at lower and lower levels of organization. The "mental image" acts to increase the threshold against the psychological deprivation; as the threshold becomes sufficient, evidence of the conscious quality of the "image" diminishes and gradually disappears.

DISCUSSION

The discussion of a special method of investigation homologous with the psychoanalytic method is beyond the scope of this paper. I very much doubt that there has been enough groundwork to form the basis for a systematic statement. The method originates in the accumulated body of psychoanalytic knowledge; its structural equivalence to the psychoanalytic method stems from the full psychoanalytic training of the investigator and from the use of genetic and psychodynamic interpretations and constructions. Its functional difference from the psychoanalytic method is the result of the special nature of the subject matter to be investigated. It may be that as knowledge of the method and of the subject matter becomes more accessible for systematic study, psychoanalytic institutes will be able to offer, as an addition to the regular training program, specialized training to those candidates with a special interest in the investigation of schizophrenic behavior.

---

against psychological deprivation. Recent experimental work with sensory deprivation, sleep deprivation, and the like suggest other thresholds against diminution of other environmental input.[17, 23] These various thresholds have some bearing on the maintenance of the relative autonomy of the ego.

The collaboration of the subjects in deprivation experiments seems analogous to what I call the progressive effort in schizophrenic behavior. A more detailed investigation of the collaborative effort of the subjects as it affects their manifest behavior would be desirable.[17] In the experimental work on subliminal visual stimulation[11] the collaborative effort of the subject is especially prominent and may create the kind of condition in which the subliminal stimulation acts as a deprivation.

These thoughts suggest that the ego can normally regulate the levels of its thresholds. One might speculate that the state of sleep requires conjoint regulation of a threshold against sensory input and another against sensory deprivation.

In order to highlight the nature of the progression and the special position of the nadir event I have excluded psychodynamic, genetic, and other considerations. Such considerations often obscure the progression, while the nature of the explanations that they offer does not make clear the special character of the schizophrenic behavior. Furthermore, I believe that increasing knowledge about the progression will in its turn change some of the current psychodynamic propositions and add others. The following discussion of the concepts that I have proposed will refer to some matters relating to method and will offer some tentative suggestions about representation, translation, and interpretation.

Psychological Deprivation   A consideration of psychological deprivation must include some study of the people who are in one or another relation with the schizophrenic. I have already discussed in a general way my perception of my role in such a deprivation and have suggested the quasi-quantitative notion of psychological distance.[3, 20, 21, 38, 43] Duration is involved as well as distance; and they bear some reciprocal relation to each other. One of the eventualities that requires special mention is the development of a cyclic, retrograding situation. To have one's problems stirred up—painfully so at times—leads not only to withdrawal but also to misperception and biased evaluation of the schizophrenic's reactions. Since he is now "on the way up" the response that he meets is enough to set him back, while the increasingly archaic level of his behavior has the effect on the investigator of rubbing salt on an open wound. This kind of retrogradation may not be overcome unless one can resolve the problem that has been stirred up. It may even call for dropping the work. The retrograding situation described provides a model that may explain many instances of chronicity in schizophrenic behavior. Someone—perhaps a nurse, an aide, a friend, or other—whose behavior seems beyond reproach may nevertheless unwittingly provide psychological deprivation which repeatedly halts the progressive effort and precipitates the nadir event and new progressions; in time the capacity for progressive effort diminishes. This is one of the conditions when the progressive effort fatigues.

On many occasions, when the new progression stops at a level at which the schizophrenic himself withdraws from the investigator, a circumscribed rather than a retrograding situation develops. Such situations permit careful observation and mutual explanations and are, therefore, probably essential for a successful investigation. I believe that other relationships with a circumscribed quality are occasionally developed by a schizophrenic. In such instances, when the details of the relationship are not known, unexpected and unexplainable "improvements" may occur and they will appear spontaneous.

Nadir Event   The nadir is an event which seems to me to be completely enigmatic. Observation is unusually difficult for many reasons. It often has to be inferred when the presenting level of behavior is lower than it was at the previous session. When it is observed it is so transient and empty of content and so quickly overlaid with the behavior of the progression as to elude attention. This latter is augmented by the fact that its occurrence within the session is an indication that the investigator is psychologically withdrawn and certainly not his most perceptive self. When the schizophrenic behavior is very archaic the nadir event is often misidentified as blocking or some other such descriptive term. When the progression is rapid enough almost immediately to restore the previous behavioral state, the nadir event may appear to be nothing more than a momentary pause.

The insufficiency of the observations of this event stand in contrast to my estimate of its importance. Much of my information about it came from investigation of the circumscribed situations that I have mentioned. Additional information accrued when the psychological deprivation had been experienced outside of the working situation. In either case, the obtaining of information depended on the relative stability and duration of the level of behavior. Any particular level of organization achieved during the progression is somewhat unstable at first and the threshold against psychological deprivation is lowered at that time. The level then becomes stabilized; if it has some duration it affords an opportunity for investigation and translation. Then there is a second phase of instability in connection with progression to the succeeding level and at this phase, too, there is a lowered threshold against psychological deprivation. Much of the time, therefore, the nadir event is inferred by extrapolation from the direction in which the behavior is changing. My reference to the nadir event as the "zero position" indicates that it is so often inferred by extrapolation.

In reviewing my scanty information about this event, I have remembered seeing something strikingly similar in a few epileptics. In the absence of the clinical records and other investigations my description is in the nature of an anecdote, but it may suggest other approaches for the study of the nadir event.

A young woman in a state institution had episodes diagnosed as epileptic equivalents. One day, as I was making rounds, she burst into an epileptic furor and came charging across the ward at me. She was no more than ten feet from me when she suddenly came to a complete stop and after a momentary blankness [nadir?] smiled a very beatific smile and entered a state of auditory hallucinations.

It is hardly necessary to explain why this instance stands out in my memory. I have an impression that I have also seen something like the nadir event immediately preceding the aura of a *grand mal* attack. The nadir is a problem for multi-disciplinary research.

From the descriptive point of view the nadir and the succeeding progression may make it appear *as if* the schizophrenic "scans" his companions for their blind spots. This may account for the fact that many observers have the opinion that the schizophrenic provokes the psychological deprivation out of sadomasochistic motives. This is a misinterpretation, however descriptively accurate it may seem. *

Progressive Effort   The use of the term "effort" is descriptive. What one observes resembles increasing concentration of attention. There have been occasions when I have observed progression from a lower to a higher level. The tension during such an increasing effort would almost be palpable. The effort diminished considerably once the higher level was achieved. The situation is reminiscent of the experience of learning a new set of abstractions. "Once such a set of abstractions is conquered . . . considerable relief is experienced. . . ." [31] What one observes, therefore, is a discontinuity in the progression from level to level (figuratively, a quantum "jump").

The capacity for progressive effort is variable. The variations that I am able to account for are those that point to a persistent but unrecognized psychological deprivation. Under such circumstances the augmented reactivity of the lower levels to psychological deprivation gives the impression of fatiguing of the progressive effort. There may very

---

* I am discussing the specific question of the relationship of the psychological deprivation, an insufficient threshold and the nadir event. My comments about sadomasochistic motivation have no reference to the psychodynamic content of any stabilized level of organization. In any particular case, the content at any level or at all levels may deal with developmental problems such as are implied in sadomasochistic and other behavior. It may very well be that developmental problems of this kind are influential in cases where the progression is halted at relatively low levels.

well be other sources which limit the capacity for progression, including developmental problems and perhaps a somatic basis.

In working with schizophrenics, it is important to bear in mind that the capacity for progressive effort is implicit. Any level is an achievement and under certain circumstances may appear to be clung to. If the level is very archaic, the predominant affect may be one of horror. This horror is probably a reference to the nadir and forms an element of an organized communicative effort. If one considers the archaic organized states to be analogous to dream structure the horror may be seen more readily as an element to be translated. It happens, at times, that humane reactions to the apparent suffering lead to strenuous efforts to provide relief. To mistake the achieved level for a "regression" to be dealt with, by whatever means, may do a serious violation to the schizophrenic's capacity for progression.

Progression Cases such as John's—often called borderline, latent, or incipient schizophrenia—seem to be best suited for observation of the progression as a sequence of behavioral states. Their capacity for progressive effort is either basically greater than, or not yet as fatigued as, it is in chronic schizophrenics, and their threshold against psychological deprivation is probably higher. Work with them is less taxing and the content, current source, and structure of the psychological deprivation can be thoroughly explored. Repeated progressions to relatively high levels of organization with their greater comprehensibility permit a translation of the meaning and the structuring of the more archaic representations. The degree of flux implied in the multiplicity of progressions is an obstacle to a more detailed exploration of the content and organization at any one level. Such information may be more readily available from work with chronic schizophrenics in whom one particular level of organization is relatively stable over a long period of time. The latter work and the work with incipient schizophrenics are complementary.

A systematic discussion of the progression, level by level, is not yet possible. The progression might be envisaged as though the levels are stacked one above the other. The picture would be that of an inverted cone.[35] The progression may also be considered as a restructuring of the behavioral functions as they are organized at each level. I do not mean to imply that the levels of any progression are identical with those of preceding or subsequent progressions. On the contrary, my impression is that there may be a considerable variability in the way in which any particular level is structured. Psychoanalytic and other evidence indicates that these levels of organization are inherent in normal behavioral equipment.[8, 9, 17, 18, 19, 22, 24, 25, 30, 33, 37, 38, 39]

The quality of unfolding manifested by the progressive effort has some of the characteristics of an epigenetic sequence. [8, 9] These characteristics are central to some of the published work with schizophrenics.[36] The content of the levels of organization—even at their most archaic— is complex and based on the experience and maturation of a fully developed individual. Some inferences may be made about infantile development on the order of inferences from the study of dreams. More extensive inferences about the mental life of infancy are probably unwarranted.

Psychoanalytic knowledge about dream structure[14] provides a useful basis for consideration of the levels of organization of schizophrenic behavior. There are two fundamental differences between the structure of schizophrenic behavior and the form of thinking described as a dream. The first is a matter of intention: "Productions of the dream work . . . are not made with the intention of being understood";[15] the progressive effort implies the intention of being understood. The second difference bears on the perceptual organization[1, 12] and the quantity of sensory intake. My impression is that there is no diminution of the quantity of sensory intake in schizophrenic behavior no matter how it may be restructured at any level. The state of sleep, on the other hand, implies a diminution of all forms of sensory intake.[14] For these reasons, the meaning of a dream will be different in many respects from the meaning of otherwise similar behavior in a schizophrenic.

As in dream structure, the structure at archaic levels determines the way ideas are represented.[16] For example, the ways John communicated with me by changing his position on the floor, moving his arms as though to draw a line, etc., point to the conditions of representability of his behavioral state. A more complicated instance may point up the distinctive structuring of behavior for representation.

> For several weeks John's behavior was paranoid. He was awake nights carrying out complex rituals to guard his room against "invasion by a madman." He complained day after day that the secretaries laughed as he passed them and he felt convinced that they were reading his records and talking about him. He would search my office for microphones and was so convinced at times that someone frightening and hostile was listening at the door that he had to open it to check.

From the viewpoint of representability, the translation of this behavior gives it the effect of a charade: "I must be going crazy. What I say is not taken seriously. People are hostile and use my records for their own purposes. No one really listens to me." A further translation is that he is looking for a friendly listener since he had tried to tell me something important to which I had not responded. His complaint was valid.

Each behavioral state has its characteristic organization of perception[1, 12] and, therefore, its own state of consciousness.[29] Perceptual qualities undergo extensive alteration. Changes of discrimination determine what is to be excluded and included. Intensity is altered so that what may be ordinarily subliminal is perceived, dim lights may appear very bright, whispers may be heard as echoing roars, and the like. I believe that at some of the very archaic levels one sensation may be replaced by another, as visual for auditory, etc. Proprioceptive and kinesthetic perception are equally involved. Complaints of estrangement, when they appear in the course of a particular level, usually indicate increasing progressive effort and in such instances serve to warn of a lowered threshold against psychological deprivation.

The level of progression reacts on the source of the psychological deprivation in a number of ways. I have referred above to retrograding and to circumscribed situations. Other developments have the effect of an attempt to modify or disrupt the situation of deprivation. The most difficult of these to cope with is a rigid, catatonic, nonperceptive state. Others include obsequiousness, seductiveness which may become openly erotic, outbursts of violence, and development of more or less fixed delusional aversions. These kinds of behavior may also be characteristic elements of the organization within a level, but the likelihood that they may indicate a continuing and undetected psychological deprivation should be explored.

It is often said that activity is necessary to build a relationship with a schizophrenic. The progressive nature of his behavior suggests to me that it is rather the schizophrenic who seeks the relationship, on his current level, and that he is active relative to his level.[32] Activity, when reported by an investigator, may reflect his efforts to cope with himself in such a way as to make it possible for the schizophrenic to reach out to him. These efforts may be protracted and very distressing to the investigator. When they have succeeded, so that the schizophrenic is more accessible, the verbal and other behavior which was successful may mistakenly be called an interpretation. In a like manner, when one has resolved a retrograding situation, the verbalization of one's understanding may mistakenly be called an interpretation. I propose to distinguish interpretations, which offer the schizophrenic new and usable psychodynamic and genetic constructions, from other interactions.

I use the term "interactions" to include all of the verbal and other behavior of the investigator and the schizophrenic during the investigative work. The content and structure of the interaction is determined by the level of organization of the schizophrenic's behavior.

Psychological distance is a central issue of the interaction.[3, 20, 21, 38, 43] What is required is to maintain a relatively constant psychological distance in a situation in which for a long time there are abrupt, extensive, and frequent changes in the level of the schizophrenic's behavior.* As I have already mentioned, the reactions of the investigator are inevitably stirred up in such a way as to bring about additional changes of level and of distance. In the work with John, where visual terms played such a prominent part, I defined appropriate distance in terms of remaining visible to him at his level. In a more general way, it can also be defined in terms of the investigator's realistic perception of the current level of behavior.[38] Psychological distance should not be taken literally. Any withdrawal from a realistic perception of the schizophrenic brings about an increase in the psychological distance whether the investigator's behavior appears overly warm or cold.

An illustrative instance occurred toward the middle of the second phase of my work with John.

> Things had been going well for a couple of weeks and I felt some disappointment when he came in one day looking tense and aloof. I had not yet learned of the effects of deprivations outside of the session. He sat down on the far end of the couch, instead of at the center as was more usual, and told me that he had been up all night "dodging back and forth between withdrawals, obsessions, and guarding the room." He chatted in an aimless way, mentioning very casually a call from his father on the previous day. I later became more alert for that very casual tone of voice—it meant "this is important." As he went on in an obsessive way I began to feel bored, until I noticed that he was talking louder and faster. I saw then that he had moved to the near end of the couch and was leaning forward peering at me. Following an inquiry and some discussion, he explained that as he was talking I had literally seemed to be getting smaller and farther away, "as if you were

---

* "Alice looked . . . in great surprise. '. . . we've been under this tree the whole time! Everything's just as it was!' . . . said the Queen. 'Now, *here*, . . . it takes all the running *you* can do to keep in the same place. . . . To get somewhere else, you must run at least twice as fast . . . !' " [5]

going to disappear into the distance." His rapid, loud talking and moving closer were an effort "to hang on."

I propose that the interactions be tentatively classified into five categories: orientation, representation, translation, clarification, and interpretation. The first three are most prominent when the schizophrenic's behavior is organized at lower levels; clarification and interpretation predominate at the higher levels. The classification is mainly an expositional device. The actual interactions, as a process, combine these categories in a manifold variability of intensiveness and extensiveness of each.*

1. *Orientation.* Under this heading I include attempts to sense a suitable psychological distance and to learn the most effective and intelligible means of translation and of responding to the schizophrenic. It is generally by way of the orienting interactions that each investigation develops its special "lingo." This "feeling out" process may require a degree of flexibility and a readiness to "switch methods" such as are described by Eissler[7] in regard to work with delinquents.

2. *Representation.* Representation is suggested for the method of communication characteristic of each level of organization. I have selected the term since it suggests a useful connection with the "considerations of representability" of the dream work.[16] The term also applies to those occasions when the investigator uses the "language" of the schizophrenic's level of behavior to convey special recognition or to offer a special response.[20, 21, 36, 41, 42, 43] This kind of communication by the investigator is sometimes indispensable. The investigator's capacity for representation (and for translation) is a special manifestation of the use of "controlled regression." [17, 22, 24, 25, 33, 37, 38] It requires overcoming of one's aversions to combining variations of tonal qualities, actions, and affects as elements of representation. The affects may be affection, dislike, suspicion, exasperation, etc.; the actions may extend to active in-

---

* Wexler's[43] vivid description of his work with Jane is a frank, sober, and very sensitive statement of what may be involved in achieving a useful psychological distance. While orienting interactions seem to be predominant in his report, they are so intricately interwoven with representation and translation that the interactions might be equally considered under any one of the three headings.

An equally vivid and sensitive report is offered by Knight.[21] Although his report is a different representation from Wexler's, it too describes the interactions of orientation, representation, and translation very effectively. It goes farther than Wexler's, in that it includes clarifications and interpretations, and provides very fine examples of each.

tervention in the management of the schizophrenic's daily life.[43] These interventions serve to clarify otherwise unsuspected elements of the schizophrenic's representation. It is likely that a full representation by the schizophrenic may require days and sometimes weeks. The investigator's sudden "intuition" [38] may, in fact, come at the end of the representation.

A problem peculiar to the more archaic levels of organization is the difficulty of distinguishing thinking from communicative behavior. One generally considers thinking to be something that goes on inside one's mind. It is a fact though that there is some accompanying behavior in the form of movements and changes of expression so that one is able to say of someone else that he seems to be thinking, lost in thought, preoccupied, etc. Nevertheless, overt behavior is ordinarily minimal when one is thinking. At archaic levels of organization the schizophrenic's behavior when he is thinking may be almost identical with his behavior when he intends to communicate. It is necessary to learn to sense the difference and to remain receptive while he is thinking. A mistaken attempt to respond, as to a communicative representation, is an intrusion and may act as a psychological deprivation.*

3. *Translation.* I have already illustrated translation in terms of the explanation by the schizophrenic of his behavior at more archaic levels. The explanation may also be offered by the investigator in the form of a translation to his own level or to some intermediate level. The translation to an intermediate level may be mistaken for what Bouvet[3] de-

---

* It occurs to me that distinctions of this sort may be made about dreams and, perhaps, about the content of analytic sessions. A dream in which the dreamer is an observer and in which he does not see himself may be a way of thinking or remembering represented by the structure of the dream. On the other hand, a dream in which the dreamer is one of the active participants would be more in the nature of a communication. A combination of reflection, communication, and recollection may be represented in dreams in which the dreamer is both observer and observed as a participator. In analytic sessions, an analysand's report in the form of an anecdote which discusses his behavior with several other people has something of the structure of the second kind of dream and it is useful to consider the anecdote from that point of view. The anecdote may also be reported as a memory in which the analysand is observing himself in the remembered situation or, again, it may be reported in such a way that the analysand is not active in the situation that he is describing. The latter corresponds to the dream in which the dreamer is the observer. I have found it useful to translate such an account, in my thinking, as equivalent to saying that there is something here to be thought about or something that the analysand is not thinking about. These considerations suggest to me that "normal" behavior may be considered as a level of organization of behavior.

scribes as a "reverse interpretation." In arriving at a translation, there may be an erroneous tendency to deal with certain elements of an archaic level apart from the context of the level. Such a tendency is indicated, for example, when an element is picked out and called a "hallucination." To do this is equivalent to referring to the spoken voice in a dream that is being analyzed as a "hallucination."

Translation seems to me to be the most characteristics interaction in working with schizophrenics. The explanations offered by the schizophrenic, and his interest in working out explanations, are a manifestation of the progressive effort. Translations offered by the investigator are often organized in one of several psychodynamic frames of reference. The usefulness, effectiveness, and meaningfulness of translations are so impressive that they are naturally recalled more readily and their relative significance may be overestimated at times. This retrospective overestimation may account for some of the diversity among hypotheses about the psychodynamics of schizophrenic behavior.

4. *Clarification.* Under this heading I include exploration, inquiry, confrontation, elucidation, educative procedures, interventions, and discussions, all of which promote an increasing knowledge of the life history of the schizophrenic and of his psychodynamics. Clarification is prerequisite to interpretation.

5. *Interpretation.* I consider that the use of interpretations in work with schizophrenics forms part of the structural equivalence to the psychoanalytic method. The development and structuring of interpretations and reconstructions does not differ in nature from the like procedures in psychoanalysis. [21, 25, 26] There are, however, many problems of conceptualization. The establishment of a working relationship and the study of its vicissitudes are often referred to as "transference analysis," sometimes with the suggestion that it may prove to be equivalent to the operational usage of transference in psychoanalysis. It is my opinion that the equivalence has not been demonstrated and that there is much more to be gained by continuing to recognize the differences than by attempting to gloss over them. It is necessary for the investigator to reflect about and to work over some of his blind spots, and there is, therefore, reason to retain the terms "countertransference" and "self-analysis." The progressive effort, the levels of organization of the progression, and the content of the psychological deprivation introduce problems into the investigation which are of a different order from the problems designated as resistance, defense, and acting out in psychoanalytic work (although these are integral to each stabilized level of organiza-

tion). Additional concepts are needed. To assume that there will be no more than an equivalence in the nature of the findings may prove to be confusing and will certainly not lead to an explanation of the schizophrenic character of the behavior.

As I have mentioned above, I include "clinical remission" as one of the levels of the progression and, therefore, as part of the schizophrenic behavior. The higher levels, including remission, may constitute what Eissler[6] has referred to as the mute clinical phase. I believe that the technical considerations that I have mentioned apply to these states. John's "state of reality" was characterized by a sufficient increase of the threshold against psychological deprivation so that I could no longer detect manifestations of the nadir or the progression. Insofar as that may be confirmed, the "state of reality" is the only level of John's behavior that I would not consider to be schizophrenic. The personality and other problems present at that level are accessible to the psychoanalytic method.

"Mental Image"   The phenomenon that John called his "mental image" of me was prominent in his representations and in his translations. His descriptions of the "image" indicated that it was quite vivid—he would often describe it while looking at me and would compare the "image" with his perception of me. At archaic levels it was a "gargoyle," an "insane monster," and distorted in many and various ways. During a deprivation, as in the situation where I seemed to grow smaller and farther away, the "image" may grow fainter and momentarily disappear. With progression to higher levels it came closer to an accurate representation of the way I "really appeared to him." The increase of progressive effort connected with movement to a higher level was represented by his subsequent description of the changes in the "image." It would become "distorted and fragmented." He would concentrate on "rebuilding it" by thinking concretely of the various parts of my body and of its various living functions. It became "clear" when he achieved the higher level.

The "image" seems to me to be an indication of the reaching out that is part of the progressive effort. At archaic levels it may be reported as a hallucinatory experience. One young woman described it as follows: "You were in my room last night and talked with me." In this case, too, there would be distortions not only of appearance but also in the form of hostile or erotic attributes. In any case, "the image" is an indication that there is a working relationship and, when the behavior is very archaic, any such indication is reassuring and useful to the investigator. It may be very difficult to delineate the presence of the "image" in very archaic states: a reference to "movies in my mind" proved in one instance to represent the "image."

I believe that the "image" functions to increase the threshold against psychological deprivation. I was led to this conclusion by the close association of progressive efforts and progression to higher levels with descriptions of the "image." My conclusion seems to be confirmed by the fact that as the threshold was increased, John's references to the "image" diminished.

If I may be permitted the metaphor, the "image" develops at the point of impact of the psychological deprivation. It acts to soothe, comfort, scold, and protect the schizophrenic, and consoles him in his loneliness and distress. It sets limits for him in his daily life and lends its strength to the threshold. As his strength increases, its ministrations become fewer and it finally leaves him on his own.[20, 27, 28, 39, 41, 42]

CONCLUSION

In order to highlight what I consider characteristic of schizophrenic behavior I kept to a minimum considerations of psychodynamics, developmental history, and the like. This enabled me to delineate, in the form of a hypothesis, the nature of psychological deprivation, the indication of a lowered threshold against such deprivation, and the ensuing nadir event. All of the manifest schizophrenic behavior appears as a progression from the nadir—a sequence of levels of organization of behavior ranging from most archaic to least archaic in their quality. The schizophrenic's "mental image" of the investigator seems to function to strengthen the threshold against psychological deprivation.

I pointed out that the probability of the development of a cyclical retrograding situation is considerably greater than the probability of the development of a circumscribed situation. The former results in what appears to be a chronic and deteriorating state; the latter may lead to a clinical remission. The capacity for progressive effort and the nature of the threshold are variables requiring investigation. The nadir event seems to be enigmatic. The sequence of states of the progression is inherent in normal behavioral equipment.

The method of investigation is considered to be homologous with the psychoanalytic method. Some suggestions were offered concerning

the nature of the interactions in the investigation of schizophrenic behavior in order to point to the need for a more systematic statement of
the investigative method.

REFERENCES

1. F. H. Allport, *Theories of Perception and the Concept of Structure*
(New York: Wiley, 1955), esp. Chap. 21, pp. 614-667.

2. L. Bellak (ed.), *Schizophrenia—A Review of the Syndrome* (New
York: Logos, 1958).

3. M. Bouvet, "Technical Variations and the Concept of Distance,"
Internat. J. Psychoanal., 39 (1958), 211-221.

4. P. W. Bridgman, *The Way Things Are* (Cambridge: Harvard
Univ. Press, 1959).

5. L. Carroll, "Through the Looking Glass," and "Logical Non-
sense," in P. C. Blackbevon and L. White (eds.), *The Works of Lewis
Carroll* (New York: Putnam's, 1934).

6. K. R. Eissler, "Notes Upon Defects of Ego Structure in Schizophrenia," *Internat. J. Psychoanal.*, 35 (1954), 141-146.

7. K. R. Eissler, "Remarks on Some Variations in Psychoanalytic
Technique," *Internat. J. Psychoanal.*, 39 (1958), 222-229.

8. E. H. Erikson, *Childhood and Society* (New York: Norton, 1950).

9. E. H. Erikson, "The Problem of Ego Identity," *J. Amer. Psychoanalyt. A.*, IV (1956), 56-121.

10. P. Federn in E. Weiss (ed.), *Ego Psychology and the Psychoses*
(New York: Basic, 1952).

11. C. Fisher and I. H. Paul, "The Effect of Subliminal Visual Stimulation on Images and Dreams: A Validation Study," *J. Amer. Psychoanalyt. A.*, VII, No. 1 (1959), 35-83. (This article offers further bibliog-
raphy.)

12. S. M. Friedman and C. Fisher, "Further Observations on Primary Modes of Perception," *J. Amer. Psychoanalyt. A.*, VIII, No. 1
(1960), 100-129.

13. S. Freud, "The Uncanny" (1919), in *Collected Papers*, Vol. IV
(New York: Basic, 1959), pp. 368-407.

14. S. Freud, "The Interpretation of Dreams," in *The Works of
Sigmund Freud* (standard ed.), Vols. IV, V.

15. S. Freud, *ibid.*, p. 341.

16. S. Freud, *ibid.*, pp. 339-349.

17. M. M. Gill and M. Brenman, *Hypnosis and Related States* (New
York: Internat. Univ. Press, 1959).

18. H. Hartmann, "Comments on the Psychoanalytic Theory of the
Ego," in *The Psychoanalytic Study of the Child*, Vol. V (New York:
Internat. Univ. Press, 1950).

19. H. Hartmann, "Ego Psychology and the Problem of Adaptation,"
in D. Rapaport (ed.), *Organization and Pathology of Thought* (New
York: Columbia Univ. Press, 1951), pp. 362-396.

20. E. D. Hoedemaker, "The Therapeutic Process in the Treatment of Schizophrenia," *J. Amer. Psychoanalyt. A.*, III (1955), 89-109.

21. R. P. Knight, "Psychotherapy of an Adolescent Catatonic Schizophrenia with Mutism," *Psychiatry*, IX, No. 4 (1946), 323-339.

22. E. Kris, "On Pre-conscious Mental Processes," *Psychoanalyt. Quart.*, XIX (1950), 540-560.

23. J. C. Lilly, "Mental Effects of Reduction of Ordinary Levels of Physical Stimuli on Intact, Healthy Persons—A Symposium," Psychiatric Research Report No. 5, June, 1956 (Psychiatric Assn.).

24. H. W. Loewald, "Ego and Reality," *Internat. J. Psychoanal.*, 32 (1951), 10-18.

25. H. W. Loewald, "On the Therapeutic Action of Psychoanalysis," to be published.

26. R. M. Loewenstein, "Remarks on Some Variations in Psychoanalytic Techniques," *Internat. J. Psychoanal.*, 39 (1958), 202-210.

27. W. L. Pious, "Pathogenic Process in Schizophrenia," *Bull. Menninger Clin.*, Sept. 1949, 152-159.

28. W. L. Pious, "Obsessive-Compulsive Symptoms in an Incipient Schizophrenia," *Psychoanalyt. Quart.*, XIX (1950), 327-351.

29. D. Rapaport, "States of Consciousness," opening paper at Second Conference on "Problems of Consciousness" of the Josiah Macy, Jr. Foundation, N.Y., March 19-20, 1951.

30. D. Rapaport, *Organization and Pathology of Thought* (New York: Columbia Univ. Press, 1951), esp. Part 7, pp. 687-730.

31. D. Rapaport, *ibid.*, p. 706.

32. D. Rapaport, "Some Metapsychological Considerations Concerning Activity and Passivity," 1953. (Unpublished.)

33. D. Rapaport, in S. C. Miller (ed.), "Seminars on Psychoanalytic Ego Psychology" (Western New England Institute for Psychoanalysis, 1955; mimeographed).

34. D. Rapaport, "The Theory of Ego Autonomy: A Generalization," *Bull. Menninger Clin.*, 22 (1958), 13-35.

35. J. Ruesch, G. Bateson, *Communication* (New York: Norton, 1951), diagram, p. 275.

36. M. A. Sechehaye, *Symbolic Realization* (New York: Internat. Univ. Press, 1951).

37. R. Schafer, "Regression in the Service of the Ego: The Relevance of Psychoanalytic Concept for Personality Assessment," in G. Lindzey (ed.), *Assessment of Human Motives* (New York; Rinehart, 1958), pp. 119-148.

38. R. Schafer, "Generative Empathy in the Treatment Situation," *Psychoanalyt. Quart.*, 28 (1959), 342-373.

39. R. Schafer, "The Loving and Beloved Superego in Freud's Structural Theory." Read at the March 19, 1960, meeting of The Western New England Psychoanalytic Society. (Unpublished.)

40. W. Van Dusen, "A Central Dynamism in Chronic Schizophrenia," *Psa. and The Psychoanalyt. Rev.*, 46, No. 4 (1960), 2-8.

41. M. Wexler, "The Structural Problem in Schizophrenia: Therapeutic Implications," *Internat. J. Psychoanal.*, 32 (1951), 157-166.

42. M. Wexler, "The Structural Problem in Schizophrenia: The Role of the Internal Object," in E. B. Brody and F. C. Redlich (eds.), *Psychotherapy with Schizophrenics: A Symposium* (New York: Internat. Univ. Press, 1952), pp. 179-201.

43. M. Wexler, "Psychological Distance in the Treatment of a Schizophrenic Patient," in R. Lindner (ed.), *Explorations in Psychoanalysis* (New York: Julian, 1953), pp. 163-172.

CHAPTER III

Introductory Notes on the Psychoanalytic Therapy of Schizophrenics

Silvano Arieti

PSYCHOANALYTIC THERAPY with schizophrenics may for didactical purposes be arbitrarily divided into two parts: first, the general establishment of patient-therapist relatedness and, second, the special techniques of the therapeutic session.

PATIENT-THERAPIST RELATEDNESS

These two parts present different didactical challenges: whereas the second is more or less easily learned by the young therapist who already has a general knowledge of the phenomenology, dynamics, and formal mechanisms of schizophrenia, the first is hard to teach, hard to learn, and at times seems to consist largely of "intuitional improvisations" [1] or of "mystical" and "unscientific" procedures. It would almost seem as if the exquisite therapeutic sensitivity of some therapists in relating to schizophrenics were an irreducible or untransmittable quality, or at least were not matched by the capacity of the same therapists to infer and thus to communicate the common or intrinsic qualities which made this sensitivity possible.

---

[1] F. Fromm-Reichmann, "Clinical Significance of Intuitive Processes of the Psychoanalyst," *J. Am. Psychoan. Assoc.*, 3 (1955), 82; A. B. Szalita-Pemow, "The 'Intuitive Process' and Its Relation to Work With Schizophrenics," *J. Am. Psychoan. Assoc.*, 3 (1955), 7.

I do not want to give the impression that I have overcome the inherent difficulties of establishing this relatedness with schizophrenics or of teaching this ability to others. However, as a result of clinical and teaching experience, I feel that an attitude of cautious optimism is justified. Although there are, indeed, some people with unusual talent for establishing this relatedness with schizophrenics, to a considerable extent such abilities can be taught and learned, and, with progressive understanding of the phenomena involved, this teaching will become more effective. An attempt in this direction will be made in the first part of this chapter.

I wish to point out, however, that although the establishment of relatedness is an absolute requirement for successful treatment, the treatment entails much more. The special techniques of the session, including interpretation of symptoms and some general orientation in the various stages of therapy, are equally important. In the space allotted to this chapter all the aspects of this laborious technique cannot be illustrated. Some of them, however, will be arbitrarily selected for discussion in the second part of this paper.

The Concept of Relatedness   The concept of relatedness, a concept frequently used in the interpersonal school of psychiatry (see, for instance, Fromm,[2] Tauber and Green[3]), does not refer only to the establishment of rapport or contact with the patient, in accordance with the meanings which were given to these terms in classical psychiatry.[4] Neither does it refer merely to the establishment of communication or of a feeling of empathy, as is more frequently stated today. It also includes

[2] E. Fromm, *The Sane Society* (New York: Rinehart, 1955).

[3] E. S. Tauber, M. R. Green, *Prelogical Experience* (New York: Basic Books, 1959).

[4] In a paper by J. Bierer, "The Specific Contribution of Individual Psychology to the Treatment of Schizophrenia," appearing in the second volume of the *Congress Report of the II International Congress for Psychiatry* ([Zurich: Orell Fussli, 1959], p. 155), it is mentioned that the principle of relatedness was developed by Adler and applied by him to schizophrenia. No mention of this appears in other publications about Adler, for instance in *The Individual Psychology of Alfred Adler*, edited by H. and R. Ansbacher (Basic Books, 1956). It is unfortunate that this contribution of Adler has not received previous recognition. It is my belief that the concept of relatedness was developed independently in the school of Interpersonal Relations and that it has a somewhat different connotation from the Adlerian. For instance, it includes the concepts of transference and countertransference. In the way it is applied in the Interpersonal school it is therefore a neo-Freudian concept.

the classical psychoanalytic concepts of transference and countertransference; however, the phenomena of transference and countertransference are considered not separately but together in simultaneous occurrence, in their influencing each other and producing a two-way stream—or rather, one stream which is the result of more than one current. In other words, it is important to take into consideration not only the feelings the patient has for the therapist but also the feelings that the therapist has for the patient, the feelings that the patient has about the feelings of the therapist, the feelings that the therapist has about the feelings of the patient, and so on, in a self-perpetuating reciprocal situation.

We could also phrase the concept of relatedness differently and say that, although it includes the classic psychoanalytic concept of object relationship, it views such relationship not only as a centrifugal force emanating from the individual but also as an interrelation between at least two individuals—more as an I-thou relationship in Buber's[5] sense; as an entity not exclusively biological and intrapsychic but also social and interpsychic.

Obviously the establishment of relatedness is important in the treatment of any patient, independently of the diagnostic category in which we include him.

In the case of schizophrenia, however, the establishment of this relatedness is particularly important for specific reasons:

1. Inherent in the illness itself is a fight against relatedness. Whereas the neurotic patient in most cases wants to be helped and to be in contact with others (although in a distorted contact), the schizophrenic seems to want to move away from the rest of mankind. He is in the process of more or less rapidly losing his grip on the world, and most attempts to establish contact with him increase his anxiety and make him disintegrate and withdraw even more. He is distrustful, suspicious, hostile, or apparently apathetic. The meeting with the therapist must curtail this disintegration and re-establish a relatedness between the patient and another person, and, through this person, between the patient and the world.

2. In the treatment of schizophrenia the various elements which constitute relatedness have functions different from what they would be in the treatment of neurotics or of normal people. In the treatment of neurotics the transference plays the most important role, with the countertransference secondary in either a positive or a negative way. In

[5] M. Buber, *I and Thou* (Edinburgh: Clark, 1953).

the treatment of schizophrenia the countertransference is just as important as the transference and at times the whole treatment depends on it.

Perhaps the difficulties in understanding this concept and its therapeutic establishment will be somewhat decreased if we start by taking
into consideration schizophrenic panic—a condition in which there is a
rapid loss of relatedness and in which a re-establishment of it may bring
about dramatic therapeutic results.

Schizophrenic Panic Schizophrenic panic is a state of acute mental
disturbance which at times precedes the onset of full-fledged schizophrenic symptoms, but which may also be followed by a return to the
previous apparently asymptomatic condition.

More or less suddenly the patient becomes extremely restless. At
times he feels as if he had been drugged. Some apparently plausible
ideas acquire predominance in his mind or possess him to such an extent
that he is not able to pay attention to anything else. He wants reassurance very badly and repeats the same question many times, but cannot be reassured. Pertinent replies make no impression on him and are
almost not heard. Nevertheless, any attempt to make human contact is
vaguely registered, increases his anxiety, and inflames his symptoms.

Although on rare occasions the patient succeeds in overcoming this
condition, most often the symptomatology rapidly becomes more pronounced. He has the feeling that something terrible is happening to him
—that possibly he is becoming insane. A little later he feels that people
think he is insane. Things seem funny, peculiar; they have acquired a
different perceptual quality and an obscure meaning. If the fear increases, the patient may become unable to make decisions, to act, and
he may lapse into a more or less acute state of catatonic stupor. If the
confusion increases, he may fall into a hebephrenic excitement.

At other times, after a period of confusion, the patient feels that
everything is clear. The light has come back. Now he understands everything and he feels completely lucid. The strange things and events
which appeared confused and obscure now have an obvious meaning.
They were not accidental, but purposely arranged. Someone somewhere is after him, against him. The patient is able to "put two and two
together" and "to assemble the various pieces of the jigsaw puzzle."
He manifests the phenomenon which I have called "psychotic insight"
and his psychosis is now well established in a paranoid pattern. But at
this time we cannot talk any longer of "schizophrenic panic"; the psychosis is fully activated. Unless therapeutic intervention occurs the pa-

tient continues to lose relatedness; that is, he continues to desocialize and to withdraw into his own private paleologic mode of experience.

A special type of schizophrenic panic which needs particular attention because of its importance and frequency is that occurring after childbirth. Many authors attribute the onset of postpartum psychoses to the stress of labor or to hormonic or other metabolic changes. Although these physical factors may play some role, the main factors seem to me psychogenic in nature. Schizophrenic psychoses are not the only conditions which develop after childbirth; all psychiatric conditions may occur, including manic-depressive psychosis, reactive depressions, and exacerbations of previous neuroses. The symptoms may occur immediately and acutely after the birth or even gradually, and at times may only be recognizable a few months after the delivery.

If the condition remains at a neurotic level, we generally have one of these two pictures: either the mother feels that she is not able to take care of the baby and is very distressed about it; or she is afraid that she may harm the child, and even kill him. These obsessive ideas and phobias are very distressing. In other cases a pre-existing character disorder becomes much more pronounced.

But in cases where schizophrenic panic occurs, the confusion is more acute. The patient presents a sudden inability to face facts. She states that she cannot take care of the baby. She wants to run away, leave her home, her husband, her baby. At other times she alternates between these feelings and the feelings that she is guilty, worthless, not even capable of being a mother. She identifies with her own mother, who was a bad mother, and with her child, who is the victim of a bad mother. Any human contact increases her feeling of inadequacy and her anxiety. The family is unable to help at all. The family generally consists of three people in addition to the patient, and these three people are perceived by the patient as strangers. The first stranger is the baby, who is seen not as a source of love but as a source of anxiety, because it will disclose her failure as a mother, her ungiving qualities, her inadequacy.

The second stranger is the mother of the patient, who, as in the past, is incapable of reassuring the patient. As a matter of fact, she seems to scold the patient for her failure to be a mother and, paradoxically, she herself seems to the patient to be the prototype of bad motherhood.

The third stranger is the husband who is also caught in a situation he does not know how to cope with. Although he tries to control himself, he cannot comfort or express sympathy for the wife who is not able even to be a real woman, a mother for his child. Instead of sympathizing with her he bemoans his destiny for having married such a woman.

Although the mother and husband try most of the time to conceal these feelings, the real feelings are conveyed to the patient. Her anxiety and confusion increase, the fear reaches the proportion of panic, perceptual reality becomes more and more distorted, and finally a full-fledged psychotic episode, hebephrenic or catatonic in type, ensues. In some cases, what follows is an acute or more or less chronic paranoid state. I have also seen lasting postpartum quasi-delusional states where the distortion never reached psychotic dimensions.

In all these cases of schizophrenic panic, whether postpartum or not, we find that a new challenge has occurred with which the patient, because of the limitations resulting from her life history and from her crippling, rather than protecting, defenses, is unable to cope.

Let us see now how some patients, treated during the early state of panic, before "psychotic insight" was reached and thus avoiding a progression toward a full-fledged psychosis, experienced the first encounter with the therapist: "I felt you were with me. I did not feel alone any more. I could not talk, but you understood the troubles I had after the birth of the baby. What you said was clear." In other words reassurance and immediate clarification were given. The therapist entered the picture, not as an examiner who was going to dissect the patient, but as one who immediately participated in what seemed to the patient an inaccessible situation. To a male patient in panic I said, "You are afraid of me, of everybody. You are frightened stiff. I am not going to hurt you." To a woman who had given birth recently, I said, holding her hand, "You are *not* your mother. I trust you, and I am here with you."

If we make some impact the first time we see the patient when he is in acute panic, the chances are good that the episode will be resolved and the full psychosis averted. This does not mean that the patient is cured or that further treatment is unnecessary. A woman, who was first seen by me in the midst of a rapidly developing postpartum psychosis, recovered quickly from the acute symptoms but subsequently received more than four years of treatment. Hospitalization was not necessary, however, and she was able to take care of her three children.

Therapeutic Attitude The above remarks on schizophrenic panic and on the first therapeutic encounter may help us to delineate those activities of the therapist necessary to establish relatedness not only with patients in panic but also with patients at any stage of the schizophrenic psychosis.

First, the therapist must have an attitude of *active and intense intervention.* He comes to participate in the struggle which goes on and not to listen passively to ideas which cannot be associated fully.

Second, there must be *an immediate attempt on the part of the therapist to remove the fear* which is automatically aroused by the fact that a human being (the therapist) wants to establish contact.

Third, there must be a *general attitude of reassurance.*

Fourth, a very *simple* and *short interpretative formulation* must be offered to the patient which the therapist grasps at once in his first contact with the patient. Of course, detailed interpretations are out of place at this point. The importance of this formulation lies in conveying to the patient that he is understood and that somebody feels with him and knows his troubles.

Fifth, some *nonverbal, meaningful* acts, such as touching the patient, holding his hand, walking together, etc., may be useful in some cases. The therapist must understand, however, that this procedure may be dangerous with some patients. For instance, a catatonic stupor may be transformed into a frightful catatonic excitement.

A *sixth* activity, which actually includes the previous five, consists in the establishment of *basic trust.* This term requires some explanation. Erikson[6] too has described fully the place of trust in the epigenesis of the ego. He defines basic trust as an attitude toward oneself and the world derived from the experiences of the first year of life. By trust he means trustfulness as far as others are concerned and a sense of trustworthiness as far as oneself is concerned.

Erikson's conception seems fully acceptable to me except that I think this period starts a little later and lasts longer, although with changing aspects. The formation of this feeling takes place, in my opinion, during the whole of early childhood, and perhaps up to the age of four or four and a half. This atmosphere of basic trust seems to me the opposite of an atmosphere of anxiety and, like the latter, the result of relationships with others. Good things are taken for granted by the baby and are expected to occur. Mother will give him the breast, she will

[6] E. H. Erikson, "Growth and Crises of the Healthy Personality," in C. Kluckhohn, H. A. Murray, D. M. Schneider (eds.), *Personality in Nature, Society, and Culture* (New York: Knopf, 1956).

keep him on her lap and will fondle him. These feelings of expectancy, optimism, trust, are vague and indefinite. The child does not possess the words used by us to describe these phenomena and his apperception of these feelings must remain at a primitive level. Possibly they consist of diffuse sensations, postural attitudes, physiological preparation for what is expected, nonverbal symbolism, and so forth.

Later the child expects not only physical things from others but also approval. That is, the child trusts that the adult will trust him. As I said previously, "There is a reciprocal trust that things are going to be well, that the child will be capable of growing up to be a healthy and mature man. The child perceives this faith of the mother and accepts it, just as he used to accept the primitive responses to the usual stimuli. He finally assimilates this trust of the significant adults, and he trusts himself." [7]

In the childhood of schizophrenics this basic trust is defective, because the parents are either rejecting or extremely anxious. That is, they themselves are deprived of basic trust and therefore cannot communicate it to the child. In schizophrenia this atmosphere of mistrust and excessive anxiety is reactivated and magnified. It is the purpose of therapy to re-establish basic trust. The therapist must convey to the patient the feeling that he has faith in him and in his human potentialities no matter how sick he is at present. In order to have such faith the therapist must like the patient and, since he cannot like every human being, he must limit the treatment to those for whom he has positive feelings and with whose difficulties he can identify. The therapist cannot offer love as a parent can, but he can offer trust.

Different therapists convey this feeling of trust in different ways; at times even by being strict and cruel, but oftener by assuming an accepting and maternal role. It does not really matter which attitude is taken. It must be the one which is harmonious with the personality of the therapist and better conveys his genuine feelings.

If we understand the importance of the re-establishment of basic trust in the treatment of schizophrenia, we also understand a basic difference between psychoanalytic therapy in general and psychoanalytic therapy of schizophrenia.

Psychoanalytic therapy in its classical conception may be viewed as an act of, or at least an attempt at, liberation. The suffering individual

[7] S. Arieti, "What is Effective in the Therapeutic Process?" *Amer. J. Psychoanal.*, 17 (1957), 30.

is liberated from unconscious burdens, fixations, repressions, defenses etc., and once this act of liberation has been accomplished, the personality is permitted to make its own adjustment.

For schizophrenic patients psychoanalytic therapy must do more than liberate. It must provide, although late and in a somewhat artificial manner, those elements which were insufficient for a normal epigenesis.

Now that we have described the positive qualities necessary for the establishment of relatedness, we must mention the two main negative characteristics to be avoided.

First, anxiety, at least to a great degree, must be avoided. A little anxiety may be tolerated and, as Fromm-Reichmann[8] said, may in certain cases even be useful. Considerable anxiety, however, would increase the anxiety of the patient, would not permit the establishment of basic trust, and would be identified with the original anxiety originally experienced with the significant adults.

Second, clinical detachment. If the patient feels that he is just a medical specimen or a "case," no affective relatedness can be established.

The ability to establish relatedness with schizophrenics is not so difficult to acquire as it may seem. One of the first problems of the therapist is the need to unlearn older models of examination and treatment that otherwise almost inadvertently would creep in. Among them are: (1) the old-fashioned routine mental-status examination, purely diagnostic in aim and consisting of questions some of which are similar to those of a district attorney; (2) strict adherence to the orthodox psychoanalytic technique, which was originally devised for the treatment of psychoneuroses and which relies chiefly on free association.

A patient of mine, Geraldine, whose treatment was very successful, told me that during her two psychotic breakdowns she met at least three persons who had the ability to "break through" to her.[9] The first was a nurse, who unfortunately was transferred to another ward; the second was a psychiatrist who was too busy with too many patients; the third was myself. This "breaking through" is an extremely important episode, experienced at times with dramatic emotional intensity. In some in-

---

[8] F. Fromm-Reichmann, "Basic Problems in the Psychotherapy of Schizophrenia," *Psychiatry*, 21 (1958), 1.

[9] For a partial report of the psychopathology of Geraldine see my paper, "Schizophrenic thought," *Am. J. Psychother.*, 13 (1959), 537.

stances it is remembered by the patient with great emotional display reminiscent of the Freudian abreaction. (This is not an abreaction, however. There is no forgetting of "the breaking through.")

When Geraldine was far advanced in the treatment I asked her to give me more details about the "breaking through" effectuated by the nurse. She said, "There was a reading room on the ward, with a piano and magazines. I went there and I looked at the cover of a magazine. A nurse stepped in. I had never seen her before. She started a conversation with me as if I was a normal person. I told her with tremendous emotion, 'You are the first person who has broken through to me.' She was not on guard, I was not on guard. She was an ordinary girl. She made me feel communication with people was worth while. Before that nothing was worth while. People were hateful."

At this point the patient burst into tears, as never before during the whole course of treatment. A little later she continued, "With most of the nurses the illness is a fault; it was not with her. I felt that the other people were on to me. She was not."

In the treatment with me during her second breakdown, this "breaking through" was not as dramatic as it was the first time with the nurse. Again, on one occasion, Geraldine expressed herself in this way: "With you I felt as confident as with the nurse. I feel it was so because you are always so relaxed and not intellectual, just as the nurse was." These words of Geraldine aroused a state of perplexity in me. I always so relaxed? That's not what my wife thinks of me. I, nonintellectual? But my friends do not hesitate to tell me that I make too much use of intellectuality in conversing with them.

I do not want to give the impression that I assume an artificially therapeutic attitude of relaxation and nonintellectuality, because to the best of my knowledge I do not. But my roles are different in different situations. I stress this point to indicate that although spontaneous and sincere, the therapeutic attitude cannot be the therapist's usual attitude toward life but requires the acquisition of a special role. When I am with my wife the accumulated tension of the problems of the day may find easy manifestations. With my friends I am a peer, and since intellectuality is a part of me, it soon comes to the surface. With the schizophrenic patient, except at an advanced stage of treatment, I am not a peer. My role is nutritional and maternal. Although there is an exchange between the patient and myself, I want to give more than I take. I do not burden him with my own anxiety, if I can help it, and intellectuality does not enter into the immediacy of our relatedness. Incidentally, I consider Geraldine an intellectual too, but the needs she wanted to satisfy in her relation with me were not intellectual ones. Perhaps what I try to describe here is the same attitude which Schwing[10] advocates in her book on "motherliness" in the treatment of schizophrenia. I differ from Schwing, however, inasmuch as I give fundamental importance also to other aspects of the treatment.

This motherliness, or immediate relatedness, need not be offered exclusively by a therapist or a nurse, or by a person in a maternal role. At times the encounter even with a layman in the role of a paternal or authoritarian figure has great therapeutic effect.

Auxiliary Drug Treatment   Before leaving the topic of relatedness we have to discuss a point which has recently acquired great importance. Have the new drugs, namely the tranquilizers, a place in the psychotherapy of schizophrenia? This question is actively debated, the staunchest psychogeneticists insisting that they have no place at all; others feeling that they actually now make accessible to psychotherapy a large number of schizophrenics who in the past would have been given only shock treatment. The drugs would make the establishment of relatedness much easier.

It seems to me that we should not adhere to dogmatic beliefs or general rules but that each patient should be considered individually. In my own experience I have obtained the best results with patients who have not used even a single tablet of tranquilizer, or similar drugs. However, I have used drugs with a relatively few patients, not because they were necessarily more acutely ill, but because otherwise I would not have been able to establish relatedness with them. In this way I avoided hospitalization. I have observed, however, that with these patients the progress has been much slower, although relatedness was achieved. How is this to be explained? My hunches are that the tranquilizers are effective inasmuch as they diminish the capacity of the patient to experience anxiety; thus the symptoms weaken, the fear of interpersonal relations decreases, and contact is established. However, the decrease in sensitivity, which in these cases is responsible for the decrease in symptoms and for the re-establishment of contact, also makes the patient less sensitive to the influence of treatment and improvement is slow.

Thus, each case has to be assessed individually. Are we going to lose

[10] G. Schwing, *A Way to the Soul of the Mentally Ill* (New York: Internat. Univ. Press, 1954).

or gain with the use of drugs? If relatedness cannot be established, if hospitalization would be necessary, with the possibility of the patient being removed from psychotherapeutic possibilities or from earning a living and thus being unable to secure treatment, drugs should be used. However, it is always much better to try psychotherapy without them. It is the responsibility of the therapist to decide. If the therapist has the opportunity of studying the individual patient intensively, mistakes will be few.

Special Techniques of the Therapeutic Session

The establishment of relatedness, as described in the previous section, is a necessary requirement and may be sufficient even to terminate or interrupt an acute episode of psychosis. As I have already mentioned, however, the treatment cannot be considered ended or successful unless the patient has understood the dynamic or psychogenetic bases of his difficulties, has learned to interpret the meanings and mechanisms of his symptoms, has built a new self-image, has changed some of the basic patterns of living, and, in summary, has achieved a level of adjustment considerably superior to the one of his prepsychotic life.

In order to help the patient achieve these goals the therapist must have a knowledge of: (1) the dynamic mechanisms and patterns of living which are likely to occur in the life history of schizophrenics; (2) a knowledge of the formal mechanisms of the symptoms not only in order to understand them but also in order to explain them to the patient at the right opportunity; (3) a particular knowledge of the symbolic aspects of psychopathologic conditions, as revealed especially by psychoanalysis.

It is impossible in an introductory paper to illustrate all these points. Only a few topics will be chosen for consideration: (1) the interpretation of delusional material and abnormal thought processes; (2) the treatment of hallucinations; (3) homosexuality in schizophrenia; (4) the patient's separation from his family.

Interpretations The importance of interpretative material is variously estimated by the various authors. We have all shades of opinion, ranging from the viewpoint of those who attribute great importance to them to those who deny their value altogether.

My point of view is that although interpretations in themselves are not sufficient to bring about recovery, they are a necessary therapeutic element. Their role, of course, varies in different cases. A statement which is repeatedly made is that the schizophrenic already knows the meaning of his symptoms better than the analyst and that therefore he does not need interpretation: what is unconscious to us is conscious to him.

This statement is correct in some cases, and especially in very regressed patients, but even in these it is not correct in an absolute sense. The schizophrenic patient does not know how to apply what he knows to the rest of his psychic life and makes a wrong use of the insight he has. The therapist must help him to connect the various pieces of his knowledge. Furthermore, in nonregressed paranoid patients, as in neurotic patients, there are actual repressions and interpretations are necessary. However, these interpretations do not need to be so frequent as some authors, for instance, Rosen,[11] advocate. One has the impression that Rosen uses interpretations as his own method of establishing immediate relatedness. (I too have suggested very simple interpretative formulations in order to establish quick relatedness.)

Other therapists feel that it is not necessary to do interpretative work; that delusions will disappear spontaneously once the relatedness we have established and the rise of self-esteem bring about a general improvement. This is true to a certain extent, but again, interpretations at times bring about a rise in self-esteem, so that it is difficult to establish what comes first. I feel that schizophrenia has to be fought simultaneously on various fronts. The effectiveness of the treatment will be enhanced by the simultaneity and eventual coalescence of these various ways.

A metaphor which I use frequently in my teaching is the following: Suppose in ancient times an enemy fortress built of ice, in a very Nordic area, had to be demolished. What could destroy the fortress? First the warm rays of the sun which would first hit, caress, embrace, and finally melt the cold fortress. Useful as they may be, however, the rays of the sun in a Nordic country would not be hot enough to melt the fortress, but only to soften it. The soldiers would have to resort to their axes to tear down the weakened walls. Schizophrenia is the fortress in the Nordic country. The warm, embracing sun is the nutrient relatedness; interpretations, as well as other techniques, are the work done with the axes.

Interpretation of delusions is not always easy. One of the things which patients have difficulty in understanding is how alleged persecu-

[11] J. N. Rosen, *Direct Analysis* (New York: Grune, 1953).

tors may represent people in their past, and the mechanisms by which unconscious identifications are disguised. It is also difficult for them to understand how some "intruding" experiences are actually projected parts of the patients themselves.

For instance, Geraldine had already reached a level at which she could speak freely about her mother and the traumas that her mother had inflicted on her. The patient was living with her mother. Since she had made considerable improvement, including the loss of all hallucinatory phenomena, I suggested that she live alone.

A few days after the separation from her mother, Geraldine started to hallucinate again. She was hearing a neighbor, an elderly woman, making disparaging remarks about her. Obviously the increase in anxiety on account of being separated from the mother played an important role. But the most important point here is that the neighbor in a certain way took the mother's place when the mother left. As long as the mother was present in her physical reality, the patient could correct the unconscious and automatic feeling of always being denigrated by her. When the real or external mother left, the inner mother or incorporated mother was heard again. However the patient had to disguise her by substituting the neighbor for her—a woman of her mother's age. The patient was able to understand these connections when they were explained to her.

Another patient, Justin, experienced the following phenomenon: He was hearing a man (whom at times he would consider an impostor, at other times "another self") say profane things. Justin felt that this other person was using his—Justin's—mouth and his voice, so that people would actually think it was Justin who was talking. This man would utter embarrassing words with homosexual content. For instance, he would say, "I like cock."

The fact was that Justin was homosexual and had had some overt homosexual experiences. However, like many homosexuals, he was rejecting homosexuality at a certain level. But the other person in him was frankly admitting homosexuality. The part of him which was repressed was also projected or externalized. The patient was told how he was really divided on the issue of homosexuality and that if he could accept his ambivalence, he would not need to resort to this strange phenomenon.

The most bizarre forms of displacement, projection, substitution, and concealment occur in delusional formations. One of the most common is the fragmentation of a person in several delusional entities. One of the most interesting is the Capgras[12] phenomenon, which is frequently described in Europe and recently has also received some consideration in the United States.[13] The patient says that an important person in his life is not the person he really is but an impostor who has assumed his appearance. For instance, the mother of the patient comes to visit the patient at the hospital. The patient thinks that she is not his mother but a horrible impostor who has assumed the mother's appearance. The patient is full of rejection and hostility toward the impostor. With this mechanism the patient discharges on the alleged impostor the feelings that he could not admit having for his mother, and the real mother is spared. One of the best ways of understanding this delusional material, and especially the fragmentations of personality and projections, is the study of dreams of neurotics with the usual psychoanalytic methods. The same mechanisms found in dreams operate in delusional formations.

Another point which needs to be emphasized is that not only the content of the delusions but also the formal mechanisms have to be interpreted to the patient. The mechanism of the concretization of the concept will be illustrated later when we discuss hallucinations, although it applies also to most delusions.

The paleologic disorder of thought can also be explained. A patient thought that when other employees in her office mentioned the word *water* they were referring to her. In her office there was a water cooler which was out of order and which had to be hit in order to permit the water to flow. When people hit the cooler she thought they meant to hit her. When I asked her why she thought so, she said, "I never walk, I run, like water, and I deserve to be hit."

I explained to her from these examples and many others that when she was in a state of extreme anxiety she resorted to paleologic thinking to demonstrate her inadequacy, and to her defensive projective mechanisms (she attributed to others the feelings she had about herself). I explained to her the basic principles of paleologic thinking as I have described them in detail elsewhere.[14]

[12] J. Capgras, J. Reboul-Cachaux, "L'Illusion des sosies dans un délire systematisé chronique," *Soc. Clin. Med. Psych.*, 81 (1923), 186.

[13] G. M. Davidson, "The Syndrome of Capgras," *Psychiatric Quart.*, 15 (1941), 513; J. Todd, "The Syndrome of Capgras," *Psychiatric Quart.*, 31 (1957), 250; S. Arieti and J. Meth, "Rare, Unclassifiable, Collective, and Exotic Psychotic Syndromes," in S. Arieti (ed.), *American Handbook of Psychiatry* (New York: Basic Books, 1959).

[14] S. Arieti, "Special Logic of Schizophrenic and Other Types of Autistic

Of course, in making these interpretations we have to appeal to those parts of the psyche of the patient which some authors have described as nuclear islands, or adult parts which have escaped the schizophrenic process.[15] These small parts still work and our appeal to them will be successful *provided the general atmosphere of relatedness has been established.*

Hallucinations Until recently it was my conviction that one of the fundamental characteristics of hallucinations was their incorrigibility. That is, until the symptom altogether disappeared, either through treatment or spontaneously, it would be impossible for the schizophrenic patient to become aware of the unreality of the phenomenon and to correct it. I have more recently found that this is not necessarily so.

Hospitalized patients approached with the old routine questions "Do you hear voices? Who is persecuting you?" are unable to give up their hallucinations. As long as an atmosphere of unrelatedness exists, the patient cannot make an effort to see and hear things as other people do, and it is unwise to attack the problem directly. However, it is also unwise to give the patient the impression that the therapist hears his voices and shares his unusual private experiences. The therapist should simply tell the patient that he does not hear these voices and will maintain an attitude of cordiality and relatedness.

Later it is easier to indicate to the patient that he hears these voices only in particular situations, or when he expects to hear them. For example, the patient may, when he goes home, *expect* the neighbors to talk about him; then he hears the neighbors. He puts himself in what I call the "listening attitude." If the patient is related to the therapist, he will be able, under his direction, to distinguish two stages: that of the listening attitude and that of the hallucinatory experience. At first he may deny the existence of the two stages, but later he may say, "I happened to think so and what I thought was confirmed. They were really talking."

Later he may admit that there is a very brief interval between the expectation of the voices and the voices, but that that sequence is purely

---

Thought," *Psychiatry*, 11 (1948), 325; *Interpretation of Schizophrenia* (New York: Brunner, 1955); "The Two Aspects of Schizophrenia," *Psychiatric Quart.*, 31 (1957), 403.

[15] A. B. Szalita-Pemow, "Further Remarks on the Pathogenesis and Treatment of Schizophrenia," *Psychiatry*, 2 (1952), 143-150.

coincidental. Finally he sees the connection between putting himself into the listening attitude and his actually hearing them. Later on he also admits that he expects to hear the voices and puts himself in the listening attitude in particular situations. (Of course, this does not occur in very sick patients who hallucinate all the time.)

For example, unpleasant thoughts which occur while the patient is coming home from work may bring about the listening attitude. "Coming home," to an empty home without love—a home which is the concrete representation for the patient of his failure, inadequacy, guilt feelings, and where an intense feeling of unworthiness is experienced—moves him toward a certain mood. At this point the patient is able to see the transition from this mood to the listening attitude.[16] As far as the content of the hallucination is concerned, it will have to be interpreted in accordance with our knowledge of pathological symbolism and especially of the concretization of the concept.[17] Patients learn to catch themselves in the act of putting themselves into the listening attitude at the least disturbance several times during the day.[18] At first they recognize the phenomenon as almost an automatic mechanism which is very difficult to control and which requires an unpleasant effort, a strong determination not to succumb. Later it becomes easier to control, especially if the relatedness with the therapist and the understanding of the historical dynamic mechanisms have at the same time diminished the anxiety. In other words, the symptom is attacked in three ways: (1) by the general atmosphere of relatedness; (2) by the rise in self-esteem and decrease in anxiety coming from a psychodynamic understanding of one's life history; (3) by the recognition of the listening attitude and a learned control of it.

I anticipate some criticism of this formulation: First, is not this procedure directed to the symptom rather than to the underlying disease? Second, if the patient acquires self-esteem and an understanding of the dynamics, do not the symptoms drop out automatically?

[16] When this paper was presented at Austen Riggs Center (March 11, 1960), Eric Erikson, in the discussion which followed, aptly commented that my technique of making the patient recognize "the listening attitude" would help him to see that he is no longer a passive agent, a victim of strange occurrences, but that he plays an active, searching role. I have found it useful since then to emphasize this point to the patient.

[17] S. Arieti, "Schizophrenia," in S. Arieti (ed.), *American Handbook of Psychiatry* (New York: Basic Books, 1959).

[18] Related to the listening attitude is what I call the "referential attitude." This symptom and its therapeutic control are discussed in another publication now in preparation.

My answer consists in referring again to the metaphor of the ice fortress: schizophrenia has to be fought on many psychological fronts. Obviously the explanation of the listening attitude is not effective per se without the concomitant use of the rest of the technique. We must also remember that in schizophrenia, as well as in many other psychiatric conditions, psychopathologic patterns of experience tend to persist for a long period of time and to return automatically. Improvement will come more rapidly if awareness of the faulty mechanism is acquired. Even so, it may take months or years before the patient can rid himself of the "listening attitude."

We have spoken of this "listening attitude," and used auditory hallucinations as an example because they are the most common in schizophrenia, but the same thing could be demonstrated in other types of hallucinations. Frequent enough, especially among so-called ambulatory patients, are the olfactory and gustatory hallucinations.

The above-mentioned patient, Justin, had the following experiences: he often smelled a very bad odor emanating from his body; at other times, when he ate with his parents or some of his close friends, he would experience "a bitter taste in his mouth." He actually thought that poisons or other substances were put in the food, not to kill him, but to annoy him and make him suffer.

In this case it was easy to explain to the patient the content of the hallucinations. He felt he was a rotten character, therefore he smelled. The rotten character, or the "smelliness" of the character was concretized and projected to the body, which in a certain way is considered part of the external world. Close friends and members of the family leave a bitter taste in Justin's mouth by exciting him homosexually, or reminding him of his homosexuality or of his failures in life. What appears to us as a metaphorical representation is actually a concretization of the concept.[19] This concretization follows smelling or tasting attitudes which the patient adopts in anxiety-laden situations.

Schizophrenia and Homosexuality The mention of homosexuality in connection with Justin leads us to another important question. There are many reports in the literature about sexuality and schizophrenia, the prevailing opinion being, at least among orthodox psychoanalysts, that in schizophrenia, especially in the paranoid forms approaching the clas-

[19] S. Arieti, "Schizophrenia: The Manifest Symptomatology, the Psychodynamic and Formal Mechanisms," in S. Arieti (ed.), *American Handbook of Psychiatry* (Basic Books, 1959).

sic picture of paranoia, there is a latent homosexuality. The opinion is also expressed that in schizophrenia lack of identification with either sex is often found.

In my opinion these statements are correct for many cases, but by no means universally so. Schizophrenic and paranoiac-paranoid patients not only may be overt heterosexuals but also may be overt homosexuals. Since my statistics are limited, I am not in a position to say whether *overt* homosexuality is more or less frequent among schizophrenics than in the general population, but it is a fact that it occurs, and it represents a considerable complication in the treatment. An important difference, however, exists from nonschizophrenic homosexuals: the overt homosexual manifestations started a little later, generally several years after puberty, having been voluntarily suppressed until then.

At first it would seem logical to assume that the same psychodynamic disturbances which led to one condition (schizophrenia) led also to homosexuality and that consequently in treating the patient as a whole we should treat both conditions. Theoretically this is true, but practically this is an almost impossible task. The two disorders, although derived from a psychologically unhealthy environment in the presence of predisposing factors, have different psychopathological organizations. An important connection, however, may exist between the two: *consciously* the patient may reject his homosexuality. Living in a heterosexual society, he undergoes additional anxiety and his self-esteem is even more threatened or injured. Especially in early youth, for instance in college, when he succumbs to the first homosexual seductions, he may go into a state of panic leading to a schizophrenic psychosis. Of course the psychosis is determined not only by that anxiety connected with the homosexuality but also by the anxiety of the whole life history and especially of the childhood experiences.

Nevertheless homosexuality constitutes an important aggravating factor and may be responsible for precipitating and maintaining psychotic episodes. In these cases the therapy should be oriented toward the patient's first recognizing his conflict and, second, accepting his homosexual orientation without anxiety. Only if this anxiety over homosexuality is eliminated can we treat schizophrenia with any hope of success. We must thus accept a limited goal and, I must add, the easiest one. In fact, in my opinion, it is easier to recover from schizophrenia than from homosexuality. Perhaps it is not difficult to understand why. There are forces operating in schizophrenia which do not exist in homosexuality. Homosexuality is a condition which may be called syntonic with the self. It is compatible with life, although in its pure forms it is not compatible with reproduction. It is also compatible with pleasure-achievement and with the fulfillment of the fundamental human potentialities. Many of the problems connected with homosexuality are derived from the fact that the patient must live in a heterosexual society.

The situation is very much different in schizophrenia. Except in moderate cases, this psychosis is not a condition compatible with life unless, of course, the patient is taken care of by nonpsychotic members of the human species. It is fundamentally a process of progressive disorganization in spite of the organization of psychotic patterns, and is not compatible in most cases with pleasure-attainment and with the fulfillment of the potentialities of man. It is thus natural that the teleologic or regenerative capacities of the organism may be on our side in the fight against schizophrenia but not in the fight against homosexuality. Of course the foregoing does not imply that the psychodynamic mechanisms which led to homosexuality should not be examined. It does not imply either that acceptance of a limited goal is a definite attitude that psychiatrists should take at all times or in all cases. I think, however, that as long as our knowledge of homosexuality, schizophrenia and of the human psyche remains approximately what it is now, this prevailing attitude is the one we should take in most cases.

Separation of Patient and Family   I come now to the final point: the situation arising if and when a nonhospitalized schizophrenic patient leaves his family to live by himself. This is always a major step.

First of all, is it advisable? On the one hand we may think that it is in the family that the troubles of the patient started, and there, probably, that they are maintained. On the other hand, we may feel that to remove the patient from his family would not really be helpful because this would be merely a removal from the external situation, not from the introjected conflicts. As a matter of fact, one might even think that this separation might re-exacerbate the symptoms. We remember, for instance, Geraldine, who started to hallucinate again when she was separated from her mother.

Actually, in my experience, separation from the family is a positive step to be considered when the other conditions, to be mentioned later, permit. It is true that the psychologically incorporated members of the family will continue to act within the patient. However, the schizophrenic patient must also mature at a conscious reality level, and this process of maturation, of striving toward independence and self-reliance, is handicapped by his living with his family. Of course minor re-exacerbations of symptoms must be anticipated and coped with immediately by discussing them with the patient or even by warning him of their possible occurrence.

Separation from the spouse or a sibling has approximately the same psychological significance as separation from the mother, with whom this sibling or spouse is generally unconsciously identified.

The other problem is to determine when the patient is ready for separation. I think we must be prepared to take some risks. Again in my experience, several patients who appeared dependent and helpless proved to be able to take care of themselves much better than the members of the family or I had anticipated. Of course, in some cases we must make return possible—a return accompanied not by a sense of defeat but by the willingness to try again a little later.

The patient will be able to live by himself if he is given more than what he is deprived of; that is, if he is given by the therapist a sense of trust, confidence, and belief in the unfolding of his potentialities. The patient should also be told that he will be able to stay again for short periods of time with the members of his family when he is in a position not to be hurt any longer by what they represent.

CONCLUSIONS

Is it possible to draw conclusions in a paper whose scope is only introductory? The writer thinks that one can at least conclude that improvement and recovery in schizophrenic patients are brought about by two major therapeutic processes: by relatedness and by insight—including of course under these two headings the behavioral and emotional changes that accompany these two processes. One or the other method is generally used predominantly or exclusively in psychotherapeutic practice, but the use of only one of them with schizophrenic patients brings about improvement only, not recovery or even satisfactory adjustment.

The establishment of relatedness is the more difficult method to learn and to practice, because it is, at the present time, less susceptible of scientific analysis. Helping the schizophrenic patient to acquire insight (and we use this term in a general sense, including in it all the understanding that a patient may acquire about his own psychological life) is a painstaking and time-consuming, but easier to learn, procedure. In some specific situations these two methods blend together and cannot be differentiated.

CHAPTER IV

Image, Complex, and Transference in Schizophrenia

John Weir Perry

THE STARTING POINT for any consideration of theory or method in psychotherapy is, according to the Jungian view, a frank and unbiased scrutiny of the psychology of the psychologist. For, to the extent that the psyche is unconscious, and hence unknown, so equally will any comprehension of it be colored by the point of view of the observer. This volume is indeed a striking testimony to the fact of individual standpoints. This is no error or fortuitous misadventure in the unfolding of our science. Not only is there sense in it; it is inevitable. Only when the object observed is adequately known, and hence within the grasp of conscious handling, can any understanding of it be deemed free of the imprint of the nature of the psyche of the observer, and then only relatively and within the limits set by the culture.

Jung's formulation of psychological types is an effort to account in some measure for this phenomenon.[1] According to this formulation, we have our several, specific predilections to look for and to emphasize one or another of the several aspects of psychological phenomena. One of us will give greatest value to the genesis of interpersonal feelings, another to the internal dynamics of emotions, or to the rational processes of communication, or to the structure of schizophrenic thinking, or to the problems of adaptation to external reality, or to the physical bases of the psychoses, or to loosening of the constrictions of rigidity, or finally to the imagery of the interior processes of the unconscious. These may be

---

[1] C. G. Jung, *Psychological Types* (New York: Harcourt, Brace, 1926).

said to be the chief predilections of the feeling, thinking, sensation, and intuitive functions, in their extraverted and introverted attitudes, respectively.

Ideally, the completely fulfilled individual would transcend such limitations and comprehend all aspects of psychic phenomena within his broadly rounded grasp; unfortunately, as human nature is designed, such a man does not yet live. Meanwhile, each of us is at his best in that aspect of the field which represents his most differentiated orientation, and there he will find his greatest skill not only in understanding and formulating events but even more in handling the actual experience with his patients. Events in that area are most meaningful to him; areas with opposite qualities are least meaningful. Yet this state of affairs should not be used as a *carte blanche* to go ahead and be as one-sided as one likes; rather, it should be the starting point for a critical evaluation of one's subjective biases and limitations, and thus for an honest effort to compensate for the deficiency.

If I were asked to state what in essence is the "Jungian way" of treating a patient, I would first of all state not a theory but the principle requiring that a theory be fitted to the psychotherapist on one hand, and to his patient on the other.[2] It is then a psychology of psychologies, or a theory of theories. The field is then accepted as inherently polyglot.

There is another area, however, in which the Jungian approach may be said to be less relativistic and more unique. This concerns the role of the unconscious imagery found in the normal and the psychotic alike, and hence the relation the therapist establishes to it and to the psychic organism of the patient. Jungians give particular value to the introverted viewpoint, the one most prone to perceive in psychic processes the trends that work toward integrating the subject or the self, and in psychic contents the trends toward symbol formation, even where instinctive drives or object relations seem to all appearances to be the sole concern.[3] In these days of thinking in terms of interpersonal relationships and communication, that is, when the extraverted bias predominates, it tends to be assumed that not much is to be gained by delving into the fantasy content that a patient offers in delusional and autistic ideas. I

[2] C. G. Jung, "The Practice of Psychotherapy," *Collected Works*, 16, Bollingen Series 20 (New York: Pantheon, 1954).
[3] C. G. Jung, "The Content of the Psychoses," *Collected Papers on Analytical Psychology* (New York: Moffat Yard, 1917); "On Psychic Energy," *Contributions to Analytical Psychology* (New York: Harcourt, Brace, 1928).

feel any such conclusion rests on a misunderstanding of what those ideas consist of.

I am going to bring into focus the role of the primordial image in schizophrenia; for the sake of clarity, I will confine the discussion to the catatonic type of reaction. The psychosis is regarded, according to this view, as an eruption of the contents of the deepest layers of the unconscious into the field of awareness, flooding it with images of death, of entering an afterlife state, of descent into an underworld, and renewal or birth in some form, along with ideas of kingship or rulership, and cosmic conflict between political or moral forces.

I will concentrate, then, on the point at which such images as these enter into the active life and personal problems of the patient. This is a vital point of connection between the generalized image and the individual issue, the point at which the dynamics of the emotional life are observed close to their source, according to this formulation of the structure of the psyche.

The Archetypal Image

Let us take, for example, the images of the king and queen as the father and mother figures. Kingship is an archaic institution that has prevailed over most of the world in the distant past. Such a king was not just an autocrat with an oversized arrogation of political power; he was, with surprising universality, the very personification of the life of the realm, of its moral law and social order, of its virility and strength, even of its fertile potency; he was the embodiment of the god, and the masculine principle incarnate.[4] He bore an affective atmosphere of majesty, and roused in his subjects affective responses of awe and reverence. The queen, on her part, typically personified the earth, the soil of the kingdom, and when the king married her he married the realm;[5] she was the embodiment of beauty and fertile abundance, rousing in her subjects such feelings as fascination and love, as the incarnation of the goddess and the feminine principle.

At one time these figures of king and queen were externalized in the social structure of the culture, but as consciousness in any culture became more differentiated and the actual rulership passed from the sacred to the secular, the figures fell back into the psychic forms from which

---

[4] A. M. Hocart, *Kingship* (London: Oxford, 1927); *Kings and Councillors* (London: Luzac, 1937). S. H. Hooke, *Myth and Ritual* (London: Oxford, 1933); *The Labyrinth* (London: Oxford, 1933).

[5] Hocart, *Kingship*, pp. 101-111.

they had emerged in the first place, and survived in historical legend, in fairy tale and myth, or in dream. These configurations in the unconscious are then taken to be equivalent and similar in kind to the historical ones; the archaic mind is seen both in the past in history and in depth in the psyche.

Archaic configurations such as these are termed archetypes. According to this view, such an image is not so much derived from the child's affective impression of the awe-inspiring father or beloved mother of the family as it is the form in which the father or mother is perceived by the child in a pre-established way; the child projects onto the parents these images from the start. Such an archetype, then, is an innate propensity to apprehend the parent in a certain configuration, with corresponding affect. Jung speaks of it as being at one and the same time an image and an emotion;[6] it is therefore an affect, and an image that conveys the meaning of that affect. It is the innate propensity to apprehend typical universal experiences in typical and universal forms.[7] The father in a typical moment is perceived as the embodiment of order and virility like a king, with the affective tone of awe and reverence for his majesty. There are innumerable archetypes for recurrent life experiences.

Archetypes are made up not only of image and emotion but also of a third feature, which is that each image has its characteristic place in a myth-sequence or process. To follow the same example, part of the nature of kingship was its rejuvenation ritual. Apparently at one time before the historical era kings were sacrificed at the end of their allotted time in order that the kingship might be renewed.[8] In early recorded history this sacrifice was not an actual killing, but a ritual death and rebirth of the king for the same purpose.[9] In the Near East, for instance, the kingship was renewed by such rites at the same time as the renewal of the year in the New Year ceremonies,[10] by which it was implied that all aspects of the life of the realm were being revivified. Now again, just as other features of the structure of the typical archaic community

[6] C. G. Jung, *The Secret of the Golden Flower* (London: Kegan Paul, Trench, Trubner, 1935).

[7] C. G. Jung, "Instinct and Unconscious," in *Contributions to Analytical Psychology* (New York: Harcourt, Brace, 1928).

[8] R. Graves, *The Greek Myths* (Baltimore: Penguin, 1955). J. G. Frazer, *The Golden Bough* (New York: Macmillan, 1934).

[9] T. H. Gaster, *Thespis* (New York: Schuman, 1950). Hooke, *Myth and Ritual*. Frazer, *The Golden Bough*.

[10] Hooke, *The Labyrinth*. M. Eliade, *The Myth of Eternal Return*, Bollingen Series 46 (New York: Pantheon, 1954).

survive in the archaic level of unconscious imagery, so these same processes that had been expressed ritually by the community can still be seen
as habitual expressions in the archetypal unconscious, and are quite
readily recognizable.

THE AUTONOMOUS COMPLEX

The archetype is universal, nonpersonal, of a different dimension from
everyday experience, and usually carries the feeling-tone of the strange
and unfamiliar. Upon this archaic, affective representation the complex
slowly builds itself out of the data of experience. The father or the
mother complex is the whole array of associations gathered around the
personal experience of the parent and is made of all the memory traces
derived from the earliest and latest emotional impressions of that
figure.

In quite everyday terms, the complex is readily recognizable in the
example of the young man with an authority problem for whom almost any older man in a position of superiority over him calls up a
problematic emotional response; or equally familiar is the plight of the
young woman who finds herself, despite her better intentions, instantly
antagonistic to any older women of a certain kind. This response, in
either case, is called an activation of the complex, which is merely to
say that the older person is being perceived at the unconscious level in
terms of the father or the mother complex, and the emotion is then
the activity of the complex itself. For a response to be unconscious
signifies that it is autonomous, arising not by the intention of the ego
but by the spontaneous play of the complex itself intruding into the
field of awareness and, by projection, distorting the perception of the
object.

I mention these familiar instances only for the purpose of naming
the components in this model of the psyche. The complex is defined[11]
as an emotionally toned grouping of psychological contents gathered
around a nucleus, the nucleus being made up of the fusion of two
components: the inner, innately derived image of the archetypal father
or mother in the form of the king or the queen, and the outer, experi-
entially derived image of the actual parent.

No sooner do I mention the actual parent than I must modify the

[11] C. G. Jung, *The Psychology of Dementia Praecox*, Nervous and Mental
Disease Monograph Series, No. 3 (New York: 1936); "The Association
Method," *Collected Papers on Analytical Psychology* (New York: Moffat
Yard, 1917).

statement and point out that the autonomous, pathogenic complexes are derived in childhood not from interactions with the parents as conscious, ego personalities, but rather from entanglements with unconscious components in them.[12] The young child's psyche has no boundaries and he lives in a state of open emotional participation with his surroundings, and is particularly susceptible to any emotional factors in the psychic atmosphere of the parents. Thus the unresolved autonomous complexes of the parents are the factors most prone to enter into and form the unconscious configurations in the child.

The complex theory then requires that we regard the parents not as unitary personalities called mother and father, but rather as composites of many part-personalities among which the most unconscious ones are the most affectively toned and the most impressive to the child and thus most apt to be damaging. The parents' own parent complexes are of course the most predominant ones.

CATATONIC SCHIZOPHRENIC PROCESS

Granting, if we may, the theory and model of the psyche as just outlined, then what does it mean for the acute turmoil in catatonic schizophrenia to abound in archaic imagery? I feel there is little doubt that the most vivid and impressive experience for the patient, and the most gripping and intense affect, lie for him in these fantasy experiences. Why should these archaic contents be more prevalent than the more painful personal problems? Even on the face of it, it appears that, according to these definitions, the nuclear contents principally appear without their complex associations.

To account for this we may point to three major factors in the acute turmoil.

One is fragmentation, not only of the structure of the ego consciousness but also of the complexes. It is by means of this that the archetypal components are dissociated from their natural context of complex associations. Fragmentation is the keynote of schizophrenia.[13]

Identification is another strong tendency in this disorder: a proclivity to find one's identity not only in an image of an object, a person, but

[12] F. Wickes, *The Inner World of Childhood* (New York: Farrar and Rinehart, 1927). M. Fordham, *The Life of Childhood* (London: Kegan, Paul, Trench, Trubner, 1944).

[13] C. G. Jung, "On the Psychogenesis of Schizophrenia," in *The Basic Writings of C. G. Jung* (New York: Modern Library, 1959); "*Symbols of Transformation,*" *Collected Works*, 5, Bollingen Series 20 (New York: Pantheon, 1956).

also in an inwardly derived image. Also, not only does the ego become thus identified but other significant persons as well are identified with such images.

Both fragmentation and identification are referable to a third major feature of the disorder, which I feel may actually account for the eruption of the primordial images. That is the inordinate strength of the archetypal processes.

It appears that when it becomes necessary for the psyche to undergo such a process as is symbolically represented in terms of death, descent, and birth, and when the ego is weak and prone to yield over to let the fantasy forms assume the lead and dominate the field of awareness,[14] then something like this happens. In the schizophrenic regression there is a concentration of energy at this deep level where the process is taking shape, robbing the rest of the psychic structures of their habitual energic charge by a shift of energy from them into the unconscious.[15] In this phenomenon lies perhaps the occasion for the breakup of the usual organization of all the psychic structures above the archaic level. One gets the impression of a tearing away and scattering of the elements of ego consciousness and the well-organized complexes, and a consequent exposing of their archetypal roots or nuclei.

I will illustrate the problem of a mother complex and the manner in which it is handled by the unconscious by presenting a case of a young woman with an acute episode of catatonic schizophrenia whom I had in therapy for several months on an inpatient service.

CASE HISTORY

The patient is a thirty-year-old, single, white woman of a profession associated with the medical field. She was brought in by the police because of bizarre ideas and behavior.

The father had died when the patient was six months of age, and the patient later blamed the mother for having forced him to go to work when he was sick and thus causing his death. For half a year, the sixth to twelfth month, the patient was taken over by relatives because the mother had a "sort of breakdown" and could not handle the care of the child. During all the rest of her girlhood, the patient lived with her two older sisters and mother under the maternal grandmother's roof along with several other of the mother's siblings: aunts and uncles both. This was a distinctly matriarchal sort of household in which the grandmother kept a controlling hand over the lives of her offspring to the time

[14] Jung, "On the Psychogenesis of Schizophrenia."
[15] Jung, "On Psychic Energy."

of her death when the patient was ten. During all these years the mother, a depressive personality, showed little interest in the two younger daughters except in a suppressive, disciplining way.

The older daughter made a somewhat comfortable adjustment to the mother by becoming more or less like her. The two younger ones, however, entered upon a mutual withdrawal into each other's secret companionship and into a state of rebellious belligerence toward the rest of the family, especially the mother. Nevertheless these two remained in their later years in a mutual dependence in relation to the mother.

The patient went through high school and junior college in good health and then enrolled in her professional education; all this time she lived in another part of the country. (She had lived in the city of her present residence for only three years together with sisters and mother; she did not really feel herself at home here, however.)

Her relations with young women friends have often been warm and close. She has been inclined to react with antipathy to older women, especially in a work situation. She has had a number of affairs with men; but more than once they were married men, and somewhat neurotic and inclined to draw upon the maternal counsel and protectiveness of the patient. One such relationship was sustained from the age of eighteen on—for twelve years.

She was inclined to use alcohol when lonely.

In the third month before her present illness she was rejected by a lover and became morose and despondent. She went into psychotherapy not long after, but had only four or five sessions and did not really enter into it fully. Two weeks before admission she was arrested overnight for an impulsive misbehavior when drunk. She became severely withdrawn at that time and delusional ideas began to form. She became acutely disturbed on the day of admission.

On admission, physical findings were essentially negative, except for a twenty-pound weight loss which led to the point of severe emaciation.

THE DELUSIONAL IMAGERY

The main outline of the patient's delusional fantasy productions sounds fairly classical; that is, typical of the disorder—the kind that one hears over and over from one case to another, if one takes the trouble to hear the full extent of them with one's patients.

She thought she had died, and that she and the others in the hospital were in an afterlife state. Crucifixions were a prevalent motif in her drawings. She was implicated in a major world conflict between the forces of Communism and those of democracy. Men were to be eliminated and their sperm kept for later use. She believed herself to be Eve in the Garden of Eden, at the beginning of creation; also Queen Elizabeth, the Queen of Peace, now to be married to the Prince of Peace, with a new message for the world; also the Virgin Mother about to give birth to a new Redeemer. She was concerned with the form of a new society in a Heavenly City.

There were various lesser images and elaborations on these beliefs; but from this bare summary one gathers that she was sustaining many varied identifications with divine and royal personages, yet that they were predominantly feminine. I would stress that the forms the imagery itself takes are in no sense abnormal, in themselves—these are the habitual expressions in the unconscious at this level—but that what is grossly abnormal is the ego's relation to them by identification and projection and submersion in them; that is what makes them psychotic delusions rather than the usual symbolic representations of the components of growth and integration.

AMPLIFICATION OF THE IMAGERY

The first step that Jung has advised for getting some sort of orientation to the meaning of this kind of unfamiliar imagery is what he has called amplification. This means an enlargement upon the scanty allusions produced by the unconscious, by drawing upon the data of comparative symbolism; in this manner the imagery is made familiar and its meaningfulness begins to emerge.

For instance, the most accessible forms found in archaic cultures paralleling this imagery are those concerning the ritual of renewal of the king and of the realm in the ancient Near East, the cradle of our civilization. There the prevailing ritual pattern of the New Year ceremonies was roughly as follows.[16] The setting was ritually defined as the center of the earth, and the time was reversed to the beginnings of creation. All that is done is a reflection and re-enactment of the cosmogonic myth. A cosmic conflict is enacted between the forces of light and dark, or order and chaos. For a while the latter has the upper hand, and the king is humiliated or sacrificed ritually; society's customary order is reversed and undone. It is a time of mourning and lamentations. Then the powers of the abyss are overcome and the king is re-

[16] Eliade, *The Myth of Eternal Return.* Gaster, *Thespis.* Hooke, *Myth and Ritual; The Labyrinth.*

juvenated, often in the form of his son. There follows the sacred marriage of the king and queen or high priestess, signifying the union of god and goddess, or sky and earth, and thus the fructification of the soil by the divine progenitor. Carnival celebrations wind up the festival.

In some way, not yet clarified by the research workers in comparative religions and anthropology, initiation rites[17] were associated with those of the rejuvenation of the king. It is maintained by some that the latter derive from the former,[18] and by others that the reverse may be true—that what we now see of initiation rites may be decadent forms of what once had been rites only for kingship.[19] Often the two rituals are simultaneous.[20] At the least there are basic features in common: the subject undergoes a process of death and rebirth, and he does it in identification with the deity of the myth.

The parallels to the patient's imagery, and to the regularly recurring forms in catatonic schizophrenia,[21] do not need to be belabored: the world center, the time of the creation, the sacrificial death and the new birth, the world conflict of opposing forces, the sacred marriage, and the rejuvenation of the realm.

Another major motif is the array of images of the feminine. It may be said that a comprehension of these archetypes is essential if there is to be any adequate grasp of the nature of woman and her own specific development.[22]

A basic symbol of the feminine is naturally the Earth Mother—the embodiment of fertility and the giver of life and nourishment—whether it be through the vegetation that grows in her soil or the animals that roam upon it. She gives both life and death, destroying and taking back into her bosom what she had only recently brought forth from it. She acts according to the timeless cyclical rhythms of the seasons,[23] of production and resorption, life and death, blossom and seed,

[17] Frazer, *The Golden Bough*.

[18] J. E. Harrison, *Themis* (Cambridge: Cambridge University Press, 1927).

[19] Hooke, *Myth and Ritual*.

[20] Eliade, *The Myth of Eternal Return*.

[21] J. W. Perry, "Acute Catatonic Schizophrenia," *J. Anal. Psych.*, 2 (1957), 137-152.

[22] E. Neumann, *The Great Mother*, Bollingen Series 47 (New York: Pantheon, 1955). C. G. Jung, "Psychological Aspects of the Mother Archetype," in *The Basic Writings of C. G. Jung* (New York: Modern Library, 1959). M. E. Harding, *Woman's Mysteries* (New York: Pantheon, 1956).

[23] C. G. Jung, "Symbols of Transformation," *Collected Works*, 5, Bollingen Series 20 (New York: Pantheon, 1956).

regeneration and degeneration. As such, she is the image not only of nurturing love and givingness but also of the fertile potential of creativity and of transformation through destruction and regeneration. An alternative symbol of these latter qualities is woman as vessel and container, who brings forth her contents from concealment to the outside, or transforms contents within herself.[24]

This image of the Great Mother is typically one member of a pair; the accompanying figure is the daughter, the maiden or Kore.[25] This maiden is the personification of youthful love and beauty in the erotically attractive and desirable potential mate. Only, as in the Persephone and the Psyche myths, she is not ready to undertake the fulfillment of her erotic life in its fullest meaning until she has come to terms with both death and the reality of the masculine principle; in other words, until she has been initiated.[26]

TRANSFORMATION OF THE SELF

The resolution of pathogenic complexes can be handled by the psyche in more than one way. Certain of them can be handled by conscious insight, that is, by the ego's becoming aware of the meaning of the feelings concerned with certain kinds of unintended experiences. A young woman with a mother problem can do much to recognize the origins and meanings of her irrational behavior and prevent herself from acting out in inappropriate and harmful ways when these occasions occur. The ego handles what it faces in the outer world and thus must become acquainted with the perceptions and feelings belonging to the complexes found in projection.

Another kind of issue—not so successfully resolved by the ego in its conscientious search for awareness—concerns the nature of the self, itself. That is, it is one thing for a young woman to have a mother problem and keep projecting it; but if she has a problematic relation to older women, either of adulation or of resentment, it implies that she thinks of herself as always the daughter or young maiden, all innocent of the tasks and responsibilities that come with adult womanhood or motherhood.[27] The entire mother problem is then seen as arising essentially

[24] Neumann, *The Great Mother.*

[25] C. G. Jung, *Essays on a Science of Mythology*, Bollingen Series 21 (New York: Pantheon, 1949).

[26] E. Neumann, *Amor and Psyche*, Bollingen Series 54 (New York: Pantheon, 1956).

[27] Jung, "Psychological Aspects of the Mother Archetype."

out of the self-image; if she did not think of herself as always the young maiden, and delegate the rest to older women, then the mother problem would lose its *raison d'être*.

As I see it, the archetypal processes come into the ascendancy in the catatonic turmoil when the self-image is standing in acute need of change and renewal.[28] The occasion for the break turns out often to be either a sudden demoralization of the ego, as in a rejection, or an activation of the unconscious contents having to do with the self, as in the intense emotions of falling in love. One may make the generalization that archetypal processes are concerned, on the whole, with the formation of a self, an observation which Jung made during the 1920's and which led him to name this purposive train of events the "individuation process," and its ultimate goal the "self." [29] The images of king and queen, as the human representatives of the god and goddess, are customarily found at the core of the process.[30]

From this point of view, it would obviously not be sufficient for the contents of the mother complex to be assimilated into consciousness only, if the entire mother problem is to be resolved. For the archetypal nucleus of that complex contains the image of the Great Mother, or the queen, which is then the inner capacity of the young woman to develop a sense of the feeling and meaning in womanhood or motherhood which has been renounced up to this time by the ego and delegated to other older women to carry for her—most especially the wives of her men friends—so that by keeping it thus in projection she can remain not responsible for it within her own psychic life. This becomes then something of a moral question. The image of the Great Mother or the queen as the core of her own potential for womanliness and lovingness and creativity is all the while an essential component in her psychic development and an important ingredient in her individuation process.

For the reasons that there is a dynamic process at work at a profound level and rudiments essential to the fulfilled integration of the

[28] Perry, "Acute Catatonic Schizophrenia"; *The Self in Psychotic Process* (Berkeley: Univ. California Press, 1953).

[29] C. G. Jung, "Two Essays on Analytical Psychology," *Collected Works*, 7, Bollingen Series 20 (New York: Pantheon, 1953); "Psychology and Alchemy," *Collected Works*, 12, Bollingen Series (New York: Pantheon, 1953); *The Secret of the Golden Flower*.

[30] H. G. Baynes, "On the Psychological Origins of Divine Kingship," in *Analytical Psychology and the English Mind* (London: Methuen, 1950).

personality are found there, one must conclude that one is not entitled to overlook the archetypal components in a psychotic process, however hard it might be to make sense of them, and it can be very hard.

THERAPEUTIC METHOD

In accordance with this view of the nature of the unconscious contents there must be added a few extra points of technique beyond those already customary in psychotherapy.

The individuation process probably takes place only, or comes to fruition only, in relationship. A helpful way to view this is to think of the therapeutic interaction as an emotional field between two psyches in which these various contents and processes come into play; since the field involves the emotional nature of both psyches, this implies that the therapeutic transaction requires the genuine participation of the therapist in terms of feeling.[31] This is not to advocate merely that we should be nice to our patients. Rather, it is meant to imply that when a patient in an acute turmoil is at some level trying to formulate a self-image, this stands in acute need of affirmation and the kind of guiding help that comes more through a feeling sort of wisdom than conceptual understanding. Such a self tends to take shape best in such a mutually animated emotional field, and much of the work goes on in terms of the very strange symbolic expressions of the archetypal process.[32] In my experience, a patient knows in a flash whether you are "with it" or not when he speaks of these things, and finds it tremendously gratifying if you are; even more, he is extremely sensitive to whether you care, and how much. If the therapist's cognizance and concern are only mild, the intensity of the process in therapy will, I think, be mild.

Under these circumstances, one should make as much effort to grasp the sense of the archetypal imagery as one would to grasp any other kind of content or emotion. Quite apart from mastering some little bit of comparative symbolism, the more essential thing seems to me to be a free and sound intuition, so that you let the patient's symbolic configurations work on you and impress their shapes and patterns on your own fantasy. It is much like hearing poetry, as far as grasping the sense

[31] Jung, "The Practice of Psychotherapy."
[32] C. G. Jung, "Psychology of the Transference," in *The Practice of Psychotherapy, Collected Works*, 16, Bollingen Series 20 (New York: Pantheon, 1954).

of the flow of imagery is concerned, for we are listening to metaphor in one as in the other; if we are open to it, we find ourselves sensing the import, in time. Actual interpretation seems to me of secondary importance, but the sense of the meaningfulness and order, primary.

A point of technique to facilitate the imagery is to have a box of crayons or paints handy in the interview, and to let the patient find his own way to use them, if he feels so moved. It helps the therapist to see the configurations; but even more, it is of benefit to the patient to get his own imagery out where he can objectify it and get a more conscious relation to it as a substantial thing going on in picture language[33] —else his tendency is to keep it out in another more difficult form, that is, in projection and hence in the concretistic misunderstanding.

With these ways of approach, we achieve in time a sense of the import that certain features in the imagery have for the personal life of the patient, and can attempt slowly to link it up with the deeply conflictful emotional issues in his background and in the current setting. Making interpretations is hardly the word to describe this; it sounds too conceptual. One might call it making connections; in part, restoring those very connections that the disorder had severed.

I should add that in Jungian theory there is no objection to the use of somatic aids to therapy; that is, no cause to doubt the need for correcting the damage done to the physiology of the body by the psychotic disorder. In 1906[34] Jung conjectured that the high degree of activation of the disturbed autonomous complexes might well give rise to some toxin that then contributed to the psychotic episode, and he repeated this conjecture in a paper on schizophrenia two years ago. For my own part, I prefer the use of subcoma insulin even to the newer drugs inasmuch as it introduces no appreciable interference to psychotherapy, and especially since the latter needs the mobilization and intensification of anxiety at points where the ego is wrestling with difficult issues. The dose of insulin automatically varies with the degree of physiological and psychological disturbance.

The present case was treated in this manner: it was begun on the twelfth hospital day, reached a dose of 220 units in two weeks, BID, and with the consequent clinical improvement came down again to 80 units in two more weeks; the psychotic process ceased to progress at the end of the following week, the seventh hospital week. The inter-

[33] Perry, *The Self in Psychotic Process.*
[34] Jung, *The Psychology of Dementia Praecox.*

views were held concurrently three times a week on the ward, and just following the termination of the morning insulin therapy.

I want to make clear my estimation of what a case study is worth. I do not feel that the success or failure of a course of therapy can be used as evidence for the justification of a theory. Many different ways of handling patients' material can prove efficacious at times, thus indicating that there are many unaccountable factors that enter into the therapeutic transaction, among which the qualities of the therapist's personality are possibly the most decisive. In supervising the work of younger therapists, I get the impression that the qualities that make the greatest contribution are warmth, concern, and an undefensive openness to whatever the patient brings; the ideal situation would be one in which the patient feels that anything he reveals is found meaningful by the therapist, who then responds to it with genuine resonance. Just how he formulates this meaningfulness, i.e., just what theoretical framework he uses, I suspect is of secondary importance, so long as he does not violate the sense that the patient's psyche is trying to convey. This means he freely lets it speak to him until he achieves some measure of grasp of it.

For this reason I believe that the best we can do at this stage of our science is to elucidate areas here and there in the psychic contents and processes so that what patients say to us with some regularity may indeed become gradually more meaningful. On the other hand, I also believe that our cultural biases inhibit our capacity to allow certain areas of psychic contents to assume the full impact of their significance.

Establishment of the Transference

I believe it is no coincidence that a patient with a preponderance of feminine imagery such as this should be one to develop a strong transference from the very outset, since the feminine principle is involved with relationship. In my first interview with her she was in restraints because of a noisy, aggressive hyperactivity. As I sat on the edge of the bed she oscillated between restless protest against the restraints and an absorbed, quiet contemplation of the feel of my arm, the tweed sleeve, and the skin of the hand. From her manner there was little doubt that she felt a compelling need for contact, and that warmth and texture seemed to exert a soothing effect upon her, as though one of reassurance. From this she would return at intervals to tearing at the restraints and trying to take the bed apart with angry, rebellious scowls and grunts. The content of talk in this interview arose from the delusional areas of concern.[35]

> After I announced myself as her therapist and asked her what she was actually going through, she replied that she was reliving the whole New Testament story. I asked her how this story went, and she began to recite, almost as a child in wonderment telling her favorite fairy tale, that "Christ was born among us and preached love and kindness and goodness, and taught us to love one another and live together in peace. It's the most important thing in life, all this."

In the second interview the patient was so deeply under the sedating effect of tranquilizers that she was practically stuporous and could speak only with effort. Even under these conditions, the need for contact was uppermost, and she reached out dreamily for my sleeve and my hand even though she could not focus on them. She managed to comment thickly that the tweeds felt nice, and that I felt so warm. She then murmured that she liked me.

The third interview, at the end of the second week, found her in an altogether different state. She was up and dressed, cheerful to the point of euphoria and talkative in a laughing vein, also a remarkably childish one.

> After telling me she liked my suit and tie (both tweed), she jokingly wrote a letter to Santa Claus in which she asked for a teddy bear; entering into what I sensed to be the spirit of this banter and its import, I asked if perhaps a tweedy teddy bear was what she had in mind; this she took up with startled delight as if I had spoken exactly to the point and she wrote an elaboration on it about wanting a "Tweedy Teddy Bear with a Tweedy Tie." In this cajoling we seemed to establish an atmosphere of informal friendliness which was maintained from that time on.

This period of a couple of weeks was the patient's phase of greatest regression. She told me later that during that time she had felt, among other things, "like a very little girl!" She regressed to several levels, which I learned about later; but what she allowed me to see now, that is, what she brought into relation to me in the transference, was the form

[35] In the following accounts of the interviews, the patient's conversation is rendered as closely as possible to her own words, but the quotation is only approximate.

of loving expression that was most basic to her, namely, primitive body-contact of warmth and texture. I was reminded at the time of Harry Harlow's revealing experiments with the terry-cloth monkey mothers,[36] and of Bruno Klopfer's interpretation of the texture and shading responses in the Rorschach.[37] The former experiments suggest very strongly that the Freudian conjectures about the oral erogenous zone as the first phase of development of the libido are given an undue and mistaken emphasis, and that the primitive and primary mode of love is not orality but the sense of warm and woolly emotional containment; the total absence of this, of course, is known to bring death by marasmus.

This primitive mode was her most basic expression of warmth, and it also represented that level of development where she had last enjoyed her mother's loving attention. Once she had ceased to be an infant, the mother had taken less and less interest in her and had assumed an increasingly suppressive and oppressive role in relation to her. Her gospel of love, then, takes on a more poignant personal significance as the image of her greatest need.

In the third week the next interview, the fourth, took a new turn. She was now in seclusion because of combative, denudative, and destructive behavior.

> She inveigled me into a contest of wills by slyly and agilely slipping past me out the door and making it most difficult for me to get her back into the room. She conceded only when she had provoked me sufficiently for me to speak with angry definiteness that this must stop right now. At this she melted and spoke tenderly, asking if I were X, her recent lover; she had loved me very much, she told me. When I reminded her that X and I were not the same, she told me the story of the breakup of her romance three months before, the rejection leaving her very depressed and lonely.
>
> She thereupon asked me if I were Churchill, and enthusiastically gave a cheer, "Long live peace between England and Holland." She declared that she and I must get to work on rewriting the Bible together.
>
> A note to me later that day was addressed to "Perry, Prince of Peace."

At the end of the third week she was full of complaints about what she did and did not want, most important of which was that all she

---

[36] H. F. Harlow, "The Nature of Love," *Amer. Psychol.* 13 (1958), 673-685.
[37] B. Klopfer *et al.*, *Developments in the Rorschach Technique*, Vol. 2, Chap. 10 (New York: World, 1954).

wanted was a little sun and fresh air and to feel the grass and earth under her feet. The sixth session was short and stormy.

> Her complaints became so forceful that she stamped out in a rage after only a few minutes, berating me for being no help, a stupid fool, a no-good doctor who did not understand anything and could not do anything that was needed; she shouted I might as well not bother to come back.

In the following session she was quite contrite over this outburst, and I reassured her that she need not be afraid of her anger—that it could not damage our relationship, and that I would always keep coming to see her regularly anyway.

The next week I did not see her because of the Christmas holidays and thus missed the eighth to eleventh sessions, an unfortunate time to be absent. However, she spoke of me continually, in terms of her Prince of Peace, or as the man she was about to marry, and with a good deal of comment about kings and queens.

Her contest of wills with me was an expression of her need to test my strength; she had been annoyed with her habit of finding herself entangled with passive-dependent and ineffectual men, and her greatest wish was to find assertiveness in men.

Her projecting upon me the image of the recent lover, X, needs little comment. It was one of the factors precipitating her withdrawal and disorder. It seems to me it arose at this point in the transference because for this kind of personality the difficulty with love is that it immediately awakens the threat of loss; to love is to invite rejection, and the two are so closely bound up together that the one complex automatically induces the other. Thus, as soon as she had expressed her need and appreciation of contact and warmth, her feelings of rejection made themselves felt, just as it had been with her lover. This was inevitable, since love and loss both belonged to the mother complex, the basic ground plan for all later experiences of affection, which endlessly repeated the history that her mother had loved her briefly, with snuggly warmth, and then lost interest. Even worse than this, the mother's becoming cold and absenting herself happened to coincide in time with the death of the father, so that again, receiving affection augured a loss not only of the mother but of the father as well. Her mood thus oscillated between love and anger, and docility and hostility. The image of the lover, X, is the image of this complex which now appeared in the transference.

Although the interviews brought forward these emotions belonging to the mother complex, it was not left at that. For transference is inclined to bring into play not only the projections of the infantile contents but fully as much the projections of the archetypal imagery which come into play to offer new possibilities of resolution. On this level, she felt that there was to be a royal marriage of herself as Queen of Peace and me as Prince of Peace. The allusion to Churchill turned out later to come from her identification with the Queen of England. Later, she told me she had felt then that we were supposed to go traveling throughout the world together spreading the new gospel of love and teaching the people how to live peaceably together. This, she was convinced, was going to eradicate all illness from the world, meaning, of course, her illness from her world. Here, then, was a symbol for the way of life that would heal her disorder—the problem of the fateful sequence of love and rejection and withdrawal.

Now we are in a position to understand the magnitude of her rage, heretofore seeming as arbitrary as the weather. She was seeing me as a doctor demonstrating great obtuseness in not playing my proper part in this effort of world healing, and in her outburst she felt justified in calling me more a hindrance than a help. Similarly her rage at the nurses was more than a simple acting out of her hostile impulses toward mother figures; her complaints about not being allowed to get out to the flowers, earth and grass all had direct reference, it turned out later, to her being the Earth Mother. She was feeling most acutely, in this inflated fantasy, the enraging disparity and gulf between her own subjective reality and the objective reality which the staff had in mind.

A little later I shall describe a crisis in the transference that brought out the pattern of affection and rejection in its most vivid colors. Meanwhile, during the following weeks (the fifth to the eighth) the transference settled into a comfortably established friendly relationship in which the patient was openly and frankly affectionate. She often reached out to hold my arm or touch my hand, sometimes telling me she loved me and was grateful to me for being so understanding of her feelings and her ideas. Always when the hour came to a close she expressed a sudden change of mood from contentment to sadness and did not want me to leave. My response to these expressions was not to interpret them, but to let them be and to comment on the growth of her capacity for lovingness.

THE MOTHER IMAGE AND MOTHER COMPLEX

By the end of the sixth week the patient was quiet, rational, and in fair contact with people around her. (She had had four weeks of insulin, with the dose now back to 8o units, which followed upon a twenty-pound weight gain.) Under these conditions the telling of delusional fantasies begins to take on a special significance. As long as a patient is disturbed and relatively out of contact, delusional contents usually come pouring out at random and in a quite disconnected way. At these times it is hard to get any consistent picture of what the structure of the imagery is like and one is left to conjecture from fragmentary evidence. Once the turmoil has settled and the patient is in more conscious rapport, there is a definite choice as to whether she will confide the story of her imagery to the therapist or not. In my experience, she will do so only if she trusts the person. Not only is there this choice, but also the rendering of the story is well on the way toward being as well organized as any fanciful fairy tale or myth. She is still quite psychotic, in the sense that she believes the reality of the imagery in the concretistic sense; it requires only the realization that the images are symbolic statements of meaning, and therefore solely an inner reality, for her to find her way out of the psychotic relation to them. Although this goal is simple enough in principle, it is of course not so easy to achieve.

At this time there came a turning point and opportunity to confide what had until then been possible only to guess. The week end before the fifteenth interview she had been quite disturbed for reasons which the staff could not determine. In the interview she gave this account:

> PT.: I thought I created three stars as I was standing by the window. You know, on . . . [two weeks before admission] I thought I created a moon, the real moon. It was very frightening to think that I had the power to do this. I had the feeling that I was the whole universe, and was making worlds and peopling them. I was making all the people on earth here, and that's why it was getting so overcrowded [a theme she had dwelt upon in the previous interview].
>
> THER.: Then your having these special powers meant that you were divine?
>
> PT.: Oh, yes [evasively], I knew I was; there was no doubt of it. . . .
>
> [Later in the interview] I was Mother Earth, the source of all life. And everything grew out of me. Yes, I was Old Mother Eve herself. . . .

It's the duty of people to grow things in the earth, to plant
and to sow and to reap. People should give up the evils of metal
and of work in the city [here she preaches with dogmatic em-
phasis]. They should stop digging [now shouting petulantly in
rage] down inside the earth to draw metals out of it. That's digging down into Mother Earth and taking things that shouldn't
be taken. They should leave them there. . . . All these machines
and cars are wrong. All those materials should be left in the earth
and we should grow things on the surface of the earth the way
we were meant to—in the soil.

THER.:   It seems your feminine nature is becoming very important to you, and you're having strong feelings about the various qualities of motherhood and of Mother Nature. But this feeling about being a goddess is of course an inner truth only, not
an outer one, isn't it? You're feeling all those qualities of hers in
yourself and beginning to realize what they mean.

PT.:   Oh no, that was real; I know I was a goddess and
Mother Earth. I know.

[She has been painting water colors of plants, flowers, and
trees, which take on a new importance to her as fruits of the
earth.]

Here, in this surprising turn of events, is the most nearly complete
identification with the full-blown image of the Great Mother herself,
the all-encompassing, containing matrix of the universe (like the "teem-
ing womb" and "nurse of all Becoming" in the "Timaeus"), the creator
of heavenly bodies, and with the earth whose soil men should fertilize
and harvest, and with the primordial human Mother Eve, ultimate an-
cestress and source of all worldly life. Her paintings of nature, another
form of the mother, were in full, vibrant colors reflecting the kind of
affectivity that she was showing in other ways. All these are components
of the basic archetype of womanhood in its maternal aspect. The feminine is given extreme stress, and it is in the form of a protest against
the masculine: she had had more to say about that the time before
(fourteenth interview), but without its full context:

PT.:   We should ban all metals and send them back to where
they had come from. Everyone lives in such a state of hurry and
fuss . . . with materialistic goals . . . there's noise and restlessness and lack of peace. There are too many people in the world
—so very many—we have to do something for them [her own
doing as Great Mother]. . . . We must establish a plan to feed
and house them. We need to take away all the big buildings,
especially the industrial ones and the businesses . . . and we
should set up homes instead, and the people should grow their

own food . . . then we need more land, so the thing is to increase the land by filling in the sea bit by bit.

I was reminded of Faust's means of redemption by the same work of increasing the land for the benefit of the people and asked her if she had heard of it; she had not, and the idea was spontaneous.

The picture is of Mother Earth being desecrated by the avarice of men who plunder her of her wealth, that is, who rob her of what should remain hidden within her and use it for their fitful striving to erect a civilization based on economic gain and science. She wants all this to be torn down and to revert to the ways of nature where the household and the soil are the supreme values. This is a strong reassertion of the matriarchal condition so centered on fertility, earth, vegetation, and nourishment as the primary concerns of life, over against the later acquisitions of the patriarchal phases of culture and the masculine principle.[38] (The question might arise whether my digging things out of her was signified by men digging things out of the earth; but it was not, since she had had these ideas before admission, and her previous therapy had not done any such digging.)

The contents and feelings belonging to her mother complex, that is, her problem with her own experience of her mother, were brought to the fore in the third month (twenty-sixth interview). At first she had been inclined to represent her politely as a "sweet, lovely old lady," which did not tally with the fact that every time her mother visited her on the ward the patient would fly into a rage at her, and would often stalk off by herself because she "could not stand mother's stupidity—she just never understands anything!" and she would then cry, "I hate her—she makes me so mad!"

> In this interview she defended her mother's part in her earliest life. During the first years the mother had been warm in feeling and prone to be cuddly, fond and attentive, but when the patient began to be a little person, the mother became more and more uninterested and even suppressive and oppressive; this gave the child no sense of freedom and no hope that she could bring her feelings and experiences to her mother with any warm response from her.

That same week she was again talking of the suppressive home atmosphere and declared defiantly, "If I want to go fly a kite, I want to

[38] E. Neumann, *The Origins and History of Consciousness*, Bollingen Series 42. (New York: Pantheon, 1954).

be able to fly a kite and have them like it!" She then spent a few days making a little model of a kite out of bits and pieces of plastic, tape, and string as a symbol of freedom and emancipation (the cross as its basic structure was one of a series of such symbolic constructions).

Her more real experience of a mother was found in the relationship with her maternal aunt, who was a loving, warm, wise individual who consistently responded to her with genuine interest. This was the only oasis of tenderness in an otherwise arid setting in which the patient and her sister teamed up together in their defiant withdrawal.

As for the father complex, this found almost no expression in the imagery except insofar as the "elimination of men" might reflect what in her view had happened to her father. During the third month, however, she told me of a hallucination she had had in the second week: Her father was leading a colorful procession of men and women up an impressive sweeping stairway (fictitious) outside her room. From that height, he called down to her, "You're my beautiful girl. You should be proud of yourself."

I felt that this vision might have arisen in relation to the transference situation, early as it was, and it was mentioned between us several times later in order to keep alive this affirmative feeling touching so closely upon her self-image and her need for the father's participation in her development.

Death and Renewal

The rest of the array of delusional imagery about the feminine was presented over the following weeks, item by item, all reconstructing the preoccupations of the first month of her psychosis.

> On the day she first became openly disturbed (the day she was admitted), the patient was with two women (mother and a friend), thus forming a triad; and the only other person she saw was a man, the doctor who came to see her; she believed everyone else in the world was dead and that they walked around only as spirit beings in the vast silence of the afterlife. On that day, she recognized herself as Mother Eve, and the place as the Garden of Eden, the First Paradise; thus everyone should be going around naked as primitives, for this was the beginning of time and of the world. She felt her watch was of solid gold, which meant that it could not move and thus time stood still.

Elsewhere I have presented and discussed examples of this image of the reversion of time to the beginning of creation so prevalent in schizophrenic productions and so universal in the myth and ritual of archaic times.[39] Let me remark now only on the fact that this idea seems part of the regular image sequence of rejuvenation and renewal.[40]

> On admission, she felt herself to have died and to be in the after-life. In the first few weeks on the ward, she felt pregnant with a divine child, and was a sort of Virgin Mary. Other women were pregnant, too, and she was concerned for their care. The ruffles on her bed concealed twelve babies under the blanket and her pillow contained a dead baby whose four limbs were at the four corners, and who could be brought to life if she could only de-liver him out of his containment. At Christmas (end of second week), she saw the Nativity taking place in a stone grotto out-side the hospital, and knew this was herself giving birth to the child. At table she sat with twelve patients, and knew this to be the enactment of the Last Supper in which she was the Lord breaking bread with the disciples; this was being televised to the world. (She painted the grotto, with a suggestion of a sacrifice of a man on an altar, and a suggestion of the Nativity.)

Those who are acquainted with symbolism of this variety will recog-nize in these forms not only the familiar themes of death and birth but also their location in the characteristic containing structure of the sacred enclosure (paradise and grotto). Mother symbolism prevails throughout these images.

The key to an understanding of the regressive backflow of libido to the infantile complexes and their emotions is to regard the child as always presupposing the mother as its natural complement, and also to recognize the archetypal basis of both in the fundamental image of the Madonna and Child, or the Great Mother and the fruit of her body; the one member of the pair is not intelligible without the other. Now if there is any theoretical statement of Jung's that may be considered most basically typical it is, in my opinion, that regression to the mother is not only a reversion to the infantile longing to possess the mother, but further and more important is a return to her to be reborn through her.[41] This means the regression takes the libido not merely to one's personal infancy but beyond this, to the archaic psyche which, in the guise of the Great Mother, receives it into her bosom to trans-form it into a new form of life.[42] He thus adds to the familiar Oedipus

[39] Perry, "Acute Catatonic Schizophrenia."
[40] Eliade, *The Myth of Eternal Return.*
[41] Jung, "Symbols of Transformation."
[42] Jung, "On Psychic Energy."

complex the accompanying Jonah complex as its natural complement.

As the patient's symbolism itself suggests, her regression to infancy revived old feelings of love and rejection in relation to the mother, but also evoked symbols of the Great Mother giving birth to the new Divine Child. I would formulate this, in terms of what happens to the self, in this manner: the libido flows back to light up that complex which represents the last time the child had the affirmation of the parent's love, that is, the last juncture at which the self was still intact but was just about to head off on a distorted development. As the libido does so, it constellates the image of a newly created self in archetypal form as the symbol of what the new potential of the self-image can be. It seems to be the habit of this symbol to appear first in completely generalized, ideal form, i.e., as the Divine Child, the pure type of all nascent wholeness; it then differentiates and represents itself in more and more differentiated form as it pertains more and more specifically to the particular individual personality concerned; as it does so the symbol shifts gradually from the divine to the human form of child.

At this point, the seventh week, the patient's symbolizing of the self turns from its earlier emphasis on the mother-child forms to the gradually proliferating imagery of the kingdom and its culture.

A DESIGN OF LIFE

In the interview following the one in which the patient first revealed her identification with the Great Mother, she went off into what at first seemed to be purely religious ideas (sixteenth interview):

> Her mood is one of open friendliness and confidence along with a slight rush of enthusiasm over her ideas. She is still relating psychotically to her imagery.
> PT.: I found what my beast was! [One she had drawn by a cross and tree.] It's the one in the Book of Revelation. [She reads in the last chapters of the "new heaven and new earth . . . the holy city, new Jerusalem . . . prepared as a bride adorned for her husband."] This is a city without evil, where there's no darkness, only light. . . . I've been feeling San Francisco here was the New Jerusalem, the City of Peace. The hospital here is the very center of the city, and it's my palace, all of gold. It's where the healing takes place [the tree of life, with leaves for the healing of the nations]. . . .
> I'm telling you all this because you understand all my ideas so well [saying this very tenderly].
> [Upon my prompting she draws the city: a finger-shaped peninsula with a circle at the center for the hospital, with hori-

zontal lines at the sides and radial lines at the top; the whole makes a rudimentary human figure with arms and hair. When I point this out, she laughs and agrees.]

Pᴛ.: We'll make symbols together, you and I. The people rule themselves . . . it's a four-square city, all gold, with jewels on the walls and gates.

On further questioning, she equated the idea of the new heaven with her own creation of a new moon and new stars. She had more to say about all the city being given over to homes for families with every-one living at home and tilling the soil, and with no more factories or mining of metals; people in the wards were to be sent home too, for the doctors to visit there. In the seventeenth interview she repeated much of this, and I ventured a guess as to what her real concern might be in it all:

Tʜᴇʀ.: Let's see. It sounds to me as if you may be wanting to turn your attention to your personal life and away from your professional concerns. Is there some problem about this?

Pᴛ.: That's right! [Here she brightens up with laughing ap-preciation of what evidently was a good guess— She spends most of the hour ranting against her work, vehemently telling how she hates it, ". . . all those dirty, filthy. . . ."]

I want to just live on a farm, and just be home and make things grow in the soil, that's all. . . .

Tʜᴇʀ.: But it seems the chief point is you want to shift em-phasis from your intellectual, professional life to a more personal, feeling life and to living your emotions—living your own life for yourself.

Pᴛ.: Yes! That's just it; I sure do! I want love and a family. Is that possible, do you think?

My guess at the connection with her professional life was not purely out of intuition, for I was recalling a painting she had made a few days before of a crucifixion of a serpent (a well-known traditional symbol). When I had asked her what the serpent seemed to mean to her, she was perfectly clear that it was the one on the medical caduceus and there-fore connected with her work. The psychological difficulty with her work was that it had become rather compulsively worrisome to her and occupied her thoughts day and night. Even worse, her mother had a way of behaving toward her as toward a husband and breadwinner, a very irritating reversal of sexual identity for her.

In seven weeks' time the patient's unconscious process had run the gamut from the regression to the image of the Great Earth Mother and the First Paradise—that depicting the beginning of creation—to the progressive construction of an image of the Last Paradise, the Bride of Christ—that depicting the end of creation. It was no coincidence that from here on there was no further elaboration of such imagery and that after this, whenever she spoke of these symbols, it was to fill in her account of what she had believed previously, for the symbol-forming work had run its full course. At the same time, her psychosis was beginning to release its grip upon her and she was less prone to insist on her identification with these great divine personages. Her talk in the interviews concerned itself increasingly with personal matters, her present relationships on the ward, and her family.

The symbolism of these paradises is readily recognizable as imagery of the archetype of the self, as Jung has defined it.[43] I prefer, because of the many connotations of this term, and for the sake of greater clarity of language, to speak of this image as the "central archetype," since its symbols usually designate centrality, whether of the world, the kingdom, the religious image, or the psyche.[44] Both the first and last paradises are symbols of the variety that Jung has described as mandalas;[45] the first designates that primordial state of the psyche at which a nascent differentiation of consciousness first causes a cleaving asunder of the opposites, i.e., good and evil. The last represents the other end: that final destination of the psyche, at which the state of division and suffering are healed in a new oneness and wholeness. In the symbol language this is achieved only by the long hard history of the redemptive process.

For a transliteration of the symbol of the sacred city, I find the idea of a design of life to be at least an approximation of its meaning. As a more calculated interpretation, I would suggest that the image of the city kingdom is the corollary of that of the king and queen: just as they personify and embody in themselves the moral, social, and physical order of the realm, so the city kingdom may be regarded as the explicit and extensive structuring of that which is intensively embodied in the royal couple. It might be called the image of the ideal culture which the individual espouses inwardly; that is, not the inner representation of the outer culture (superego) so much as the psyche's own inner organizing of its structure of meanings and values.

The patient's drawing of the sacred city as a rudimentary human

---

[43] Jung, Psychology and Alchemy; *The Secret of the Golden Flower*.
[44] Perry, *The Self in Psychotic Process*.
[45] C. G. Jung, *Psychology and Religion*, The Terry Lectures (New Haven: Yale Univ. Press, 1937).

figure speaks eloquently for the argument that such a city is fundamentally a representation of the self—her own inner culture.

Such an interpretation rests upon and illustrates an important point of theory: that the unconscious psyche itself strives to produce cultural creations out of its own instinctive roots,[46] and to integrate the collective culture just as much as it works to integrate the individual personality and its own inner culture.

RESOLUTION OF THE TRANSFERENCE

I suggest that lovingness is the quality most strikingly intruding into the conscious scene because it is the factor the archetypal process is promoting. This naturally entails the coming into play of these emotions within the transference relationship.

At the end of the week of the interview last described, the patient had dressed up especially for me in a new pink dress of which she was quite proud, and had her make-up carefully done. Sensing the import that was all too obvious, I asked her what she felt about me (twentieth interview):

> PT.: I love you very much, doctor—very much indeed, [this with earnest, simple, sincere feeling].
> THER.: What is it about me that makes you feel that way?
> PT.: You understand me. You really understand what I try to say and understand my ideas. I'm coming to look well because of good doctoring, I guess [smiles at this bouquet tossed to me].
> [Now, turning her attention to her difficulties with relating to too many people too much of the time:]
> I want to retire to a farm and just be alone.
> THER.: There certainly is a strong wish to leave the professional and impersonal interests and get back to living and filling your more personal life.
> PT.: Yes, I need to be alone some of the time, and then if I am, I can feel more need for people. The other way, I just fight away from them.

At this, I reassured her that her introverted needs as such were valid enough, but that they were different from withdrawal, and we discussed the difference.

In the twenty-second interview, she went further into her loving feelings:

> (Her condition is excellent, with good color, alert, and perfectly coherent.)

[46] Jung, "Symbols of Transformation."

A (a friend on the ward) is her "very special friend." All the patients are friends up here. They cut up together and have a good deal of fun. At the dance the evening before, her sexual feelings were strongly stirred. She is worried about them and wonders what to do with them (this in a solemn, reflective manner). (I ask what sort of thoughts there were of this kind.) She had been having "crazy ideas" (laughs a little in embarrassment). She thought I was making it all happen by means of medicines; giving her shots and pills to give her these feelings. (I explain carefully about all medications. She then seems satisfied and a little embarrassed at having thought such things.)

Touch means so much to her, whenever she touches or is touched. (I remind her of the response to touch in the opening interviews.) Yes, she was very aware of that; it meant a lot. After all, it's the only way she can feel really sure.

(At the end of the interview, she takes my hand, caresses it, scrutinizes it carefully, and tells me she loves my hands, "beautiful hands.")

She was recognizing fully the strength of her erotic feelings and impulses, and was permitting expression of them in the transference relation with little reserve. Yet there are the familiar paranoid ways of interpreting an impulse from the unconscious as coming from outside; therefore, if she felt herself falling under the spell of a loving feeling, she saw me as a sort of Svengali contriving to conjure them up by the most mechanical devices. On the other hand, she was quite frank about her profound satisfaction with touching which had been so clearly manifested at the start.

Her telling of her "cutting up" with her friends on the ward deserves mention as an allusion to a fact of her personality. She had been in the habit of stirring up strife and contentious feelings whenever her emotional life seemed otherwise to be getting somewhat empty and boring. Especially was she prone to this in relation to her mother and siblings. These are games of setting up little plots and dramatizing antagonisms for which the boyish component in such a young woman has a great predilection (i.e., the animus).[47]

In the following interview matters came to a head:

(Again in excellent condition; color good and manner coy.)
    She says she wants to know all about me; can't we talk a little about me for a change? (I respond that she is the one we are interested in.) She has lots of feelings she can't handle here,

[47] Jung, "Two Essays on Analytical Psychology."

and she doesn't know what to do with them. She wants me to kiss and fondle her, and approaches, wanting to be held (I hold her off, gently but firmly). She asks to be allowed to leave the hospital, or at least for us to go out walking together.

She tells me of the delusional ideas she had had of an impending invasion by the Communists. The men of the world were all to be eliminated by the women who would keep their sperm in jars to be used in case of invasion.

In response to this proferring of her love, I tried as well as I could to find the middle ground between two pitfalls: on the one hand not wanting to rebuff her hard-won feelings which she had risked exposing to me and, on the other, not wanting to let her gain any impression through these very aggressive maneuvers that I could be seduced into erotic feelings or expressions toward her. I therefore left her free to declare what she wanted to do, but responded by pointing out the difference between the primitive bodily expressions of warmth—inviting all the power of the passions—and the more conscious variety of feeling where warmth can be conveyed back and forth in perfectly manageable ways, such as words. At this level, I told her, she already knew how I felt toward her and could count on it.

The next interview followed the week end, in which she became suddenly disturbed when her mother visited her, and remained so afterward.

She comes in looking pale, unkempt, with characteristic petulant frown, abrupt staccato speech, and rather angular motions of expression.

(I remark that it seems to have been a bad week end for her.) She agrees and tells me that some of the ideas she had had when she first came recurred to her the previous day: she saw me as one who whipped patients around from horseback; a patient's scar made her think I had beaten her up; another abdominal scar on a patient suggested to her that I had impregnated that patient and operated to cover up; she thought I gave things to patients to dope them up; she had felt hypnotized by me.

When she had first come, she thought the doctor's scar meant he had died and was sent back; she also believed she and the others had all died.

With this outburst of imagery, all told to me as if they were odd ideas she had once had, I could interpolate the affect with little difficulty: she saw me as sadistic, power-driven, sexually dangerous, and unscrupulous, and she had had ideas of the hostile elimination of men by women, and of dying, that is, of losing touch with the real world of warm human relationships. So I ventured to make the obvious connection with what had happened in the last interview:

> THER.:   You remember Friday and your very frank expression of feeling for me? How did you feel after it?
>
> PT.:   I was very angry with you later on. Very mad, indeed! [This is spoken quite frankly and openly.] In fact, I could rip you limb from limb, and tear you in little pieces! I need a physical expression of love as well as words; Z came up to me and kissed me on the mouth, and it made me feel very good.
>
> THER.:   It seemed then that I was not accepting you in a way that convinced you, I guess. The way you speak, you see me as aggressive, whipping, and hurting.
>
> PT.:   Yes, you won't let me express it physically [mad and hurt].
>
> THER.:   But you know I've been giving you real feeling as warmth and concern, and you already know whether I like you by the way things feel when we talk together. But to try to change this to a different kind of relation would not be fitting or appropriate, or the real meaning of it.
>
> PT.:   But why not? I love you and need both kinds of expression. I could choke you!
>
> (She walks up behind me with anger cloaked in a playful guise to make it acceptable; she puts her hands around my neck as if to choke me. I hunch my shoulders very slightly, in surprise, but then extend my neck to leave her free and show I am not afraid of her anger. We laugh a little. She then caresses my neck.)
>
> PT.:   You see [triumphantly, but in joke], you jumped when you thought I was going to choke you! Are you afraid of me?
>
> THER.:   No, I'm not, and that's why I offered you my neck. I know your real feeling.

In this outburst of enraged emotion it is not difficult to discern the projection and locate the sadism. I think I can with fair honesty disclaim the charges that her angry fantasies were making. Rather, over that week end she was perceiving me purely as the elemental male, one who asserted a completely phallic sexuality, without the slightest sense of responsibility to the relationship or to the woman's part, and power-driven and manipulative in gaining mastery over woman. All this is as primitive a male sexuality as her erotic seductions toward a purely body-contact type of sexual reassurance are a primitive female variety. When thwarted, she was thrown willy-nilly over from the role of the primitive loving woman into the purely destructive one, whose archetype is the

Terrible Mother who chokes the life out of a man, dismembers him, and cuts him up.[48]

When things come to this pass any human relationship inevitably threatens to break down, with these primordial images and passions entering to take over; great desire is naturally accompanied then by great destructiveness, its natural partner. At this point, the only remedy is a conscious way of relating with conscious feeling that can appraise what really is going on between the two persons.

From this time on, the patient made no further overt seductive moves toward me, but none the less remained loving, trusting, and open, allowing herself to make affectionate gestures perfectly freely; for my part, I felt no further need to be self-protective or defensive about these expressions. The interviews for the next three months were concerned largely with discussions of her ward relationships, family relationships, and her relation to me; in lesser part, she spent some time every now and then filling in the details of her fantasy formations which she had had previously while ill.

IMAGE AND ISSUE

It was my intention at the outset to focus upon the point of junction of the primordial image and the complex. This is the delicate area where interpretation is vital inasmuch as the patient is inclined to by-pass its personal and emotional meaning and avoid the communication of the affect, letting the image be her sole expression.

Three instances stand out in the course of these interviews. In the third session I pointed out to her that her wish for a teddy bear was not going to be passed over as a childlike letter to Santa Claus, but was acknowledged by me as a request that she might bring her warmth to me. In the seventeenth her comments on the order of society in the New Jerusalem could easily have passed by as idle religious fantasy, but were recognized as significant statements about her own coming way of life. In the twenty-fourth her recitation of her previous fantasies about my cruelty might easily have been interpreted as mere statements of what was finished and gone in her imagery, but the slight suggestion about her anger released the actual rage that was cloaked there. Each was a vital issue.

I see these crucial passages as moments at which we restored the lost articulation between the image and the complex—its natural context. I feel that often this is all that is needed in the way of interpretation—

[48] Jung, "Symbols of Transformation."

this is why I earlier called it making connections rather than interpretations. It illustrates the principle that the image is the representation of an emotion in a complex.

FORMULATION OF THE PROCESS

As soon as one begins to make theoretical abstractions from experiences of this kind, one is sure to do violence to the nature of the events and make mistakes; however, one must attempt it, cleaving meanwhile closely to the text.

The bare bones of the structure of the unconscious process seem to me to be this: it began in her identification with a primitive "Earth Mother" in a primitive paradise, with her seeking a primary means of contact in the transference in terms of touch and temperature. It ended up in her identification with an evolved spiritual Madonna in an evolved paradise, and with her working out in the transference a relation of affection and trust.

Symbols of the feminine abounded throughout the process: the Earth Mother, Eve, Eden, creatrix, moon, the Virgin Mother, grotto, Jerusalem (often called "Mother Jerusalem" in ecclesiastical tradition), the palace, the queen, and the many ideas of death and birth; in her paintings there were more: the tree of life and the cross as the tree of death,[49] her soul as a woman with a cup depicting the Twenty-third Psalm, and numerous representations of plants and flowers associated with the Earth Mother.

She made it apparent at every turn that her solid identification with the feminine in the form of the mother archetype was in protest against the masculine. In her delusional imagery she saw the women of the world eliminating all the men, and in true matriarchal spirit keeping their semen for later use in fertilization. She painted a picture of the serpent being crucified, a male symbol (Aesculapius) associated with her professional vocation; another sacrifice she depicted was a man beheaded on the altar in the grotto before the nativity. She visualized her ideal society in rebellion against the elaborate culture of science, industry, and mastery over nature, and was at the same time in rebellion against her own nonpersonal and compulsive professional concerns and way of life, and also against the masculine role of pseudo husband assigned to her by her mother.

This struggle between feminine and masculine bears on an issue involving the opposites in the form that Jung describes in the tradi-

[49] Jung, "Symbols of Transformation."

tional terms *Logos* and *Eros*.[50] *Logos* is concerned with discriminating, abstracting, understanding, and the impersonal; *Eros* with relating, interweaving, entangling, experiencing, and the personal. Man has a component of the feminine in him (the anima), and woman has of the masculine (the animus), each living in the unconscious as autonomous complexes or part personalities.[51]

I would interpret the patient's fantasies as efforts to reassert her basic Eros values against the heretofore overly dominant Logos ones; that is, of her native womanly nature over against the animus. In simple terms, she now wanted to live for love and creativity and not for work. On the one hand, she would re-establish the supremacy of Eros at an elemental level: this was symbolized by Mother Eve and the Paradise of Eden, by primitive people, sexual love, and the birth of babies. On the other hand, she would re-establish the supremacy of Eros on an evolved "spiritual" level: this was symbolized by the Virgin Mother, and the Paradise of the New Jerusalem, by a people redeemed by a gospel of love, kindness and peace, and by the nativity of a divine child. In the first case, Eros amounted to body contact and instinctual relations; in the second, to warm feelings and personal understanding.

As to the question of the genesis of the disorder, I would put it in terms of her mother-daughter psychology. One could say that she was only setting up a symbolic world in which the father was again absent as he was in her early life. Certainly the grandmother had been a matriarchal Great Mother, powerfully constellating the mother image by way of the mother's mother complex. However, a psychotic turmoil is more dynamic and aimful than merely recreating old configurations of childhood, although these are also present. She had lived thus far as a young woman whose identity was always that of a daughter and maiden, leaving the rest of her womanly nature unconscious and in projection upon the mother and mother figures. The needed development was then for her to explore the meaning of the rest of her feminine nature, of motherhood, of the dimensions of love that go beyond sex play, and of creativity, and to assimilate them into her life.

[50] Jung, *The Secret of the Golden Flower.*
[51] Jung, "Two Essays on Analytical Psychology."

CHAPTER V

The Curative Function of Symbols in a Case of Traumatic Neurosis with Psychotic Reactions*

Marguerite A. Sechehaye

T HIS IS A CASE OF A WOMAN, sixty years of age, whom, according to her wish, we shall call Demeter.[1] When she was forty years old, she experienced a severe trauma: her child, a girl of fourteen, was taken away from her. After this shock, the patient fell into a state of serious prostration, inertia, and depression, which, however, was not a typical state of melancholia.

Because of her depression, Demeter had consulted a number of psychiatrists and psychoanalysts who diagnosed her case as either a manic-depressive psychosis or as a melancholia. They treated the patient by means of rest and psychoanalysis but without success. And no one paid any attention to the amazing procedure which Demeter used to procure long remissions. This treatment consisted in regularly spending her days in a library, more particularly a public library. Demeter had noticed quite incidentally that these visits improved her condition, and led to a total remission of more or less considerable length. Alas, this recov-

* Translated from the French by R. Burdet and Patricia Ann Sherman.
[1] Demeter is the Greek name for Ceres, goddess of agriculture. She had a daughter, Proserpine, who was taken away from her by Pluto, god of the lower regions.

ery ceased as soon as the patient stopped her visits to a library. She did this several times.

One day she came upon two of my books: *Symbolic Realization,* and *The Diary of a Schizophrenic.* Although her own case differed completely from the cases cited in these books, Demeter saw a likeness in the role played by a symbol in the healing process. She therefore thought that the author would probably understand something about the amazing agent which healed her, and that she would understand the probably symbolic value of the library. And so she wrote and asked me to study her case and try to cure her.

In this letter she also revealed the events which she considered the direct cause of her sickness:

> I fell sick at the age of forty, consequent to the abduction of my daughter, an event that was fully approved by my country's Court of Justice which is entirely under the influence of the Church.
>
> When I am sick, I am unable to do anything, any work whatever, to make any appointment and least of all to speak to people. I avoid everybody. I lose all contact with both people and things. Inside and mentally I *know* that I live, but I *feel* that I do *not* live, that I am like dead, similar to the feeling just before losing consciousness when being anesthetized. I suffer the entire time from not feeling alive. I must stay in bed tortured by this impotency but not really tired. And I am hostile.
>
> You will say that this state is an affliction, but I tell you it is a torture! In these periods I see and hear as usual and I don't feel my body changed. It's my heart and my memory that are affected. Dead. I began to feel I was dying inside when I had just recovered from pneumonia. But I believe I did not realize this feeling of being dead, or half alive, until it was over, thanks to the library. The public library is the only thing which for a period of time has cured me. I was then as I had been before the abduction of my daughter.
>
> This experience has been repeated eight times in a period of nine years. Now I am absolutely sure it is only the library which cures me. Before the war, I consulted a number of doctors who treated me—psychiatrists included—but nothing succeeded in improving my condition in the least. No one ever showed the slightest interest in the library and yet, I repeat, this was the one and only thing that helped.
>
> At present I feel sick again, having stopped spending my days in the library; but your book has given me hope. I feel sure, in all my affective being, that you who have found "symbolic realization" will also find the meaning of the library. I resemble your patient Renée in one respect: Her symbol has struck me. I also

have a symbol, but no one wants to understand it. I am sixty
years old; at my age a long psychoanalysis is hardly indicated and,
anyway, it would be impossible for me to stay in your city for
this length of time. I believe, however, that with analytic knowledge one could cure me taking the discovery I accidentally made
of the library as a starting point.

I must confess that on reading this letter I remained skeptical. Was
this really a symbol usable in therapy or had the reading of Renée's
case merely led the patient to some self-suggestion? I furthermore wondered whether some form of persecution might be involved. For I had
considerable difficulty believing that the abduction of a child would be
officially sanctioned by the Court of Justice; moreover that the Court
would be totally subordinated to the Church.

I felt that I must first of all ascertain the facts for diagnostic purposes—the therapy, consequently, would depend on the reality of these
facts. If the abduction were real, the event could be considered a trauma
capable of calling forth Demeter's psychoaffective disorder. But if the
event was entirely invented, or was a strong exaggeration of minor accidents, the patient's complaints could be regarded as delirious elements
of revindication.

The information I could gather revealed to me that the facts were
not as extraordinary as I had first thought. When I could speak to
Demeter and examine copies of the documents leading to the abduction, I found that she had been telling the truth. Moreover, I questioned
a psychoanalyst who had treated her a few years before, and he assured
me that the events had taken place in the manner related and that she
had not exaggerated them.

And so I agreed to undertake psychotherapy with Demeter. After
144 interviews her symptoms of inertia, indifference to and loss of contact with her environment, "moral affliction," the feeling of "nonexis-
tence," and blocked affectivity had disappeared. The patient had reac-
quired her capacity for feeling and acting without needing to visit the
library.

This recovery has now lasted nearly six years and, up till now, no
relapse has occurred. I saw Demeter several times after the treatment
and always found her well, thankful, and regretting only that she had
not started treatment earlier. Because of her sickness she had lost twenty
years during which she could have made herself useful to her country.
But happily, Demeter is more active than she was before becoming

sick and also is more interested in her apostleship, i.e., her work for freedom, and the rescue of oppressed children and adults.

This case seems to be interesting for the following reasons:

1. The patient's age and the duration of her malady (twenty years).

2. The particularly symbolic form of her spontaneous healing attempt.

3. The immediate disappearance of the disorder by the discovery of the symbolic aspect of the abduction trauma—and this without its being necessary to make conscious to the patient what the trauma had represented to her unconscious.

4. The complicated diagnosis. (Practically all the psychiatrists and psychoanalysts who examined and treated Demeter diagnosed her case as a manic-depressive psychosis or as a melancholia. However, in the light of the present analytic data, the diagnosis should be revised, I believe, to a traumatic neurosis accompanied by a psychotic state. We shall return to this point later in our paper.)

ANAMNESIS

Demeter was next to the youngest of seven children; she was six years the junior of the youngest sibling but one, so that she had had but little contact with her brothers and sisters. At Demeter's birth her mother was forty and her father seventy years old. All of the family was in an excellent state of health, except the youngest, who as a child already suffered from rheumatism. The family belonged to the upper industrial circles, was conservative, and much attached to its religion.

In Demeter's memory, the picture of her mother is always associated with an inexplicable feeling of uneasiness. She describes her as a cold, haughty, reserved woman who never spoke to anybody and was extremely conscious of the prerogatives of her class.

> My mother [says the patient] regularly spread around her the fear of the unknown; she was always mysterious, always silent and icy. Everything was prohibited with her, especially conversing with the people outside, for they were not our equals and would contaminate and corrupt us. It was prohibited to go outside the park, and to go to school, as this would have brought us into contact with other children. I was not allowed to study for fear of fatigue. It was also forbidden to swim or to ride. She isolated us from everybody and everything; the only exception was a painting lesson twice a week to which I went accompanied

by a governess and where I was indeed in the presence of other children. My mother taught me neither cleanliness nor order, and she never spoke to us about sexual things. At the age of seventeen I was totally ignorant. And although my mother looked after me physically, I hated her and had but one wish: to run away from her.

This description seems to indicate that Demeter's mother had a schizoid character, with psychopathic tendencies, and that she played the role of a continually frustrating mother to her daughter.

The father does not seem to have played a dominant role in the family. Demeter describes him as a good man but completely absorbed in his business. He paid little attention to his children. When he was at home, he retired to his room, which contained an extensive library where he read a great deal. She was still very young when her father died.

Concerning her brothers and sisters, the patient said little but her resentment was nonetheless clear:

I never had any intimate relations with my brothers, but I remember how they teased me, calling me a baby and always repeating that I was nothing, knew nothing and—being a baby—would never be able to do anything. I have always been alone and abandoned and I have never received a word of affection or encouragement. And so I never had a strong wish to live; on the contrary, I even wished I had never been born. The only thing which interested me were the children in the village. When by chance I went outside the park, the poverty of the hungry children shocked me. Ever since that period I have wanted to alter this order of things and I still want to do so now.

Would these starving children not have represented to the patient's unconscious the frustration of love she experienced in her family?

When Demeter was twenty-four, an insurrection broke out in her country. Contrary to all her family stood for, she threw herself into this patriotic adventure and became an ardent member of the liberation party. She wished to marry one of the combatants, a man of great intellect and heroic courage, but who had no financial means. Demeter's mother, horrified by what she considered a degradation that would dishonor the family, was opposed to the marriage. Demeter, however, took no notice of her mother's opposition and broke with her family. Four years later her husband was placed in a high post by the revolutionary government. But shortly after this he was imprisoned by the opposing party, which again had come into power. To protest, he went on a hunger strike and died after seventy-five days, a martyr to his political convictions. He left his wife and a daughter, three years of age, whom we shall call Josy. After the death of her husband, Demeter became more and more active in the movement for the liberation of her country, visiting many areas and leaving her child at home in the care of her mother and sister-in-law. But her desire to educate her daughter in a spirit of great liberty, in accordance with her husband's and her own ideal, incited Demeter to have Josy educated outside of all family traditions. She therefore placed her in a boarding school to make her independent, strong, well educated, and dedicated to the unfortunate.

Demeter, while living in a small town in the neighborhood, met a man and conceived a daughter by him. "I purposely wanted the child to be illegitimate," she told me, "in order to protest against the middle-class and religious conventions opposed to love and life." Thus Demeter remained clearly opposed to the principles of her class and scandalized anew her family and that of her husband, particularly her husband's eldest sister. This person had transferred to her niece all the possessive affection she had felt for her brother. She constantly usurped Josy's visits, pretending that Josy's paternal family had both the wish and the duty to look after her. Our patient, however, did not accede to these demands for she feared that her sister-in-law would use the child's visits to wean her from her mother and to instruct her in the religion Demeter dreaded.

One day Demeter received a letter from her daughter saying that her aunt had arrived at her boarding school and that she wished to take Josy home with her for the holidays. The aunt had also written personally stressing the fact that Josy's paternal family wished to see the child, and gave her word of honor that she would bring Josy back to school as soon as the holidays were over.

Since Demeter had no confidence at all in her sister-in-law, she sent a friend to fetch Josy from the boarding school. The child made no objection and only asked the time they would be leaving. Then she left the room to get ready. A moment later, however, the head of the school came in and agitatedly said that Josy had disappeared. Demeter informed the police and frontier posts without any result, and for a fortnight she remained in total ignorance of where Josy might be and whether she was dead or alive. At last, a card written by Josy to the head of the school informed her that she was on a journey.

Josy's aunt had had her carefully instructed in the religion dreaded by

Demeter. She had given the child the assurance that her father, whom she much admired, had expressly wanted her to receive this tradition and that her mother by not having seen to this had shown a lack of maternal love; finally, that her younger sister was an illegitimate child and proof of her mother's misdemeanors. It is easy to understand that such revelations had a particularly traumatizing effect on the girl, and she consequently decided to go with her aunt.

The lawyers Demeter consulted found that the costs of the abduction had not been borne by her sister-in-law, who was very poor, but by the political party which had a great interest in regaining the child. In fact, as the daughter of a national hero, Josy's conversion to her country's traditions could help to reconcile the old and new parties. The lawyers therefore advised Demeter not to make any official protest; but they encouraged her to bring her daughter back personally, since she had a natural right to do so. And so Demeter went back to her own country and, with a friend—an ancient comrade in the strife—organized the re-kidnapping of her own child.

Unhappily, the friend became fearful at the last moment and backed out. Demeter felt betrayed and abandoned, and this was another shock to her. But it was the next day that she experienced the trauma which made her become seriously ill. She calls this "the shock of the document."

That evening Demeter sat in the parlor of her hotel. The door opened and a young man came in accompanied by a priest. The young man held a large parchment at the end of which were red seals attached by red tape. He showed the document to Demeter and drew her attention to the fact that it was signed by the President of the Court of Justice. Then he handed her an official copy of the document. The text said, in substance, that Josy X had requested the Court of Justice to relieve her of her mother's tutelage and place her under the protection of her aunt and the General Guardian. Mrs. X must therefore renounce the legitimate guardianship of her daughter. The young man handed Demeter a pen and requested her to sign the document in acceptance.

The presentation of the document was a brutal shock. She said to me:

> It was so sudden, so unexpected, so terrible and horrible, that it perverted my judgment. I thought: "If my country's jurisdiction declares me guilty and without the right to keep my daughter, it must mean that I am guilty indeed." I had lost my self-confidence and had become feeble and impotent. So I gave in and I signed

the document. And I, the victim, had suddenly become the person punished in the place of the other person who deserved punishment for having stolen my daughter. As a rule, the kidnapping of a child is considered a grave offence, and the guardianship of a child is not given to the person who carried her off.

Next day, having recovered her judgment, Demeter was terrified at the thought of having signed such a document and hastened to consult a lawyer. He advised her to oppose the so-called "request" of her daughter. But in spite of all her petitions, journeys, and considerable expense, Demeter obtained no relief and her mental condition became aggravated.

Some months later, the process was terminated by a judgment *in camera*. Demeter was informed that the Court of Justice had decided to deprive her of her natural guardianship of her daughter and to transfer it to Josy's paternal aunt. No further explanation was given. Demeter was shocked not only by this decision but also by the fact that the whole procedure had taken place behind closed doors notwithstanding her lawyer's efforts to make it public.

And then came the final blow. At Christmas the patient received a letter from her daughter accusing her of being a bad mother, since she had not educated her in her father's religion. It also stated that Josy would never return to live with her.

This caused the patient to give way completely. She gave up the struggle and soon was bedridden with a broncho-pneumonia so severe that she was between life and death for six weeks. When she had recovered physically, she felt changed. She felt not really alive, but dead. And in spite of the feeling of "being dead," she suffered terribly and was in great despair. She spent her days in bed, was indifferent to all things, and became exclusively preoccupied with past events. She could not forgive the doctors for saving her from penumonia, for she suffered at the thought that her daughter was now being educated in the old conservative way. Moreover, Josy believed her mother to be seriously at fault. "It would have been better," she thought, "if the child had not been alive."

Henceforth, renouncing a daughter who had disavowed her, she said to herself, "She is my daughter no more; indeed, she never was my child." And she explained to me that it was in order to keep sane and free from too much suffering that she had thus given up her daughter. This defense mechanism by which the patient blocked out the object of her affection proved to be incapable of improving her condition. Demeter withdrew totally from social life, was bedridden most of the time, and refused to see anybody. The only preoccupation that gave her any relief was reading. "It was my only means of escaping from my thoughts and suffering," she explained, and in this way she began going to a public library. Demeter came to notice some improvement from visiting the library and about six months later she felt as well as before losing her daughter. So she took up her work again with a feeling of relief. But she soon relapsed into her depressive state with the same feeling of being dead. In order to escape from these feelings, the patient returned to the library and again noticed that her visits promptly brought her some relief and that after several months she was feeling quite well.

> When I had had this experience three or four times, I came to realize that it was indeed the library that cured me. Since then, I turned to it whenever I felt a recurrence of melancholia. But if a library is to be of any use to me, it must necessarily be a large, clean, well-ordered, and easily accessible room. If I have to make an effort to reach it, it is not the same thing and it does not operate. But if the library answers to the conditions mentioned, I become as I was before the kidnapping of my daughter.

The main drawback to this curious treatment was that the patient relapsed whenever she discontinued it. Our very active Demeter naturally wanted to take up her political and social work as soon as she felt better. She therefore resented having to spend half her time in a library in order to be in good mental condition the rest of the time. She consulted psychiatrists and psychoanalysts hoping that they could explain the mysterious curative power of the library and thus free her from her tiresome obligation. But no one, according to our patient, wanted to see the library as a symbol open to analysis. They all considered the phenomenon a curious coincidence with the spontaneous ups and downs inherent in the cyclic nature of the malady. And only Demeter felt sure that the library must have a symbolic value when she read *Symbolic Realization*. "At that moment," she said, "I had the conviction that what I had hitherto obscurely felt was true, and that the library had a deep significance which, if found, would cure me."

Many diagnoses had been made of this patient's condition. My own observations during the initial interviews led me to consider the diagnosis as a traumatic neurosis complicated by psychotic phenomena. The evolution of treatment would show whether this provisional diagnosis could be sustained, or whether new aspects of the patient's psychoaffective structure would make its modification necessary. We will discuss this question further at the end of this report.

Course of Treatment   The analysis evolved, as usual, in two phases: the collection of material (traumatic events, childhood remembrances, dreams, associations); and the interpretation of the material's contents.

I must say immediately that the psychotherapy was not conducted along the classical lines of a Freudian analysis. Our patient was in a psychotic state, so that analysis was certainly not indicated. The reader, consequently, will find in this account neither a regular analysis of resistance and transference nor an interpretation of dreams and their associations. This does not in any way mean that the patient would not have had such transference or resistances. On the contrary, one of the first elements brought by Demeter to the therapy was her fear of attachment to the therapist and of thus risking a new deception. "After my misfortune I had promised myself," she said, "never more to love anybody nor to have any affective contact with a human being." This conscious resistance was, however, soon overcome by my promise that I would not abandon her.

Analysis of dreams was not possible either: in the first place, because they referred almost exclusively to the abduction and thus formed a repetition-symptom inherent in any traumatic neurosis; and second, as is often the case with psychotic patients, the dreams represented to Demeter realities more emotional and more real than reality itself. The patient had not the slightest interest in free associations and approaches to her unconscious conflicts as the therapist proposed. This inability to perceive the conflicts' reflections in her dreams did not arise from a resistance; rather, it was dependent on the patient's psychotic state. Having said this we will now examine the essential points of the analysis.

During the first part of the treatment, the patient principally related the history of the abduction of her daughter and its consequences; the principal themes were her resentment against the clerical authorities "responsible for the abduction of Josy and at the root of all misfortune in the world," her contempt of capitalism and, last but not least, the moral suffering she had endured for twenty years.

While relating this, Demeter constantly referred to her infancy and it was easy to establish a parallel between her present feelings and what she had felt in her childhood.

Religion is obscure and it wants one to be ignorant. My mother disliked books and she forbade us to study and to know things. . . . By stealing away my child they have taken away my power and activity. . . . My mother interdicted me to act; everything was forbidden. I was deprived of seeing people, of mounting a horse. . . . My country's government and clergy send me my own money penny by penny to pay for my treatment. Evidently, after having broken my health, they don't want me to recover my strength. . . . My mother was not interested in me.

These juxtapositions show the unconscious connections the patient was making between the past and the present. As Freud says: "Behind a traumatic neurosis often hides a neurotic structure predisposing the patient to being overcome by a recent shock."

The second part of the treatment was devoted to the interpretation of the symbols brought by the patient. The symbol "library," however, which appeared important to Demeter, plays, paradoxically, only a secondary role in her recovery. Another element in the drama proved to be the primary trauma: the presentation of the document which officially sanctioned the abduction of the daughter. This event had been told many times by the patient, but its emotional contents had been suppressed. And the document had not only served its traumatizing purpose but also reactivated an infantile complex that had remained deeply unconscious.

The complex character of the presentation of the document is proved by the state of ego annihilation into which Demeter was thrown at that very moment. Although the patient had earlier been able to control her emotions and undertake action suitable for the defense and the recovery of her maternal rights, she presented at that critical moment a clearly pathological comportment. Let us recall the events: Demeter received the visit of a young man, accompanied by a priest. The young man unrolled a parchment. At its lower end were big red seals attached by means of tape, equally red. In the document she read that a minor child, Josy X, had requested to be relieved of her mother's tutelage and to be put under protection of the General Guardian and of her aunt. The young man asked Demeter to sign the request and the patient, subjugated, signed.

This woman, who was in the habit of constantly meeting political and social personalities, felt herself suddenly not only annihilated but even guilty for wishing to keep her child—guilty, "since the law denies me this right." This abrupt ego decline can only be explained by the destructive effect of an underlying complex suddenly activated by emotional stress.

The patient experienced a feeling of intense relief and liberation merely on realizing that this event had been the crucial point of the drama and that it had precipitated her psychotic state. I therefore initially centered my therapeutic efforts around this precise point so fully charged with dynamism. In fact, the reality for Demeter was indissolubly bound to the symbol representing it. By a presymbolic participation of magical order *reality was the symbol and the symbol was reality*. This emotional reality inherent to her complex was re-experienced by the patient with unimaginable intensity as she related the traumatic event. The manner in which she tells the episode, the symbolic elements she discerns, the associations rising in relation to them, show that the affair with the document plunges its roots into the deepest part of her unconscious!

This complex had been, in fact, the structural organizer of Demeter's personality. We know that every individual carries within himself a bisexual tendency. In a normal girl, the feminine tendency should naturally predominate; but if conflicts or traumas come to disturb her sexual development, there will be loss of balance and the masculine tendency, instead of disappearing, will be reinforced and become an integral part of the personality. As Freud has shown, Demeter, like all little girls, had wanted a penis; the more so, because she had been brought up with older brothers who jeered at her girlish feebleness and endlessly repeated that she was nothing and always would be nothing. Moreover, her brothers were granted large amounts of liberty whereas she was deliberately deprived of these things by a mother who considered study and liberty both superfluous and wrong for a woman.

So intellectual power became for Demeter the exclusive and envied apparatus of the male sex. This caused her to identify with her brothers. Oedipal tendencies would have compensated for this trend toward masculinity, but they had little opportunity of developing in Demeter. Her father paid no attention to his children. To his little girl he appeared as a distant and rather mysterious being who constantly retired to his library. Very soon she also acquired the habit of withdrawing to her father's library and, unknown to her mother, of plunging herself into one of his fascinating books. The library became for her a place of refuge and a means of acquiring some intellectual power. After marriage and motherhood, Demeter found in her child a symbol of her power (the child representing to her unconscious the coveted penis). This is why Demeter was so eager for her daughter to receive an education proper to make her "strong, active, and independent," these being the very privileges of which she had been deprived by her own mother. Hence we understand how the presentation of the document was felt by Demeter's unconscious as a symbol of castration. The Court of Justice represented the castrating mother who refused her the right of possession of her own attribute of power: her daughter. But although the symbolic meaning of the document was perfectly clear to us, it was not clear to the patient, who was quite unconscious of it.

Space is not available for a full account of Demeter's associations, which constitute a proof of our hypothesis. The following, however, were the principal ones:

> The document that was terrible, horrible, is written on *parchment*. Parchment is made of the skin of a sheep or lamb. I called my daughter "Lammi" when she was small, which means little lamb. A lamb is sacrificed in the Gospel, like my daughter was sacrificed for an old Oedipean madwoman, my sister-in-law. The parchment carries a text and a signature exactly as the Table of Law carried the Ten Commandments of God. God, that is the Chief Justice, the President of the Court, who signed the document. A priest is there and he assists in this infamy, the sacrifice of my daughter, like the priests of all religions, always present at the sacrifices. It is a *bloody sacrifice*, for there are seals on the parchment and tape, red like blood, the blood of my child that is sacrificed. And the young man bearing the document is slim, very slim; he stands up straight like a *knife*. It is the knife which has served for the bloody sacrifice of my daughter! *This is the horror of the thing which has made me sick and which took away my power: they have sacrificed my child!*

These images rising to the patient's consciousness gave her an intense emotion. She realized suddenly that the shock had been caused much more by the symbolic significance of the document than by the unjust deed. The whole scene is re-experienced, not in the sober way in which it actually took place, but under the hallucinated aspect of a cruel and bloody sacrifice. And this vivid reminiscence acted on the patient as a powerful catharsis.

After this, we had two choices in continuing the psychotherapy: to try by means of associations and progressive interpretations to make the patient conscious of the complex character of her trauma; or simply to establish connections between the patient's present and her infantile past while remaining on a symbolic level.

We chose the latter because of reasons of limited time and of relatively well compensated masculine tendencies, but particularly because of the specific character of the psychosis. For Demeter, similar to schizophrenic patients, experienced the symbols as more vivid and real than the facts of reality. Interpretation of the symbols, in the sense of rationalization, would have deprived them of their dynamism. Since one of the fundamental symptoms of our patient was the affective indifference to which she had sunk, the awakening of her sensibility appeared to be a clear sign of being well on the way to recovery. So we contented ourselves with establishing manifold relations between the trauma experienced in her adult life and its origins in her infantile past. I showed the patient that the feelings she had toward the protagonists of the drama were the same as those which she had formerly experienced in relation to her parents. And I brought the striking fact to her notice that the actual personages had not even changed. They had revived and become magnified in the redoubtable figures of government, Court of Justice, and Church. The patient then began to realize that, if the document had made her lose her capacity for action, this was because the child represented her power and that by losing the one, she also lost the other. Demeter was much relieved by making this conscious. She exclaimed:

> Yes, this is quite true! The child was my power and the document, by depriving me of my child, deprived me of all my power. I had no right to it any more since justice had taken it away and this is why I could no longer work.

A new connection was thus developed between "the inhuman Court of Justice [directed by the Church]" and the patient's mother, who had also been "inhuman." Apparently for Demeter action meant power. She also made the discovery that the Church, like her mother, gave her a feeling of inexplicable anguish and the fear of things mysterious and unknown. She said:

> Indeed, what terrorized me in the document was the unknown, the mystery surrounding it. My mother made a mystery of everything, and particularly of sexual matters. The anguish I felt toward her and toward the Church was the same; they both forbade me all action, all knowledge, leaving me in anguish and darkness.

These few associations, selected from many similar ones, show clearly the relation between the trauma of the document and the experiences in childhood with a castrative mother.

Demeter had succeeded in surmounting her castration complex by trying to acquire intellectual power in a number of ways, but particularly by reading. She did this since childhood. Later on, political activities and the birth of a child cicatrized the narcissistic wound. But the trauma of the document reinstated the castration anguish by depriving the patient of the object of narcissistic compensation: her child. This brought back the terrifying thought of being deprived of "something precious and essential" without which she would be impotent. The fact that the patient felt the presentation of the juridical document as a bloody sacrifice proves that the kidnapping of her daughter was felt by the patient's unconscious as a brutal castration. The presentation of the document indeed created a double stress: an undeniable trauma to the adult ego (a trauma that every normal mother would have felt in a similar case), but at the same time a reactivation of the ancient narcissistic wound. It was the combined action of these two traumas that broke the balance and that prevented the ego from establishing a system of defense adequate to the situation. This is why the patient was obliged to have recourse to emergency defense mechanisms and her ego functions blocked. On this basis she suddenly felt annihilated, her judgment falsified, her perception of reality weakened, and finally her contact with the environment broken.

This castration anguish can equally be traced in the depressive state that followed the trauma. The patient had indeed the impression of "being dead," which made her suffer intensely. The feeling of being dead is often a form of castration anguish. Demeter's child had become part of her by a process of introjection, so that sacrifice of her daughter amounted to her own sacrifice, or her own death. Moreover, the patient lost all feeling of her proper value, and of her right to live. So Demeter abandoned herself to a progressive destruction in which nothing could relieve or comfort her and everything left her indifferent.

The Library   Next came the interpretation of the symbol of the library in which Demeter spent the major part of several years. Once she realized the library might have a symbolic meaning she felt that if this were found, she might recover her mental health.

The library was revealed to have several significances and to comprise various symbols as did the document. One of these symbols is the catalogue, which is consulted initially. Her associations are so transparent, and her unconscious and conscious so close together, that comment is superfluous.

> The use of the catalogue is to create order. It establishes organization and clearness in what is vague and confused. It is also a means of information, allowing us to find in history books the history of powerful people. Thanks to the books indicated in the catalogue, we learn the truth about the past and about facts that were never taught us. The catalogue also indicates books on anatomy. I studied anatomy a great deal and wanted to be a hospital nurse.

The library also represents a means of mending ignorance imposed by one's mother:

> My mother read very little; she was opposed to instruction as is the Church, encouraging justice to hold a trial with closed doors in mystery and falsehood. Ignorance is the unknown. And it is the unknown that has destroyed my daughter. Had I had more extensive knowledge they would not have been able to take my daughter away for I would have defended myself.
> *Books!* How my daughter loved them! Later on, it's she who would have instructed me. *It's my daughter who is in the library; there I rediscover my spiritual child* who no one can steal away from me.

Later, the patient brings other images and symbols relative to the library:

> There you find long, undivided tables with a number to each place: it's *equality and justice to all people*; no differences are made between the readers. And then there are the lamps, straight, with two branches like those of a balance with a pair of scales: the balance of justice. There, too, the scales are the same for everybody. Equality means justice. These lamps bring to my mind the statue of Justice holding a pair of scales. Justice, this horrible woman, ugly and blindfolded, her eyes blind to the needs of children. This is the only justice I knew. This horrible woman. But now I know another one. *You are justice, the real one!* You have re-established equality on the scales; you have lightened the too heavy one, the one of the unjust and ignorant Church and of opulence and you have added weight to the other scale, the one of the oppressed workers, miserable children and myself.
> And then the library is light and clean. The Church, which prevents instruction, is dark. And the Court of Justice must neces-

sarily be dark too. My mother never taught us the truth. In my
maternal language everything that is clear and white is called
beautiful.

The library, like a *hospital*, can cure people. It has the same
vast dimensions and silence; one feels protected there from the
external, hostile world, where one receives mortal shocks. One
must remain a long time in the library, like in a hospital when
one is seriously ill. One must wait patiently for many months
until the treatment is finished.

Probing deeper into the matter, Demeter now compares the library
to her maternal home:

The library is *full of life* whereas my mother's house was full
of deadly silence. My mother was opposed to life, to children, to
love, as is also the Church. And if you didn't agree with her, she
tyrannized you. Around my mother there was solitude, mystery,
ignorance and impotence. In the library there is life, knowledge,
truth and [intellectual]   power. The library restitutes life to me!

We have dwelt upon the associations and the symbolizations relative
to the library in order to illustrate more clearly the symbolic processes
by means of which the library promoted the patient's partial recovery.
This was, in fact, a spontaneous attempt to heal.

For by means of the library the patient's ego succeeded in successfully controlling the state of impotence into which it had been thrown.
On a fantasy level, Demeter converted herself to an *upright Court of
Justice*, where there are no closed doors and where she or anyone can
freely take note of the books, that is, documents, and by studying the
history, judge the cause itself. By the *mechanism of repetition*, which
is a primordial element in traumatic neurosis, the patient symbolically
repeats in an active way the events she passively experienced. As
Fenichel, after Freud, remarked: "In this repetition the ego doses its
effects and chooses its moment." With Demeter, the ego repeats the
traumatizing situation in a reassuring and curative manner where she
can dominate the danger instead of being crushed by it. And this is
the library's first function: to help her somewhat to integrate the traumatizing event, adapt herself to it, and to manage the situation. She does
this by choosing the documents as she wishes and by taking note of
them openly and quietly at her own rhythm. On a deeper level touching
the patient's castration complex, the library fulfills a *compensative function*. Because the books instruct, they convey clearness and truthfulness
to the thoughts. To Demeter's unconscious, instruction was intimately

related to her daughter; it had even become a substitute for the lost child when Demeter says, "My books are my spiritual child."

Second, there are also medical books in the library, so that Demeter can study anatomical charts and particularly those representing the genital organs. In this way she can magically recover the lost object, the penis, formerly symbolized by her child. This is why the patient so often says, "By consulting these anatomy books I refound my strength and my power." Moreover, while visiting the library, Demeter identifies with her father, who used to retire to his room and plunge into his books.

Third, the library brings still another form of compensation. In fact, it represents the ideal home, the house wherein cleanliness, order, liberty of thought and action prevail, all things so totally absent from her maternal home. The patient's oral tendencies receive their satisfaction, too. Are not books her mental nourishment? Demeter, moreover, associates the library in an almost direct way to the maternal breast, when she explains: "The cupola on the public library in my town always reminds me of a breast; it has the same shape, this breast, which nourishes the child and gives strength to it."

And last, the library fulfills a function of no small importance: it offers *refuge* and *restoration* to Demeter. In her view, it represents a hospital, a place where people who suffer receive attention. Here again we find a double meaning. On the one hand, as a hospital, that is, a refuge from life, the library is a protection against the renewal of painful stimuli, a place of rest after the commotion caused by the trauma. The ego, crushed by the task imposed on it, tries to escape from all responsibilities and to live in a passive, regressed way requiring but a minimum of effort. On the other hand, the state of depression and of moral pain seems gradually to diminish, because of the library.

The sojourns in the library probably allowed Demeter to achieve a kind of "mourning labor." In a first movement the patient tries to reestablish the introjection of the lost object (her daughter) by means of books which she incorporates intellectually. In a second movement she tries, on the contrary, to loosen the bonds linking her to her child; she endeavors to break away from her remembrance and, while parting from her, to replace her with a substitute that will carry no risk of suffering: books and instruction. This is why Demeter says, "I no more needed my child materially since I found her again spiritually in the library."

It is the combination of all these factors, which correspond to various psychical stratifications, that confer upon the library a power so eminently curative.

The Role of Transference   And yet the library was unable to cure the patient, because she remained under the obligation of constantly renewing her visits to it. This could be expected to be altered by the treatment. The analytic situation allows the primary neurosis to be replaced by a transference neurosis in the course of which the patient will be able to express her conflict with all the elements relative to it. During the initial interviews the patient manifested her fear of again attaching herself to a person who might deceive her. This negative transference lasted but a short time, and the rest of the analysis was followed by a positive transference during which the patient felt fully confident that she would be cured. This positive transference has been a great support to the healing process and it has shortened the treatment. It allowed Demeter to re-experience the intolerable feelings caused by the traumatic event without fear of being submerged. These feelings had remained vague, syncretic, and more or less unconscious; the corresponding harmful emotions could in this way be assimilated and dominated by the ego. The patient considered the analyst "the good mother" who understands and protects, and this allowed the resistances to be reduced to a minimum. "I have never had the slightest difficulty in talking to you on any topic," said Demeter, "and this is something quite new to me. And you never caused me any pain although we had to discuss painful subjects."

In this case it was not advisable to hew too strictly to the rule of neutrality in the therapy; on the contrary, it was desirable to offer the patient an atmosphere of relaxation and security by taking sides against the real injustice that had been inflicted. Abraham and Fenichel are of the opinion that the principal task of therapy consists in bringing to the traumatized patient the relaxation and the reassurance he so very much needs and in the absence of which the analyst is incapable of achieving his therapeutic goal.

Demeter's retirement to a library was a form of spontaneous therapy and she transferred this into the analytic situation. Not only did she seek moral repose, help and security from the analyst, she also actively repeated—by way of catharsis—the trauma she had passively undergone. She brought this to consciousness and succeeded in assimilating it. By offering her an opportunity of understanding what had happened within her, the analyst restored the power which she had been deprived of by ignorance. The patient also transferred to the analyst the affective potential symbolized in the library's lamps, which represented justice. The therapist had become justice personified, who gave her back the rights of her child and restored the balance cruelly broken by an unjust destiny.

> You are the lamp that illuminates [she said]; you have enlightened and instructed me about all these obscure symbols, all this mystery surrounding me. You are Justice with the pair of scales, for you have given me my right; you have undone the injustice and the infamy of the closed doors. This is why I am cured. I am no more in any need of the library, I have recovered my capacity for work and action.

But if Demeter saw in the library the ideal maternal home, she transferred to the analyst the image of the foster mother, giving protection, care, security, love, and nourishment.

> You are the cupola of the library; the cupola is the mother's breast. You are what my mother should have been and what she failed to be. I thought I never could love any more. I have always detested my mother and, since my misfortune, everybody. Now this nightmare is over. You have done me an immense lot of good, much more than you seem to think.

And so all through the analysis the patient substitutes the mother-analyst for the library-hospital. But in place of treatment by the library, which was undetermined and unconscious, the treatment by the analysis, as we have noted, allowed Demeter to re-experience the anxiety of the traumatic situation, to become conscious of the pathologic emotion tied to it, and to dominate it. And further, it helped the patient to abreact her infantile traumas. It is interesting to note that this abreaction remained strictly on a presymbolic, magical level. Not for one moment did the patient realize the meaning of the castration represented by the symbolic figures in the surrender of the document: bloody sacrifice, man-knife, red seals.

Let us also note that the transference could be terminated at the end of the treatment even though not subjected to an orthodox analytical interpretation. Demeter has remained sincerely thankful and friendly toward the analyst, but without any fixation on her. This ability to give up dependent, infantile behavior is one proof of sound recovery.

STRUCTURE OF THE CASE

It is difficult to establish the exact structure of so complicated a case in which, moreover, we were bound to remain within the confines of the traumatic neurosis, the patient having no understanding of her original neurosis. Yet the patient's associations and the whole context of her analysis were sufficiently clear to allow us to assume the existence of an underlying neurosis, and more particularly a castration complex.

Abraham claims that individuals with a tendency toward depressions and traumas have always experienced frustrations in their childhood and, more especially, early narcissistic wounds: loss of vital narcissistic satisfactions, repeated minor humiliations, penis envy, castration, Oedipal frustrations, feelings of abandonment and solitude, etc. The patient's history revealed that she had undergone privations of all kinds, both early and late, and that these had created a neurotic structure in her. We find this structure reflecting itself throughout the patient's traumatic neurosis. One might almost say that the latter constitutes a screen for the initial castration trauma. This would explain why the ego was invaded and unable to master the situation, its energy having already been mobilized for maintenance of the earlier suppressions.

Indeed, the repressed hatred against the castrating mother was strongly activated by the traumatizing process, as we have shown before. The Church and the Court of Justice symbolizing the mother renewed at that moment her castrating action. In terms of the unconscious, the object, valorizing the patient and representative of her instrument of power (her daughter), was turned against her and refused to belong to her. This provoked an intense aggression against the object itself and the patient desired to destroy it. However, because of the introjection, the patient was destroying herself by wishing to destroy the object. So she defended herself against the eruption of her aggressive impulses by blocking them off and keeping them outside her field of conscience. Thus was created the state of inertia, passivity, and withdrawal from all external activity into which the patient relapsed. One might be astonished to find in the patient's depressive state with its prominent moral pain no expression whatever of feelings of guilt. This can be explained both by the fact that this was not a state of genuine melancholia and by acknowledging that the existing feelings of guilt were suppressed by the obvious injustice the patient had undergone. Eminent jurists had decided in her favor, and Church men had criticized the demeanor of the Church in this affair. So the events could produce a rationalization of the aggression and suppression of any neurotic feeling of guilt that might arise. Moreover, these events allowed the patient to give expression to her new and intensified vindicative tendencies and to express them freely. And we wonder if it is not due to these aggressive tendencies that Demeter escaped a genuine melancholia with impulsions toward suicide that was projected outward, thus protecting the patient against complete self-destruction. Yet it is unquestionable that if a complete analysis had been done, a strong culpability, due to the aggressiveness felt against a very frustrating mother, would have been disclosed.

Behind the obvious castration complex are hidden other elements of an anal and oral order. We realize this when we think of the importance the patient gives to property: "It is wrong to possess." This is, moreover, the only domain in which Demeter shows a conscious feeling of guilt. She abhors banks. "My husband used to say that banks made me sick every time I went there." And she gives a considerable importance to cleanliness. She dreads everything that is soiled and likes nothing better than an empty space glittering with cleanliness!

But the most important element is the oral frustration. The patient's mother does not seem to have loved her, for she gave her cold chills and left her in a state of affective isolation. By way of compensation, Demeter has a feeling of deep compassion for deprived and abandoned children with whom she unconsciously identifies. She has need for maternal security and protection. This was never expressed in words, but it revealed itself in her show of confidence towards the therapist. She believes the therapist could be a mother who would support her. Thus one day Demeter brought me a cushion-sack made of red plastic, stating: "I chose red for it is placenta and I am bringing you myself as well."

During the short lapse of time in which this patient was treated, even deeper layers of her psyche were disclosed, stratifications ranging from the castration complex to the oral. And yet, curious as it may be, although the patient took full cognizance of the symbols relating to her complexes, she never realized their exact nature and contented herself with re-experiencing them intensely in the manner of a "presymbolic magical participation." This sufficed to cure her.

Diagnostic Problem

Now that we have seen the case as a whole, let us reconsider the problem of differential diagnosis. Although this proved to be rather difficult, a solution was gradually found in the course of treatment. The opinions of the doctors consulted by the patient had been varied. Some psychiatrists had considered a form of manic-depressive psychosis; for others melancholia was a possibility, whereas a few considered Demeter to be suffering from paranoia. It is to this last diagnosis that I rallied initially. For the patient manifested very strong revindications and she had formed projections that seemed to trace back further than the trauma of the abduction. On the other hand, the circumstances seemed so extraordinary that I could reasonably question their exactitude. But as I received authenticated information and got to know the juridical documents, the patient's way of thinking and reacting appeared more adapted to the circumstances than I had initially thought them to be. Close analysis of the factors inherent in the circumstances, and of factors relative to her character, subsequently contradicted the hypothesis of a paranoid structure. The principal factors are as follows.

1. *Reality of the trauma.* Demeter had undeniable and repeated frustrations during her childhood. Later on she experienced, by the kidnapping of her child, a most serious setback. Moreover, she twice experienced a revolution, which caused a great political and social confusion throughout the country and which, like all revolutions, provoked extreme reactions in numerous participants. One can say that Demeter's ideas were shared by half her compatriots, and by many of the most eminent ones. Her husband, whose thoughts and political aims she fully shared, is considered in his country as a liberator and national hero, and to such a degree that the government allocates a pension to Demeter in spite of the action brought against her. So it would be difficult to consider her political and religious ideas as pathologically querulous. Real paranoiac patients, moreover, base their revindications on facts which, if true, are usually insignificant, fragile, and totally disproportionate to their reactions.

No mention whatever of mental disease was made in the judgment. If the judges had suspected any mental disorder in Demeter, the Court would undoubtedly have taken this into account by asking for a psychiatric report.

2. *Absence of ideas of grandeur.* The patient never showed any overestimation of herself, and she was not conceited about the signs of honor given to her or about her friendship with prominent political personalities. Such circumstances would certainly have caused an exaggerated ego expansion in an individual with paranoiac tendencies.

3. *Absence of revindications transposed to other themes.* When De-

meter was freed of her complaints by psychotherapy, she did not transfer her revindications to other themes, as is usually the case with paranoiac patients.

4. *Acceptance of reality.* Although she was ill at that time, Demeter was quite capable of submitting herself to the reality principle when she realized that any further steps to recover her child would be useless. She renounced further efforts at once; a paranoiac patient would never have done this.

5. *The confident character of the patient.* Contrary to the well-known distrust of paranoiac patients, Demeter always showed great confidence in others and more particularly in her therapist. And, remarkably, she kept this confidence on ascertaining that my political and religious opinions were different from her own. She was always very respectful of the opinions of her adversaries, if she knew them to be sincere. Paranoiac patients, on the contrary, are known to be most touchy!

As to the diagnosis of manic-depressive psychosis, this was formulated because of periods of depression followed by periods of improvement. We know, however, that these phases of amelioration were not of an inherently spontaneous and cyclical character but that they depended directly upon the visits to the library. The doctors, not giving consideration to the symbolic and compensatory role the library played, could very well have considered them circular phases. A depressive state, however, existed beyond doubt.

A diagnosis of melancholia cannot be sustained either. The patient never displayed the intense feelings of guilt, self-accusation, ruin, and suicidal tendencies which are characteristic of this psychosis.

And last, a diagnosis of hysteria was also formulated. Let us recall that Freud has shown how much the symptoms of this condition resemble those of a traumatic neurosis, so that the two are apt to be confused. Yet the absence of a divided ego, of conversion symptoms, of sudden emotional motor discharges, makes us dismiss this diagnosis. Clearly manifest in the patient's symptom picture are the symptoms of a traumatic neurosis: blocked affect; ego crushed by a destiny felt as cruel and implacable; a feeling of emptiness and death; agitated sleep, with stereotyped dreams relative to the trauma; endless repetition of the experienced event; and withdrawal from the world to a purely passive state with marked regression to infantile dependence. These last two symptoms (withdrawal from the outside world and infantile regression) have been particularly accentuated in this patient. Their intensity and duration, their singular quality and resonance, make it impossible to consider them as simple reactions of a neurotic order. The fact, also, that the patient has spontaneously found a symbolical-magic method of intermittent self-cure, and that she has also been open to the symbolic realization method, proves to us that she had returned to a stage of massive regression to which neurotics do not generally retreat, i.e., a stage where the individual experiences the symbol as a reality and sees it, as Demeter did, in a manner as magical as it is intensive. That is why most of the psychiatrists who examined this patient diagnosed her as psychotic. Actually, it was for me more a matter of *psychotic reactions to a trauma* than of an authentic psychotic personality organization.

The gravity and nature of the patient's reactions can be explained only by the existence of a collateral neurosis, with deeply imbedded roots. Freud has drawn attention to the fact that one frequently finds a neurotic predisposition in traumatics. Fenichel and Rado express the same idea when they write: "A qualitative awareness of certain aspects of complexcs permits the stimuli to provoke traumatic states." This was, in effect, the case with Demeter. If the experienced catastrophe, representing a polar attraction, was the determining cause in the outbreak of the illness, the infantile conflicts play, for their part, a complementary role no less important. Furthermore, the anguish and deep insecurity resulting from the legal action, which in some way sanctioned the sustained injury, awakened in the woman a whole collection of early frustrations, leaving the ego in a state of disorganization and central depression.

Throughout psychotherapy this primary complex was always present, although in a latent form and as a superimposition on the relived trauma, without ever emerging at the conscious level. It is perhaps upon these previous upsets in maternal relations that the psychotic character adopted by our patient's reactions are incumbent. Besides, we know today how often severely traumatized subjects may react in the same way as certain psychotics do. At the same time, in the present framework of our analytic and psychiatric knowledge, we are able to put infinitely more finesse into the establishment of the diagnosis of mental illness. Many authors, rather than attempting to apply a definite psychotic or character-neurosis label, prefer to classify some of their patients as "limited" or "borderline." The term *borderline*, although indeterminate, nevertheless describes very well what is meant: complex cases which, in certain aspects of their symptoms, touch on psychoses without, strictly speaking, being rated as psychotics. Thus the diagnosis which seems to us most applicable to Demeter's case is that of borderline and, if one wished to be more explicit, *"psychotic reactions to a traumatic neurosis."*

CONCLUSIONS

We realize that our case offers many more problems than we have considered. Before concluding, we must take up two points of methodology which appear essential. First, the *choice of method*. It is unquestionable that the psychotherapy adopted here succeeded in curing the patient in a relatively easy and rapid way. Yet it is also evident that there has been no real change in the underlying neurosis, since this has not been touched by the therapeutic action.

The question could be asked whether a deepened analysis conducted along classical lines would not have allowed an approach to the fundamental neurotic structure. But, as we explained initially, the choice of a classic psychoanalytic approach was counterindicated from the outset for two reasons: the first of these was the patient's age. At an age above sixty, an attempt to reach the foundations of her personality would very likely have caused a dangerous confusion, and without certainty that the patient would ultimately arrive at a better balance than the one she had reached before the trauma; second, because of the sublimations which had succeeded relatively well with her. The masculine tendencies inherent in her castration complex had indeed been canalized and sublimated into well-adapted political and social activities. And it is questionable whether her age would have had the strength to find as good a form of expression for the normal feminine tendencies disclosed by a deepened analysis.

The patient had well perceived the danger of plunging into the depths of her primary neurosis when she wrote: "I don't believe that at my age and in my case a real and long analysis would be necessary." For my part, instead of considering this affirmation as an expression of neurotic resistance, I interpreted it as the effects of self-defense against possible disintegration of her personality. And it was not accidental that the patient chose a symbolic way of self-expression. For only a psychotherapy of this kind could really offer to this patient a climate of understanding, reassurance, and symbolic and magical realization. This is the more true because the symbolic mode comprises an infinite scale of factors which, although imponderable, are charged with much dynamism. A mere attitude on the part of the psychotherapist, a gesture or a word, provides the patient with an essential gratification, an affective plenitude, loading him with favors. His annihilated ego becomes thereby capable of facing pathogenic emotions hitherto insufferable. The deep tendencies, momentarily disinvested of their sublimation-object, regain quite naturally the trails they left in the patient's psychism. This explains the rapidity of recovery and also its solidity for the patient, who has remained well these last ten years without needing to visit the library.

The second point we must mention concerns the *differentiation between the compensation symbols and the need symbols*. This important problem is often met in psychotherapy with psychotic patients. Indeed, how can we discover among all the symbols of a patient the ones that correspond to an essential need which, having been frustrated, must absolutely be satisfied? How can we distinguish them from those which are but endless compensations and the satisfaction of which is counter-indicated? The difference between these two groups of symbols is sometimes very subtle. Yet there exists one criterion which allows their certain discrimination: the compensation symbol is always indefinite and, like a drug, operates to bind the patient, whereas the need symbol, only once realized in an adequate way, acts definitively. As soon as the need has been met, the patient detaches himself quite naturally from the symbol and transfers his interest to forms more evolved and more penetrated by reality.

Yet in order to obtain this result, one essential condition must necessarily be fulfilled: the realization of needs must absolutely be effectuated by the therapist and it cannot be left to the patient himself. This *sine qua non* is directly derived from primitive structure of the superego in psychotic patients. This superego had made them feel the frustration as a refusal on the part of the "wicked mother," later represented by "hard reality." The result is that satisfaction of the need, or even the desire of need satisfaction, represents something sinful to the patient, as it is forbidden. When in her childhood Demeter had been deprived of instruction, activity and power, she had felt this as an interdiction on the part of her mother against having these assets. Later on she managed to more or less dominate the interdictions of her superego. But the trauma of the kidnapping of her daughter, by reactivating the ancient frustrations, intensified the maternal interdictions and threw the patient back into anxiety and impotence. Therefore, in order to draw her out of this state, the psychotherapist had to become the "good mother" to the patient's unconscious (as for psychotics), the "real justice," who restitutes the right to life, action, and power. And this sufficed to render to the patient at last the maternal love she had been so much deprived of and to let her receive it in the precise way in which her unconscious desired it. So we can explain the solidity of Demeter's recovery, which persists without failure in spite of all the difficulties which any person is bound to encounter in active life.

CHAPTER VI

Dynamic Structurization in Schizophrenia

Gisela Pankow

DYNAMIC STRUCTURIZATION OF THE BIRTH SITUATION WITH PARENTS OF SCHIZOPHRENICS

Principal Problems Schizophrenia may occur because parents are beings who speak. If this sentence opens the chapter, it is in order to present a formula incorporating more than ten years of experience with schizophrenia, and especially with the analytical psychotherapy of schizophrenics. This formula concerns only the phenomenological aspects of schizophrenia in the original philosophical sense of structure analysis. At this stage of our research, we cannot yet elaborate a theory as to the origins of psychosis. But our therapeutic experience seems to confirm that there would be no schizophrenia if there were no body experience and no speech.

In order to show how the reciprocal relation between language and body experience affects parents, we focus on the birth situation as it is assumed by the parents, because this material contains the most efficacious and the most significant dynamic structures of the parent-child relationship.

Recent publications concerning mothers of schizophrenics[1] and the remarkable analysis concerning the structures of families of schizophrenics[2] have proved that schizophrenia does not appear as a mere accident. There is a specific family background that cannot be overcome

[1] Y. O. Alanen, *The Mothers of Schizophrenic Patients* (Helsinki: Academic Dissertation, 1958).

[2] R. Schindler, "Zehn Jahre bifokale Gruppentherapie mit Schizophrenen," lecture given at the *2nd International Congress for Psychiatry*, in Zurich, 1957.

by the schizophrenic. In a very instructive way Schindler has analyzed dynamics in families of schizophrenics through sketches, and he refers not only to the mother but also to the father and the other siblings. Schindler succeeded in elaborating a treatment of the schizophrenic's family based on the analysis of family dynamics.

On the other hand, Bateson[3] and his team have in particular analyzed communication between the schizophrenic and his mother. If, in spite of these important papers, another contribution to the problem of the schizophrenic's family is added here, it is in order to elaborate another point of view that concerns the integration of the third generation in its theoretical and therapeutic aspect.

As a child is created in his parent's words long before his body is prepared for birth, an important part of psychotherapy with schizophrenics consists of working out with the parents the family situation—the role the parents had—at the time of the conception of the child, especially as this role concerns the parents' relationship with their own parents. Through such working out, parents can be made aware of distorted family structures and can be helped to get rid of ties that bind them to their own parents. When they are able to renounce their infantile relationship with their own parents, they can become parents themselves. At this moment, they can recognize their child as the "fruit" that means something that is different from themselves. In this way the schizophrenic child can get permission to exist.

These specific interventions undertaken with parents of schizophrenics have remarkably improved the basis of psychotherapy with psychotics. But such therapeutic experiences cannot yet be considered equivalent to a theory concerning the origins of the psychoses, and particularly of schizophrenia. Indeed, the family background is important, and no psychotherapist who treats psychotics will deny this very important factor. But we cannot yet prove exactly in what way these factors intervene on the causality level.

Whenever possible, I try to see the mother of a schizophrenic patient three times before I see the patient himself. During the first consultation I only listen. In nearly all cases these mothers talk about their children. During the second consultation I try to work out the mother's relationship with her own parents. I have never seen a mother of a schizophrenic who was not tied to her own parents. Lewis B. Hill once stated in my presence that schizophrenia appears in the third gen-

---

[3] G. Bateson, D. D. Jackson, J. Haley, J. Weakland, "Toward a Theory of Schizophrenia," *Behav. Sci.*, 1 (1956), 251-264.

eration of obsessed mothers, and my research confirms Hill's experience
in nearly 85 per cent of my cases. (Recently a more than fifty-year-old
mother of a schizophrenic woman shouted in my consultation room:
"You want me to give the freedom to my daughter that I never had in
my own youth!" I tried, nevertheless, to treat the schizophrenic daughter
because there was an obligation to a colleague. But when the patient
began to improve, the mother discontinued the treatment.)

During the third consultation I try to focus on the specific family
situation which governed at the conception of the schizophrenic child.
I work out what place could have been given to the child they were waiting for in this family, and confront the mother with the fact that for
her, her child was not a "fruit"—something that is no longer a part of
the mother's body but an independent body that can take its own place
in the family. My technique consists of helping the mother to recall her
child's biological birth. Then I remain silent, and the mother works out
fantasies showing in what way mother and child are still in an unfin-
ished birth situation. I continue my silence because it is pointless to
separate a mother from her child if the mother does not yet exist herself
because she is still tied to her own mother. As the grandmother has such
an overwhelming role in the birth event, it is not very difficult to bring
this material out. I try to show the mother that the most important person during pregnancy was neither her husband nor the child in her
womb, but her own mother. She took power and authority functions, so
that the father could not become a father and the mother could not
become a mother. Thus the family structure was severely distorted, and
the mother unable to recognize her child as a fruit.

When I have cut the tie between the mother and her own parents, it
is possible to confront her with her birth fantasies demonstrating how
the schizophrenic child is still in her womb. I try to permit the mother
to have a child that is something apart from herself. When she is freed
from her own mother she is able to understand this intervention.

Having seen the mother three times, I then see the patient three
times. Afterwards I try to see the father. Sometimes, if appointments
are difficult for him to arrange, I see him before I see the patient. My
indication for successful psychotherapy of schizophrenics is based on this
first approach with the parents. I have met very chronic patients who
were cured of schizophrenia because there was this possibility of "permitting" the child's birth with the parents. Mothers of schizophrenics
are usually about forty years or older, and it does not seem necessary or
feasible, to start classical analysis of their neuroses. Only once did I

treat a very anxious mother for some months because it was not possible to separate the schizophrenic daughter from her; I wanted to help her understand what her daughter signified to her. There was, however, no attempt to treat her neurosis; I tried only to work out family structures at the birth of this daughter in order to help the mother to have a child that was no longer a part of herself. In all other cases I have seen mothers only once or, more generally, three times. My intervention concerning recognition of family structures is such a severe shock for these mothers that three sessions are sufficient to enable treatment to start with the child. These mothers change remarkably when the schizophrenic child improves and begins to lead a life that is no longer connected with them. The mother's improvement occurs whether the child lives at home or not. The mere fact that a part of the mother begins to be a human being in its own right gives the mother a chance to become herself, too.

For the parents of a schizophrenic, it is not permissible to have a child that is a fruit. For a schizophrenic, it is not permissible to exist.

A Schizophrenic Daughter Seen by her Mother   Several years ago I treated a schizophrenic adult female patient who improved remarkably after one year of treatment. One day, in an apparently good phase of treatment, she entered my consultation room, sat in an armchair and told me that she did not want to lie on the couch any longer. I left her completely free with regard to the couch.[4]

Suddenly the patient, while sitting in the armchair next to my table, opened her umbrella and turned the outside of it toward me. From time to time she shouted: "Oh, you must feel very fine now. You are so marvelously protected!" She twirled her umbrella around and thus, hidden by it, she attacked me verbally. I remained silent. For more than a half hour she repeated her attacks, about four or five times asking me if I felt well protected. Finally I got up, went around my table and looking into her face said, "I have to see your mother." Immediately the patient's expression changed. She looked quite normal

---

[4] I suggest to patients that they may lie down on the couch if a certain stage of the reconstruction of their body image is completed. These problems have been discussed in my books cited below and I will elaborate them in greater detail in my book which is in preparation (*The Body Image in Psychosis*).

G. Pankow, *Structuration Dynamique dans la Schizophrénie. Contribution à une psychothérapie analytique de l'expérience psychotique du monde* (Bern: Hans Huber, 1956); *Dynamische Strukturierung in der Psychose. Beiträge zur analytischen Psychotherapie* (Bern: Hans Huber, 1957).

and folded her umbrella up. Then she said, "Today I shall not pay for my session; I suffered too much." I answered that I understood her suffering, and said that she would have to suffer still more in order to be born. I told her that her mother should make an appointment by phone. The patient left me saying that she would like to tear up the money she had to pay for her session.

I received no call from the patient's mother. But three days later, at her appointed hour, the patient entered my consultation room accompanied by her mother. "Here's my mother!" she cried, pushing her mother toward me. As this mother was more than seventy years old and had lost her husband ten days before, I answered, "I have the impression that you mistake yourselves for each other. Sometimes I don't know whom I treat, you or your mother. As your mother is old, she can stay with me; but not at the expense of your session. Will you please arrange for your own session?" My patient smiled and gave me an envelope she had prepared which contained the money for the session. It was the only time that the patient had paid in this significant way.

When I was alone with the mother, I noticed that she wore a special look: a mixture of ecstasy and unreality. Many psychiatrists would speak of a paranoid look. When she was comfortable in her armchair, I asked her if she knew that her daughter was under treatment with me for mental disease, and that the convent to which her daughter belonged was paying for the treatment. She told me that she was aware of it. Then I asked her when she had first noticed that her daughter was ill. With a faraway look and a strange, rigid smile she told me in very stiff language that she had never noticed her daughter was mentally ill until the day she had refused to work in the convent. This refusal to recognize mental disease in a child is characteristic for mothers of schizophrenics. I tried to discover something about her pregnancy. She replied that she could not remember because it was so long ago. I tried to help her by telling her that her relationship to her husband seemed to have been very tense at that time. She smiled her stereotyped smile. Now I tried my direct attack in order to clarify what this child signified for her. I asked her: "When you carried your last daughter, was there any difference in your body sensations during pregnancy compared to the other pregnancies?" She answered: "*I had the impression of carrying a canary.*" I did not understand and remained silent; I only tried to realize the significance of the fact that this mother had felt she carried not a human being but a bird.

After quite a long silence—I neither asked any question nor gave any explanation—she told me that her strongest desire at the age of seventeen was to become a nun in the religious college where she was educated. She had been unable to realize this ideal because her parents had not wanted her to become a nun. Thus the patient's mother brought out two things: first, that there was a strong dependency on her own parents during adolescence and, second, that she had carried throughout her life old desires and ideals of a religious vocation. All this material appeared when I tried to locate her daughter's body in relation to her own body by referring to the event of pregnancy.

In order to free this mother from juvenile desires and to cut the tie with her own daughter, I told her, "You give the impression of living a part of your own life in your daughter's body. She is a nun and actualizes a desire you could not realize yourself on account of your own parents. If you want your daughter to escape from mental disease, we must cut this old tie between you and your daughter. She is herself, and you are yourself. Each one has to live her own life."

I was then struck by her relaxed and much more real look. My intervention had taken about forty minutes. Then I spoke with the woman about her husband's death and about her own life. After fifteen minutes she left me with a warm look. I asked her if she would agree to pay the same fee for this consultation as the convent paid for her daughter. She did so. During this consultation, my patient had stayed in the waiting room until about fifteen minutes before the mother left me. In the evening I asked myself whether my intervention had not been too cruel for a woman more than seventy years of age who was meeting a psychiatrist for the first time in her life. When my patient came to see me for her session the following day she lay down on the couch without any invitation; she seemed happy and relaxed. After a short silence she told me that last night her superior had given her permission to call on her mother. She said, "My mother was very pleased to meet you. She told me that it was *the first time in her life that she had been able to speak about me.*"

Let us interrupt here and try to understand what had happened. Unfortunately it is not yet possible to publish the cure in more detail because my patient might be recognized by her family background. The only fact I can reveal at this time is that my patient was able to work through Oedipal material immediately after my meeting with her mother. Five years after treatment she no longer has any trace of schizophrenia, and I hope to publish the complete analysis in a few years.

Reciprocal Relation Between Part and Whole My research approach to schizophrenia is a phenomenological one; it is concerned with structure analysis. I worked for years with schizophrenics trying to enter their world merely by speaking with them. My guiding question was: "*Who is the other for the schizophrenic?*" Whenever I tried to understand object relations of schizophrenics, I noticed that there were no object relations in their actual life history. The longer I worked with them, the more I was obliged to recognize that schizophrenics have no object relations which can be compared with those of neurotics. Even if a schizophrenic calls the analyst "mother," there is no proof that the analyst enters into his life history, because he may also call another person present at the session "mother." This common example shows how the schizophrenic recognizes parts of himself in other persons. But he is able to recognize himself as well in things because he is *everywhere.* For a schizophrenic, there is no difference between inside and outside.

If we again ask ourselves the principal question "Who is the other for the schizophrenic?" then there is no possibility of speaking about object relations in their life history, as in the case of neurotics. Freud[5] observed this fact and said that in the psychosis there is no longer any reciprocal relation between the ego and the other. But I found that there is still a reciprocal relation between the part and the whole. My theoretical and therapeutic approach to schizophrenia was based on the elaboration of this reciprocal relation which I first discovered with the schizophrenic,[6] and which is now presented in its aspect as a dialogue with the parents.

Let me return to the example of psychotherapeutic intervention with the mother of the schizophrenic patient discussed above.

My interview with the mother was based on what I discovered during the previous session with the patient. As mentioned above, the patient had been silent for about forty minutes. I tried to understand the scenario she worked out with the umbrella, and I made an approach to what I call "the relation between forms of bodies." I do not push the patient to elaborate associations because the psychic underground is so fragile that psychotic material is brought out very quickly. I try only to lead patients on to the recognition of forms, and to the reciprocal relation of forms. Looking at the patient's body in relation to the umbrella, I thought of a newborn child hanging onto the placenta. Thus I suc-

[5] S. Freud, *Gesammelte Werke* (London: Imago, 1940, 1946), Vols. X, XIII.
[6] See my previous works cited.

ceeded in finding a dynamism which included patient, analyst, and ob-ject. Not only must this dynamism be understood on the level of a simple image of birth; it also has to be referred to the recognition of structures. I took the patient's gesture with the umbrella as a *language* she spoke without words. As her gesture with the umbrella was a mes-sage for me, I was involved in the scene. This session thus took on the aspect of what I call "a situation involving three." In the present in-stance there are two persons—the patient and I—and one thing, the umbrella. The speech the patient made demonstrated how she tried to get rid of me, but she did not succeed in liberating herself from me. She sat for about forty minutes in her armchair and did not move, but only shouted: "You must feel quite well protected!" What apparently pro-tected me and prevented her from looking at me was the umbrella. I had the impression of a parachute and thought: "She cannot come down to earth in order to be born because the tie between mother and daughter has never been cut. As there has never been a separation be-tween mother and daughter, both constitute one being." The facts to be understood in this case are the relations between bodies. These rela-tions concern parts that should be recognized as parts, if the conception of the body as a unity is still possible. In the situation with the um-brella, I took the patient as a part of her mother and confronted her with this form of existence, telling her: "I have to see your mother." The patient immediately folded the umbrella. To see her mother as a sepa-rate being helped the patient to be separated herself from her mother.

It is theoretically important that the mother showed the same re-ciprocal relation between the part and the whole that her daughter had revealed (see page 156). After the intervention with the mother, I suc-ceeded in elaborating with the patient the Oedipal dynamics—which it had been impossible to do for a year. Instead of seeing her father as an anonymous cruel man, or a wild dog, the patient could, for the first time, recognize desires for him. This therapeutic success motivated me to try to understand the basis of my intervention.

There are analysts, especially Peerbolte[7]—who focus on the biologi-cal facts of birth. But more dangerous than birth accidents, as for instance the tangling of the umbilical cord around the neck, is the fact that there are mothers who never forget the event, and who *speak* about it all the time. Their children carry the umbilical cord around their necks even to an adult age. This tie is as real for them as on the

[7] M. L. Peerbolte, *Prenatal Dynamics* (Leiden: A. W. Sijthoff's Uitge-versmaatschappij, N.V., 1954).

day it strangled them. We must then, work out in dialogue these reciprocal relations between the body of the mother and the body of the child. Even if there have been birth traumas, psychotherapeutic interventions can help, for the mother and the patient can speak to the analyst, who leads them to recognition. Thus the patient as well as the mother has to discover that each has existed until now only because together they formed a unity. The following formula expresses the characteristic relationship between a mother and her schizophrenic child in an instructive way: *The mother was a part of her own child; the mother did not have a child. The child was a part of his own mother; the child did not have a mother.*[8]

Filling of Gaps in Family Structure   It is impossible to work out Oedipal dynamics with patients if the parents cannot recognize themselves to be parents. When the parents are tied up to the grandparents, the patient cannot become more than a part of his mother's body.

Some further examples will demonstrate how these gaps of parents who are no parents lead to characteristic family structures. In the following case, I had to fill the gap with a father rather than a mother.

One day in my office I saw a schizophrenic girl accompanied by her mother. I asked myself how this mother could have such a daughter. I had seen the mother alone twice and had to admit that she was not tied to her parents. A severe test would perhaps have shown tendencies to obsession, yet not to a degree that would be called neurosis. The father, on the other hand, was obsessed and neurotically tied to his parents. Unfortunately, his obsessional system was involved with his daughter's. The schizophrenic girl was a twin, but the two sisters had always been different.

These daughters were the object of their father's greatest love. He told me that since their early youth he had tried "to work out a system to teach them morals." He wrote plays, therefore (in terms of his intentions, "morality plays"), and arranged for each daughter to play a role opposite the other. One daughter had to be "pure," the other "spoiled." He told me that his schizophrenic daughter had always been the "pure one," and the other daughter, whom he loved less, the "spoiled one."

---

[8] I have worked out the reciprocal relation between *to be* and *to have* in its characteristic reaction on schizophrenics in two papers that will appear this year. G. Pankow, "Structures rigides et structures souples chez les psychotiques," in *La Psychanalyse* (Paris: Presses Universitaires, 1960), Vol. VI; "Dynamic Structurization and Goldstein's Concept of the Organism," *Am. J. Psychoanal.*, 19 (1959), 157-160.

The schizophrenic daughter succeeded at high school, the other did not.

One day the "spoiled one" announced that she had a fiancé and wanted to marry. Although this marriage worked out very well for her, the father told me that he had been unhappy since the event because his "system no longer worked in the right way." I tried to confront him with the understanding that he had put parts of himself into his daughters' bodies, and that the day he was forced to face the fact that the daughter who had married was no longer a part of him, he became frightened. I told him further that perhaps there now existed a new system for him: since the "spoiled daughter" had become the "pure one," the other one had to be ill. He agreed.

He then became aggressive and questioned me about the specific length of treatment. I replied that I would need two months in order to see if his daughter could be treated, and that we had to work out the possibility of putting her into another family because the results of treatment would be better in this way. At this moment, he interrupted and cried: "You think about curing my daughter! I only thought she could go and see you in order to change a little. She cannot live without her mental disease." He left, and some days later wrote that he did not want treatment. (It is actually better if refusal occurs before treatment begins. Too often, the threatened parents interrupt the treatment after the patient begins to improve.) As this father needed his daughter as a refuge for his own "spoiled part," it was impossible to start treatment.

In another case (recently published)[9]—that of a thirty-seven-year-old schizophrenic philosopher, the father was severely obsessed, the mother warmhearted, but inhibited because of her husband. I met the parents three months after I started treatment as the second analyst in a ten-years' analysis. The father was interested in his garden, and I used this point of contact. Focusing on plants, I was finally able to help him understand that some plants, even with the best care, could not develop like others. In this way, the father was able to recognize his son as a being that could not be directed and limited by his father's will. The mother told me: "In fact, this son carries in himself all the bad parts of his parents." She finally understood, by my intervention, that the child had to be something that was not she. I succeeded in this intervention after having cut the tie that bound the mother to her own parents. Thus these parents were able to become parents, and the schizophrenic son had permission to exist.

[9] G. Pankow, "Der Ring am Fuss der Zigeunerin. Ein Zugang zur psychotischen Welt eines Philosophen," *Der Psychologe*, 11 (1959), 145-150.

DYNAMIC STRUCTURIZATION OF THE BODY IMAGE
WITH A NEGATIVISTIC SCHIZOPHRENIC PATIENT

Main Aspects of Modeling-clay Technique How does one enter
the world of the schizophrenic—this world where there is only himself
and nobody else? Even if the schizophrenic speaks about other persons
and we think that they could be important figures in his life history,
we discover sooner or later that what he, for instance, calls "father" is
only a part of himself. Therefore it is useless to elaborate associations
concerning his life history because in this way the psychotic material increases, and there is no longer any basis on which to work.

In psychosis we need another kind of technique. I ask the patient
to take modeling clay and to model something for me. This clay work is
a message revealing the manner in which a patient, in relation to his
analyst, lives in his body. Therefore, the clay model is equivalent to the
body image and implies the two fundamental functions that I have described elsewhere. First, the body image reveals the manner in which
the patient lives—that is, experiences the reciprocal relation between
the part and the whole in a spatial figure and especially in his own
body. This attempt at the spatial structure of the body image is elaborated by means of the *external outline* in the sense of a container. The
other function of the body image concerns the *internal content* as the
thing signified by a container and leading to historical structures.

My therapy with mental patients consists of reconstructing their
world by at first structurizing an organic relation between the part
and the whole. It is important to state that a neurotic patient is able to
find the reciprocal relation between the part and the whole because for
the neurotic the conception of the body as a unity is always possible.
This cannot be attained by a psychotic patient. The dissociated body
(*le corps dissocié*) of the psychotic patient takes the place of the body
in pieces (*le corps morcelé*) of the neurotic patient.

The principal difficulty is to make the patient touch the modeling
clay. One patient told me recently: "Each acceptance of a form in the
sense of an external outline is a menace for me. [Pause.] The moment I
accept a definite form, I shall be lost."

The modeling-clay activity obliges the patient to recognize the body
as limited. This fact may evoke enormous anxiety. I have worked out
several ways of approach in order to handle transference with the modeling-clay method which will be published for the first time in my book,

The Body Image in Psychosis. In the present paper I can give only one example of the method without other references to my modeling-clay techniques.

Patient's Dissociated Body Image   I want to present a part of a treatment of a schizophrenic patient that was published in a different form in 1956.[10] I have chosen this case because the patient was very ill, and when I saw her recently—five years after her treatment—in the presence of two other people, there was no longer any trace of psychosis. She was completely changed, even in her physical aspect, and she now enjoys happiness she never before knew in her life.

Miss Valerine, as I shall call her, was a high-school teacher forty years of age. She resembled a porcelain doll in her size and fragility; she was quite pale and was one of those beings who had never completed the development of her youthful body. The patient was motionless except that from time to time her eyes abruptly changed direction.

I learned that she had been unable to work for a whole year and that a month earlier she had had four electroshock treatments and six insulin treatments in a hospital. A psychiatrist and a psychoanalyst consulted because of her lack of response to the previous treatment suggested that I try analytical psychotherapy.

The details of the patient's case history were meager. She was born in Switzerland where her father directed a business before the First World War. Her father was from Alsace, of German origin, and he became French by his marriage to a rich French woman. The patient had a brother five years older and a sister two years older than herself. Valerine was thus the youngest and, as I discovered later, an "unwanted child." "They did not expect me."

The principal difficulty in the treatment was that the patient would not speak. Finally, after four sessions of body relaxation, according to the method of Schultz[11] which I modified for mental patients, I suggested that the patient should draw and model clay for me. Without making any interpretations, I succeeded in establishing a certain contact with her. In cases of negativistic schizophrenia, the analyst must enter into the patient's life as soon as possible, otherwise treatment is not possible.[12]

[10] I want to thank the publisher, Hans Huber, for permission to refer to my text of 1956.

[11] I. H. Schultz, *Das autogene Training* (Stuttgart: Thieme Verlag, 1954).

[12] There was no somatic therapy for this patient. But for very excited patients, tranquilizers help the start of analytical treatment.

In the twenty-seventh session, that is, at the end of the second month of treatment, the patient brought me what she called an *Oriental temple*. This temple was only a façade. After having slept for some minutes on the couch, Valerine said:

> I have slept. Between the columns there is the incarnation of Buddha: [pause] a being in a squatting position with several hands. The face is uncommunicative. He is impassive as he meditates in the position of the Lotus Flower. [Pause.] *The child's interest is the whole.* [Pause.] The guardian lets him enter. He is a pilgrim.

After a while the patient sat down on the couch with a lost and bewildered expression and told me, "I look for tick-tock that I cannot see. It is in the next room."

Would it be possible to enter into this room? At the following session Valerine brought me what she called *the house on pillars*, telling me: "I wanted to make a staircase. I have made this house instead of making a staircase. These are his two wives." There was a staircase with a blue carpet (four by six inches), made of red blocks forming only three steps, a set of which descended symmetrically on each side like a bridge. Four red pillars crowned by four balls were planted at the four corners. There were two layers of yellow, one placed to serve as the floor and the other as the roof above which rose the four balls.

For the first time, the patient had created three persons in a closed room. Sitting on the carpet on the last step was a brown-colored person whom the patient called *the man of the house*. Behind him, between two pillars on the left, Valerine showed me *the wife for the outside world*, and sitting on the floor was *the wife for the inside world*. These women had the same brown color as the man. Here is my dialogue with the patient:

> THER.:   Who are you?
> PT.:   All the three. [Pause.] I have lived with them. I think there is somebody going away. A house quite alone.
> THER.:   Where is this person, whoever it is, going?
> PT.:   It seems to Europe. [Pause.] The one who is inside has no dress. I have not had enough time. She must hold herself erect. Therefore I have made two legs. It is a woman, nevertheless. [Pause.] If this has a skirt, then there is no need of feet. You can see, nevertheless, that this is a leg. *A skirt and two legs that would be mutilated.* That is why I have made the skirt without legs. It is much more difficult to make feet.

THER.: What are the roles of the two women?

PT.: The one who is outside is the one of whom he is proud. The one inside is the one whom he needs. [Pause.] All this happens in a country far away. There is no sense in the relations with the women. [Pause.] The one outside loves him more in a physical way; the one inside tries to make him happy. The one outside should be admired. [Pause.] These are the two imposing aspects of the wife.

Let us try to understand in what way the psychosis had destroyed the situation involving three persons. There was no longer a situation involving three persons, but one involving two persons, for the two women were tied to each other. One being the opposite of the other, these two women formed a block. The man went away.

Let us now look at the women's bodies. The woman inside had two legs that she might stand upright. She needed no dress. The woman outside had a skirt and therefore needed no feet. What can be understood by the obscure remark, "A skirt and two legs that would be mutilated"? The patient referred to a woman's body, unifying legs and a skirt as a mutilation. Instead of a separation, there would be a union of these two opposites. The patient considered such a union to be very dangerous. Perhaps we are here at a center of destruction.

Dynamic Structurization by Means of the Phantasm of the Flower Man During the two following months, that is to say, up to the fifth month, treatment was extremely difficult. There were some interesting clay models, some of them representing parts of the body: a red hand (thirty-eighth session), a white hand (forty-third session), a head of a sphinx (fifty-third session). But I did not succeed in finding a connection between these parts of the body and the body in its unity. Although the white color dominated, the patient's negative feelings toward the analyst threatened a discontinuance of the treatment. I should mention that until the present there has been only empirical psychological knowledge about colors. But Dolto's[13] long experience with children confirms that white implies the highest degree of aggressiveness.

"One part of me will not heal," the patient told me during the forty-second session, showing a block of clay with two immense horns —one indicating "the road of sin," the other "the road of holiness."

Why was it not possible to continue this analysis as a classical analysis of obsession? Because the reciprocal relation between the body in its external outline and in its interior content had been destroyed. In

[13] Discussion remark in Dolto's Psychoanalytical Seminar in Paris.

obsession, there is a bisexual body image. In severe cases there can even be a certain tension felt as a separation between parts of the body, as I have shown in a case on the borderline between obsession and hallucinosis.[14] But in obsession there is no split of the body image; for an obsessed patient the conception of the body as a unity is still possible. I want to elaborate now that for our patient Valerine the conception of *the body as the thing contained within a shape has been destroyed, and not only suppressed as in obsession.*

The statue of the Flower Man, which Valerine brought for the eighty-fifth session, permitted me to enter deeply into these disturbed relations between the body in its external outline and in its interior content. This was a red body, measuring five inches in height, sitting on a block covered with violet paper. The body had no head, no neck, and no arms.

Why did the trunk differ from other trunks? The patient had put an unreal creation in the place of the chest and the head. The stomach had the form of two immense petals. Immense masses forming an open and folded stomach could be seen better from the side. The base was created by the folding of the outside petal, this forming a projecting part which was unsupported.

Why is a person not accustomed to working with schizophrenics frightened when looking at such a model as the Flower Man? There are zones of destruction in this body, not only because of the absence of a head, neck, and arms but especially because the interior of the body is open. Kulcsar[15] has confirmed my experience that zones of destruction in a clay model indicate the degree of the dissociation of the body image, and on this basis he worked out a test revealing the degree of psychosis. This research material profoundly confirms Fisher and Cleveland's approach,[16] and I showed in 1956 [17] that the most characteristic and most important factor in the statue of the Flower Man was *the loss of the boundary between the inside and the outside of this body.*

Valerine showed me her work and said:

[14] G. Pankow, *Dynamische Strukturierung in der Psychose. Beiträge zur analytischen Psychotherapie* (Bern: Hans Huber, 1957), Part III, Chap. 4.

[15] S. Kulcsar, "Trouble du schéma corporel intérieur dans la schizophrénie," lecture given at the *2nd International Congress for Psychiatry in Zurich,* 1957.

[16] S. Fisher, S. E. Cleveland, *Body Image and Personality* (Princeton: Van Nostrand, 1958).

[17] G. Pankow, *Structuration Dynamique dans la Schizophrénie. Contribution à une psychothérapie analytique de l'expérience psychotique du monde* (Bern: Hans Huber, 1957), p. 70.

These are a man's legs. [Pause.] I did not know what to put on him. Something will come, something that will make a being which would not be a real man. For some days past, this is in my head. [Pause.] I was furious with you. By and by I gave you up. Something which does not claim not to be you. [Pause.] I asked myself, if people were not as they are, how would they be. When I ask this, they smile. Evidently there is no solution.

During the following session (fifty-ninth), I learned that Valerine had decided to continue with the treatment. For the first time in a year she tidied up her cupboard and began to think about the next school year. Then she speaks again about the Flower Man: "My fellow of the other day—*everything that is underneath is the stuff waiting for what it is to be.* This must not represent any particular thing. [Pause.] All this lies on his stomach. [Long pause.] Are there patients who succeed in telling everything that they think?"

"The stuff waiting for what it is to be." This remark gave me hope that the patient could one day begin to organize the stuff out of which to create a body which she had lost.

On the other hand, it is very important that the patient had unified in the statue the muscular legs of the man and the stomach formed like a flower. But did this stomach only represent a digestive organ? The interior part was differentiated in such a manner that it resembled a woman's sexual organ. But on the other side, the stomach had a phallic aspect. From the side could be seen the protruding view of these petals. Thus if we only consider the external outline we could speak in this model of a bisexual aspect of the stomach.

The Flower Man helped the patient to recognize the lost content of her body image. In our research work we call such a dynamism that helps to reconstruct the spatial structure of the body in its external outline and its interior content a *phantasm*. The phantasm of the Flower Man evoked the notion of the stuff which the patient recognized as being capable of organization. Thus the stuff, in its potentiality and not yet in its actuality, was the first attempt at the reconstruction of the lost body. This reconstruction filled up the destroyed zones in the statue of the Flower Man, and this structurization also implied a reconstruction of the external outline as well as that of the internal content.

As the phantasm of the Flower Man helped the patient to complete the body as a unity, Valerine became able to develop fantasies in the classical sense of imagination. I think that it is not a mere coincidence that the Flower Man provoked the question as to whether there were patients capable of telling the analyst everything. Thus the Flower Man must have hidden something that helped the patient to recognize desires.

Two sessions later, Valerine showed me what she called *the opposite of the Flower Man*: a white head measuring about three by three inches. It was a head without eyes, without ears, and without a mouth. The neck was placed on a piece of the chest, which lengthened into a white blanket about three and a half inches wide. The blanket was rolled up twice toward the inside. Valerine told me: "*This is the opposite of the other fellow.* He has with him everything that he will become. It is taken at the opposite pole. [Pause.] *Between these two poles, there is a hiatus. But I do not know what this hiatus is.*"

> THER.:   What do you call these two poles?
> PT.:   On a superficial plane, one would say that one of them is well planted on the earth; the other is not. [Pause.] On a deeper level, I do not know. I have the impression that the first one will succeed; this one will not succeed. He has a basis; this one has no basis. [Pause.] He has no vitality. One does not know what he will become. He even has no organs in his head. He has no eyes, no ears, and no mouth. He has no organs.
> THER.:   And this blanket?
> PT.:   It is contained in the blanket. He does not know when his stuff will be organized. [Pause.] The other one has a basis. This one has not.

Later on during the same session, Valerine discovered a new aspect of the organization of the stuff. I asked her if these statues represented sexualized beings. She answered that the white man could turn into a man as well as into a woman. "At the bottom we are sexual beings. Therefore, all this has no sense. I cannot understand by what means I could manage to reconcile these two alternatives." I answered that this was her problem. She continued: "If I look at them, *they are not men, men who are waiting.* They have no sex. [Pause.] Perhaps that is because I have not the courage to differentiate them." Thus Valerine recognized that she had lost the notion of a sexualized body. But the split between the head zone and the leg zone was so severe that I needed two more months to cure it.

Healing of the Split in the Patient's Body Image   In the sixty-third session, the patient started what she called her *revolt*. Walking on her knees in my consultation room, she seized a photograph of me and cut off my head; the portion of the picture containing my legs she took with her. She knew, as she told me, that there was also my person in it. But the split between the person and the legs was so strong that she could not get beyond it. During the following session she stayed in my consultation room on the floor behind an armchair, her dress wet from rain. She wept from time to time, calling me "Madam—mother." I simply explained to her that this behavior was contrary to her taking my photo.

After this, in the ninety-first session, the patient brought a *dancing woman* in modeling clay. The body was violet and sat on immense petals of a red flower. For the first time, Valerine spoke about the *desires of her body.*

> There are two kinds of *desires* in my body. For the first time they come one *after* the other. One yesterday evening; one this morning. [Pause.] The one of this morning is quite simple: it is physical and psychological; it only concerns the sexual organs. The one of yesterday evening is quite different. I find much more difficulty in repulsing it. [Pause.] It is in my breasts. It goes all over my body; I would like to indulge in a caress.

Thus a movement of the sexual organs and a movement of the heart were unified for the first time. The split between the legs and the person was cured. In six months the split in her body image was repaired and Valerine was able to begin the analysis of her life history. This treatment enabled her to resume her profession as a high-school teacher after having traveled for some months. The whole treatment took one year and a half. I had no contact with the patient after this. She only sent me a Christmas card each year, for which I thanked her.

I saw the patient in March 1959 in my home in the presence of a philosopher and a psychoanalyst who had met her with friends when she was very ill. As I mentioned above, we did not see any trace of a psychosis. She was completely changed, even in her physical aspect, and looked much younger than she did five years before, when I finished the treatment.

CONCLUSIONS

The method of Dynamic Structurization has been elaborated in order to describe a process leading to the reconstruction of destroyed psychical structures. In this paper, I present the method of Dynamic Structurization for the first time, in reference not only to schizophrenics but also to their parents. There are *gaps* to be filled in psychical structures for the parents as well as for the schizophrenic himself.

The *gaps* in the parents' psychic structures concern what I call the family situation. By "family situation" I mean the role the parents had at the time of the patient's conception. This role especially involves the parents' relationship to their own parents and shows how parents of schizophrenics are bound to their own parents. As parents of schizophrenics are not parents in reality, the terms "father" and "mother" are employed for a relationship that does not fulfill the function involved in these words. There is a dissociation between the significant and the thing signified. I try to reconstruct these destroyed family structures by liberating the parents from their own parents. When these parents can become parents themselves, they are able to recognize their child to be a fruit, which means something that is no longer a part of themselves. Until this is done, there is no place for their child as a separate being when they speak of him. There is no dynamic relationship between the child and his parents because in these families the child is only a part of the parents.

The same *reciprocal relation between the part and the whole* helped me to understand my empirical method of modeling-clay work with schizophrenics. I succeeded in applying this method even with severely ill patients when there was some help from somatic therapy (tranquilizers) at the beginning. The modeling-clay method is a message revealing the manner in which a patient, in relation to the analyst, lives in his body. It is an equivalent of the body image and implies the two fundamental functions I have described since 1956. The first function of the body image concerns spatial structure, and refers only to the recognition of forms, that is, to *recognition of the external outline*. When a schizophrenic patient is able to complete in his clay work, or by speech, a destroyed body so that it can become an organic unity, the patient theoretically can be relieved of schizophrenia. The moment he recognizes his body to be a unity, the patient is able to distinguish inside from outside, and so he can overcome "the loss of boundary," to take Fisher and Cleveland's formulation.

But the reconstruction of the spatial structure is not sufficient to be rid of mental disease, as the human being lives not only in spatial structures but also in *historical structures*. It is very difficult to help a certain group of patients (who will be described in more detail in my new book) to discover that the external outline of a spatial structure could have the role of a container involving an internal content. *The recogni-*

tion of the internal content leads the patient to understand that a container *has* a content. If this container is for example the patient's body he has to recognize that the inside of his body is differentiated, as well as other parts of his body, and belongs to him as a person. Thus the reciprocal relation between to *be* and to *have* introduces the one who has and the one who does not have. Thus the other person can appear, and interpersonal relationships are possible.

I call certain dynamic images that help to reconstruct the spatial structure of the body image in its external outline and in its interior content *phantasms*. These phantasms help the patient to reconstruct the body image primarily in creating its boundaries and thus realizing inside and outside. On this basis, the phantasm also introduces interpersonal relationships because it leads to the interior content of differentiated forms. At this moment, life history is possible and analysis in the sense of object relations can begin. In general, with a young schizophrenic (that is, up to twenty-five years of age) I need two to three years of analysis after having reconstructed the lost unity of his body image.

CHAPTER VII

The Quest
for the Golden Mean:
A Study in Schizophrenia*

Arthur Burton

> If a body meet a body
> Carrying a spade, and
> If a body has a rake,
> Need either be afraid?
>
> —KIERKEGAARD

ALTHOUGH NO AVAILABLE THEORY of schizophrenia allows us either to understand the genesis of the illness or to modify it with suitable precision, there have been enough sucessfully treated cases to provide the glimmerings of such a theory.[1] This latter work might in a sense be considered merely the covering of the quicksand in which we have often become entrapped. One such was the attempt to treat the schizophrenic as though he were a neurotic, which has resulted in a nihilistic despair for the therapist. Again, Jung[2] speaks of a toxin in schizophrenia after a certain point in the maldevelopmental process is reached; and the remarks of Freud on schizophrenia have been quoted so often as to not require reiteration here. I question whether we could have avoided

---

* I am indebted to Walter Rapaport, M.D., and Arthur Anderson, M.D., for making the study of this case possible.

[1] I think here of the work of Benedetti, Fromm-Reichmann, Rosen, Sechehaye, and Sullivan, among others.

[2] Personal discussion with C. G. Jung on May 9, 1958.

these conceptual cul-de-sacs, for such has been the history of science. The treatment of schizophrenia requires an evolutionary kind of maturity not cheaply bought, and the necessary insights are not to be obtained by revelation. Now, with the maturity which comes from what we have learned through therapeutic interaction with schizophrenics, we must test new models which, while based to some degree upon our models of the dynamics of neurosis, do not blind us to the new phenomena.

Schizophrenia is now so pervasive as to constitute a social as well as a personal process. Is reality, then, becoming so difficult for man that we are confronted with a generalized schizoid or schizophrenic retreat? Can we find some clues to this illness in the relationship of the schizophrenic to his proximal field, i.e., his family, and possibly to his more distal social field? In an earlier paper[3] I showed that the "heroes" Albert Camus[4] so vividly presents in his novels may be independently diagnosed as schizophrenic. But Camus is not writing about schizophrenics—he writes about Everyman, and the tremendous impact of his work is just that we all see ourselves as Meursault, Jean-Baptiste Clamence, Janine, and the others. Can it be that in the prismatic lens of the strict medical tradition of organic models and analogues, we have missed the relativity of the schizophrenic *being* in his field—i.e., the dynamics of the schizophrenic way of life?

Case histories of the psychotherapy of schizophrenics reveal one finding which occurs with increasing and startling frequency, a finding further enhanced by personal experience as a psychotherapist of schizophrenia: As one is able to put aside one's own fears of the schizophrenic, it is possible to enter a deep and meaningful relationship with him. We are able to *encounter* the schizophrenic as a human being rather than as a set of symptoms and to relive with him a maturation experience profitable to both patient and therapist. Each psychotherapist is dimly aware of the schizophrenic aspect within him, and the personal specter of regression is an alluring one to his unconscious. Because we fear these things we may deny the *encounter* with the schizophrenic while yet engaging and encouraging it.[5] We live out certain of these aspects with

[3] A. Burton, "Schizophrenia and Existence," *Psychiatry* (Nov. 1960).

[4] A. Camus, *The Outsider* (London: Hamish Hamilton, 1946); *Exile and the Kingdom* (London: Hamish Hamilton, 1958); *The Fall* (New York: Knopf, 1957).

[5] It is an interesting observation that novitiates in psychotherapy are eager to treat schizophrenics and will tackle such cases without hesitation, often to come to a sad end. Such treatment is for them the hallmark of a finished and accepted psychotherapist and there is a compulsive aspect to it. It is

our patients; but we cannot see them to a complete culmination because they lead to a total engagement which is sometimes enduring and always painful. I will attempt to show later that such an *encounter* is the essence of the treatment of schizophrenia.

In a number of earlier papers[6] I have attempted to formulate my own understanding of schizophrenia and its treatment. These papers represented stages of my growth in this area. In this chapter I want to bring my ideas into a current matrix and to illustrate them with the treatment of a case. If some redundancy is inherent in this process, I want to beg indulgence in advance.

Being and Becoming

The process of growth is the process of *becoming*. *Being* is a stage in the process of *becoming*. The potential for the development of a self-structure is the most significant of psychical facts and is never lost even to the most regressed schizophrenic. In schizophrenia the patient loses sight of his *becoming* potentialities because to *be* and to *become* is threatening. He loses status as a being since the continuum of *becoming* is absent. There are many rationalizations for this feeling of threat. Thus, for example, the schizophrenic fears that he can establish his own existence only at the expense of someone else who must become ill or die in his place. Most often this is a significant relative. He thus lives through some "other," of whom he is a part and for whom he provides an immunity of a kind in life. And indeed we know that the improvement of the schizophrenic in psychotherapy is often at more than an economic cost to his mother or father. Thus any movement toward or away from objects—including, of course, persons—is full of hazard. He fears to love and fears to not-love. *To be* is then literally a question; and *to become* a most dangerous event.

Schizophrenics have a need *to-be-as-before* rather than *to become*, and *to become* is only a matter for others. Under these circumstances, it would appear that the schizophrenic, whose future is blocked and whose present is questionable, looks for a solid foundation in the "past," and a significant aspect of the therapeutic task is to confront him with the

---

a rare event, however, when such a psychotherapist can actually *encounter* the patient.

[6] A. Burton, "Paradox and choice in schizophrenia," *Psyche* (Heidelberg) (in press). "Schizophrenia and Existence," *Psychiatry*, Nov. 1960. "Aggression and Self-realization in a Young Woman," in A. Burton, R. E. Harris (eds.), *Clinical Studies of Personality* (New York: Harper, 1955).

present and to give him insight into the projective future. The dynamics of regression are sufficiently well known, but in schizophrenia it is not simply a matter of regression in the usual sense. The neurotic has at least reasonably well-defined historical stages to which he can regress. The schizophrenic does not because his ego was never individuated at any level to begin with. He must, therefore, fall back upon the archaic—those areas of prehistoric attainment which are more or less common to all people, and which are not governed by the conventional time-space concepts of physics. Thus my patient Doria said to me, "I want you to take me back six thousand years." "Where does that place us?" I asked. "In the realm of King Tutankhamen." This was more than idle statement. With the onset of Doria's illness, she became interested in archeology, and for good reason. She sought the foundations for her *being* in the archaic past in terms of the Queen archetype so well illustrated by Perry.[7] To be Queen is to be related to the King, to produce Kings, and to be the model of womanhood and motherhood in the land. It is a recognized fecundity, without danger and with universal approval. It is a necessity to the future of all people everywhere.

The oceanic nature of the schizophrenic unconscious cannot be confined to the circumscribed scope of the neurotic's—it ranges far and wide. He is, so to speak, in it whereas the neurotic watches from the cliffs above. Once the bonds of reality and of temporal-spatial constructs are thrown off, communication becomes unique, idiosyncratic, and significantly symbolic. *To-be-as-before* then means that we must draw upon the far-reaching images and symbols in a reintegrative process before the patient can accept the *here-now* and its structure. But the archaic makes the therapist uneasy and he quickly and arbitrarily returns the patient to the *here-now* or its life-historical antecedents. If the schizophrenic is to *become*, to be present in the *here-now*, he must first be affirmed in the past on a symbolic level in terms of the deepest understanding. (This is essentially what Sechehaye does in her symbolic realization.) Only then can he exist as a being in a temporal-spatial framework. Probably the most frequent comment made by schizophrenics to their therapists is, "You do not really understand me, do you?" By this he means, "You do not really understand my archaic self—my other existence—which must be so foreign to you."

Obviously one cannot sit and wait forever for a conventional transference to develop with a schizophrenic. The patient will never come into treatment or, if he does, there will be a sterility which presages

[7] J. Perry, this volume, Chap. IV.

little therapeutic movement. We must understand that the schizophrenic finds it overly threatening to deal with coeval temporal-spatial
matters in a framework of human existence. If we accept his need *to-be-
as-before* and thus begin with a medium which permits expression in the
form of archaic symbolism, then growth can be stimulated. We do this
through such materials as pigments and plastics which allow for oceanic
and boundaryless expression—where the part/whole and container/non-
container[8] aspects can be expressed and brought to consciousness. All of
this takes place within the framework of the *encounter* with the therapist of which I will speak again below and which is crucial. It is not then
specifically a problem of re-repression, as Redlich sees it, but of symbolic
expression for later repression. When the patient is once again a unity
in his being, and existing in the *here-now*, repression of the unconscious is a normal stabilizing event.

The question of *choice* in connection with mental illness is an obscure one and usually avoided in discussions of schizophrenia. We believe that patients in some way select their symptoms, but we are not
certain how they do this. *Choice* is also often confused with will and
consciousness. Obviously, the schizophrenic does not *choose* to be a
schizophrenic as such—but he does in some way perceive and interpret
the events of his environment in a schizophrenic way. These are his
values; they have meaning for him where previously there was no meaning at all. He thus *chooses* a new set of meaningful values, albeit the
choice is an unconscious one. All human beings have such **choice** and
it is but a question of conscious or unconscious selection.

Now, if a schizophrenic does have a *choice* to be a schizophrenic,
can he choose not to be? Certainly one decides whether or not to live,
i.e., the philosophical question of suicide, and this is also a decision
each man makes. I believe the question can be answered positively providing certain conditions govern. If the patient can become a "whole"
rather than a "part" of the "other," then he will *choose* not to be a
schizophrenic. This seems on the face of it a bit mystical, and we can fall
into an easy trap of our own making. We can confront patients with
their *choices* and rest there. This is obviously a misunderstanding of
the situation. In the psychotherapy of every schizophrenic a point is
reached where the patient must be confronted with his *choice*, but this
can come only within the framework of the new relatedness which is
the therapeutic encounter. The way the patient wants to be is the patient's decision to make and not the therapist's. The latter's counter-

[8] G. Pankow, this volume, Chap. VI.

transference and counteridentification do not change regardless of the *choice* the patient makes, for we want for the patient only what he wants for himself. The right to be as a "whole" is something the patient cannot have because it has not been possible for him to have the *necessary courage to be.*[9] This he must find—if he is to find it at all—in his own special and unique way and no one can show him the way. He can only be accompanied in an intimate way. We may put this as a form of symbolical *Journey to the East.*[10]

NOTHINGNESS AND THE ABSURD

For the understanding of the universality of dread and its relationship to the great void—*Nothingness*—we are indebted to Kierkegaard.[11] *Nothingness* is not to be understood simply as death. If this were so, then events would follow their natural biological course. *Nothingness* is a conception of the living—a feeling of emptiness and loneliness before which all else retreats. In this connection a quotation from Edith Weigert is appropriate. "An intense yearning arises for full identification, for the oceanic feeling of perfect union, the bliss of primordial symbiosis, but the demonic images of anxiety to be possessed, exploited, annihilated, or to possess, exploit, and annihilate the other drives him into flight." [12] *Nothingness* is the absence of full identification, of the feeling of union, and its manifestation is anxiety, dread, and flight. Schizophrenia is the extreme manifestation of *Nothingness.* The schizophrenic comes from the same cradle as do the Holy Barbarians, but he does not dare defy culture. He remains within its realm but retreats in a form of illness which is socially and ethically approved. In a sense, he sees himself as an untouchable among the accepted—but society sees him as ill.

In a former paper[13] I employed Camus' conception of the *Absurd* to show that all men live in a world of existential absurdities which they must personally reconcile. This reconcilement is possible for most people at a cost—and they pay this cost. This is the situation for the average man in a world which since 1922 has seen seventy million people displaced, dismembered, or destroyed. The schizophrenic reacts to the *Absurd* by denial, falsification, and retreat. The logical polar opposites

[9] P. Tillich, *The Courage to Be* (New Haven: Yale Univ. Press, 1952).
[10] H. Hesse, *Journey to the East* (New York: Noonday, 1957).
[11] S. Kierkegaard, *Fear and Trembling; The Sickness Unto Death* (New York: Doubleday, 1954).
[12] E. Weigert, this volume, Chap. XIV.
[13] A. Burton, "Schizophrenia and Existence," *Psychiatry* (Nov. 1960).

of death or revolt are not open to him, and so he falls back upon his primordial and archaic experience and sets up communication systems which are strange and bizarre to us. He becomes his own object and thus brings order to absurdity, i.e., to him he is now predictable, as is his world. He clings to these conceptions with a fanatic desperation and resists the therapist's attempt to wean him back to the world of the *Absurd*. He is unwilling to accept Kierkegaard's "leap into faith" without assurances of a very special order.

To abridge Camus, the *Absurd* is the substance of *Nothingness*; it provides the basis for the void and the denudation of values by which men live—it is the equivalent of *nonbeing*. It is contrary to the need "to lose oneself in an all-consuming passion—to be devoured—to be attached to an all-embracing cause" (Weigert).

Schizophrenia, then, in my view, is a problem of existence, i.e., a very problematical mode of being-in-the-world, and the schizophrenic can perhaps best be understood in this way. The therapeutic problem is to replace the *Absurd* with a creative force—Eros—and this can be done only through a living-out with a person—let us say, the therapist —who has himself faced the *Absurd* and its consequences.

PHENOMENOLOGY

The psychic contents of the schizophrenic, but not the interaction of patient and therapist, can be formalized into a number of categories or, as I have called them, vectors. These vectors confront the participants at some stage or other in the treatment. They are important because they have to be dealt with in their own right and, if permitted, they mask the underlying reality of the *encounter* and its significance. They have been discussed elsewhere[14] but bear affirmation because of their extension:

1. The schizophrenic feels both omnipotent and completely helpless in a strange matrix. It is disconcerting in therapy to see him now at one and then at the other of these polarities, with resolution seemingly impossible. These polarities have a historic significance in terms of his personal development in relation to mother/father, and prehistorically in terms of his primordial past. People accept one or another of such polarities toward a power they do not understand and fear, such as God, the cosmic world, parents, etc. It is an attempt both to deny and

[14] A. Burton, "Paradox and Choice in Schizophrenia," in A. Burton (ed.), *Case Studies in Counseling and Psychotherapy* (Englewood Cliffs, N.J.: Prentice-Hall, 1959).

to pacify the *power*; but for the schizophrenic omnipotence and help-lessness sit side by side in a "double entry" and there is no bridge be-tween.

This is the way it was in childhood. There they reigned supreme only to find that the world would not be arranged to suit them and that fantasied omnipotence could not enduringly change the "double bind" they were in. Helplessness has its own rewards in passivity and is its own form of omnipotence. It permits an overt surrender and peace, but of course the energy which is aggression must then be diverted to fantasy. Man has always dreamed of the total vanquishment of na-ture—of absolute biological control and prediction—but he has just as frequently needed to be at one with nature and an integral part of it. (And there are those today who advocate a simple return to it.) This need to conquer—and to be a part of a grander cosmic scheme (the divinity)—has long rent man asunder. These mystical/animistic needs are a definite part of the archaic heritage of the schizophrenic. In ther-apy one comes to recognize them, but one is not trapped by them. They are projected upon the therapist and through the *encounter* their pro-tective immunity is safely uncovered so that less omnipotence and help-lessness are needed and a partial integration is possible. Frequently I have challenged these needs directly[15] by refusing to believe them and the patient comes gradually to understand their foundation and thus take a more consistent position in relation to reality.

2. Not a great deal is known of the body image although the con-cept has been with us for some time. The most recent work is that of Pankow[16] and Fisher and Cleveland.[17] Psychotherapists of schizophrenia have long been aware that there were body-image distortions in their patients. Only later was it seen that as the schizophrenic improves, his body-image concept changes. I have wondered whether there are body-image hierarchies in schizophrenia which are at variance from the non-schizophrenic,[18] i.e., is there a normative organizational principle—pos-sibly a cephalo-caudal one—which following disorganization becomes

---

[15] See also, for example, the work of Rosen.

[16] G. Pankow, *Dynamische Strukturierung in der Psychose. Beitrage zur analytischen Psychotherapie* (Bern: Hans Huber, 1957); Structuration Dynamique dans la Schizophrénie. Contribution à une psychothérapie ana-lytique de l'expérience psychotique du monde (Bern: Hans Huber, 1956).

[17] S. Fisher and S. E. Cleveland, *Body Image and Personality* (Princeton: Van Nostrand, Inc., 1959).

[18] A number of experiments by the writer are now in progress on this point.

integrated as the schizophrenic improves? Is there some relationship between the body-image organization of the mother and the schizophrenic child—are the body-image nurturant zones the fundaments of interpersonal relationships and must these be restructured before the schizophrenic can function? These are problems which need experimental answers. On a clinical basis I can confirm the findings of Pankow that the schizophrenic has a spatial or structural difficulty in differentiating the "inner from the outer." The container or vessel properties of the ego are confused so that the ego boundary merges with the life space. We say that the schizophrenic is everywhere. This confusion is not only horizontal, i.e., spatial, but also historical. A body has a history only insofar as it is a body in a spatial-temporal continuum. Otherwise its history merges on many levels with *all* history and cannot be differentiated. I can see why Pankow first deals with the body image of her schizophrenic patients before she copes with the patient's life history material.

We have unfortunately made too little use of *all* of the avenues of communication with our schizophrenic patients. Body language is particularly effective at certain stages, but we are uncertain in its use.[19] Furthermore, there is a severe tradition in psychology that psychotherapy is a verbal process and the patient must not be touched. These latter fears, it must be pointed out, are our own and not the patients'. Fortunately, body language operates unconsciously as well as consciously, and so the presence of two people together without physical contact is effective. Then the use of paints, plastics, clay, and drawings permits such language to operate in surrogate fashion. Doria, the patient described here, picked her face continuously so that it was a mass of sores. This was one of her prominent "social" symptoms. The dynamic meaning of this face-picking is left for the case description below. However, when she did this in my presence, I gave her my hand to hold. After a time she would reach for my hand rather than pick her face. An association was thus set up between her most prominent symptom and her bodily relatedness to me.

3. The patient says, "My life is all sex—but then there is no sex." This statement highlights the sexual vector. Sexuality is the bellwether of the integration of the ego in western civilization. The neurotic re-

---

[19] See, for example, the comments of C. A. Whitaker *et al.*, "The Involvement of the Professional Therapist," in A. Burton (ed.), *Case Studies in Counseling and Psychotherapy* (Englewood Cliffs, N.J.: Prentice-Hall, 1959).

presses his sexuality for he cannot cope with the guilt his impulses create. The schizophrenic is pansexual and nonsexual. He would like to have the substance to repress, but it is not clear to the unconscious what is to be repressed. The ego is so sexually submerged that it gives up mediating altogether.

What the schizophrenic means of course is that he has lost the meaning and value of sexuality. He has had enough of the act itself, and often perversely, but it has not provided unity and closure with people. He tends to look to his sexuality for his deliverance; but then it is also his cross. In the treatment of a schizophrenic I find that this area is best left until the patient, with a certain readiness, broaches it. With some it is the first interview—it is then a screen—but most often it is late in therapy. It comes when the patient has established a relationship with the therapist and as a necessary adjunct of the transference and countertransference. The definitions of masculinity and femininity are first borrowed from the therapist, and then become the patient's own.

This is often the area in which the therapist's anxiety reaches its maximum. Some of the most primitive and archaic symbolic material provided by dreams, painting, and delusions deals with sexual and reproductive material. The patient must again give birth symbolically—and be reborn—in the therapy and here we have the crux of the entire treatment.

4. In what I have called the "ethical sense" vector I have drawn together a number of facets of the patient's cultural response to people and the need for love. This is probably a much less pure vector than our other four, but possibly the most crucial. Love is a continual preoccupation of culture and not simply for reproductive reasons. It is manifested in the arts, religion, philosophy, law, and in every social institution. It is constantly dinned at us by radio, television, and similar group media. Love is often considered a private domain, but it is very much culturally oriented. Society sets the scene and the limits; it sanctions and punishes love in complex ways beyond belief. It expects all people to be able to love and is puzzled when they cannot, or when they do so in perverse ways. But culture is threatened when people cannot love, and so the inability to love becomes an illness in a formalized way. The loving quality is absent in the schizophrenic—this is his illness—and so his ethical continuity in culture is lost. He restores this first with his therapist in *their culture* and with a partially new set of ground rules. Then he may be able to tackle the proscriptions of culture.

5. Communication is a variable which implies a meaningful energy transmission to and from people. I suppose there is intracommunication as well as intercommunication, but I will set this aside for the moment. Communication is a set of signals of many orders within a value system. Signals of no or little value are ignored, since no one can respond to all the signals the environment provides. It is, therefore, a matter of sensitivity and selectivity. Just how the signal system operates in schizophrenia we are not yet certain, but Bateson *et al.*[20] have made a fine beginning analysis. The code is set by the child's field or world, but his mother is apparently the chief coder. If her code is consistent, then communication is straightforward even though it may contain "noise." If it it is inconsistent, i.e., if the code is changed in the middle of a signal, then the response may be to a part of the signal only, or to multiple parts, or to none of it. (To experience the anxiety this generates in an adult one has only to receive Morse code which comes in this way on a radio receiver.)

Something like this must happen to the schizophrenic-to-be child so that eventually the "noise" comes to meet autistic rather than inter- and intracommunication needs. This creates a narcissism that is best served by paleological communication, idiosyncratic in nature. It is belaboring the point to make a complete and unified theory of this kind of model. A theory of schizophrenia need not be dependent upon unitary models; rather, it must depend upon such models at several levels of integration. The communication vector helps explain one aspect of human existence—but one aspect only—of *being-in-the-world* in relationship to the dynamic field of the individual.

In psychotherapy one begins with the patient's own communication system and works from there. The metaphors are meaningful and meaningless until the framework of the *encounter* is set. Then metaphor, simile, image etc., can be transformed by symbol analysis. A consistent code now becomes possible where it was not before.

Function of Symbols

If the process of psychotherapy with schizophrenics were confined to the bringing up of conscious material, it would go hard with them and with the therapist. With the schizophrenic it is not simply a matter of consciousness, for he is already overly conscious of the *Absurd*. (In this connection, I can never recall seeing a mentally deficient schizophrenic,

[20] G. Bateson, D. D. Jackson, J. Haley, and J. Weakland, "Toward a theory of schizophrenia," *Behav. Sci.*, 1 (1956), 251-264.

i.e., a dull one, with the exception of the "simple" variety, which I do not believe is schizophrenia at all.) It is rather a matter of a *qualitative* consciousness of another order. Frankl says,

> In schizophrenia the ego is affected both qua consciousness and qua responsibility. The schizophrenic is "creaturally" limited in respect to these two existential factors. The ego is "hypotonic" in regard to consciousness, while the sense of responsibility is likewise curtailed. The schizophrenic person experiences himself as so limited in his full humanity that he can no longer feel himself as really "existent." These are the qualities of the schizophrenic experience which made Kronfeld call schizophrenia "anticipated death." [21]

How can one provide consciousness of existence through free association and abreaction in the conventional manner? And how much can be abreacted out? There is a definite limit to the motoric or acting-out aspects of the therapeutic situation. Fortunately, there is a psychotherapeutic aspect which is curative and which lends itself excellently to the analytic situation. This is the function of symbols. Sechehaye[22] has been the most consistent worker in this area with schizophrenics. She has shown that a symbol has a dynamic with a curative power and that this operates without regard to conscious knowledge of what is taking place. The symbol *pari passu* is integrative and uniting on an unconscious level, as is insight on the conscious one. It also offers immediate symbol gratification and emotional reinforcement.

The patient brings the healing symbols to the *encounter* but their dynamism must be a part of the transference situation. Without this they have only limited-time healing power. Symbols contribute to making possible the *encounter* in the first place, which the patient could not otherwise face, and helping to eclipse a process that might be ever enduring. Symbols, unlike signs, are not limited to any structural or temporal level and they have universal import, as Jung has shown. They are common to every man, but also unique to every individual. What is symbolized is the relationship to the eternities—life, birth, death, love, being, world, hell; just those events which are most crucial to existence.

[21] V. Frankl, *The Doctor and the Soul* (New York: Knopf, 1955), p. 250.
[22] M. A. Sechehaye, *La réalisation symbolique, un catalipeur de la structuration du moi schizophrénique* (Bâle: Karger, 1957); *A New Psychotherapy in Schizophrenia: Relief of Frustration by Symbolic Realization* (New York: Grune, 1956).

The realization of self through symbols makes possible a deep and meaningful *encounter* which goes beyond the transference and its analysis. It is no longer necessary to bring everything to a verbalization. The symbols, even if not interpreted, are the standards through which the vale to *becoming* are carried.

THERAPEUTIC ENCOUNTER

In the history of man it has most often been the arts—painting, drama, the novel, and poetry—which have presaged a change in the innermost portion of man. This avant-garde message is usually met by the public with indifference and bewilderment, if not downright rejection. Ultimately we can look back on the arts and see the significance of what was then being said. Man's condition in the twentieth century has been the subject of a number of artists and writers, including such people as Sartre, Camus, Malraux, Eliot, Picasso, and Klee. What are they telling us about man's existence? Tillich[23] puts it this way:

> The combination of the experience of meaninglessness and of the courage to be as oneself is the key to the development of visual art since the turn of the century. In expressionism and surrealism the surface structures of reality are disrupted. The categories which constitute ordinary experience have lost their power. The category of substance is lost: solid objects are twisted like ropes; the causal interdependence of things is disregarded: things appear in a complete contingency; temporal sequences are without significance; it does not matter whether an event has happened before or after another event; the spatial dimensions are reduced or dissolved into a horrifying infinity. The organic structures of life are cut into pieces which are arbitrarily (from the biological, not the artistic, point of view) recomposed: limbs are dispersed, colors are separated from their natural carriers. The psychological process (this refers to literature more than to art) is reversed: one lives in the future to the past, and this without rhythm or any kind of meaningful organization. The world of anxiety is a world in which the categories, the structures of reality, have lost their validity. Everybody would be dizzy if causality suddenly ceased to be valid. In Existentialistic art (as I like to call it) causality has lost its validity.

The artistic creation—in its symbolism—defines the feelings of man and of his culture. What the expressionist and existentialist painters and writers are saying is precisely what the schizophrenic says in a differ-

---

[23] P. Tillich, *The Courage to Be* (New Haven: Yale Univ. Press, 1952), pp. 146-147.

ent way. The schizophrenic, like the artist, draws attention to his condition of *Nothingness* and the emptiness and loneliness which occupy him. He becomes acausal in his autism, and thus departs from the reality of others. Artistic movements are protests and are designed for self-healing. As such, they cure the wounds of culture. Some such expressionist process is possible—yes, necessary—for the schizophrenic.

Weigert in discussing the problems of communication between doctor and patient in psychotherapy speaks of the need the patient has for the therapist as follows: ". . . he turns to the psychiatrist with two essential needs that underlie his symptomatology—a deepening of his self-understanding by a freeing of self-expression, and an improvement of his adjustment to reality, based on more meaningful communication with others." [24] I would like to paraphrase this description of patient needs for the schizophrenic in this way. The schizophrenic has his own reality and is not at the moment interested in any other until he can see a continuity of the world in it. Neither is he interested in self-understanding as such. What he wants at first is a symbiotic life situation which will allow him to recapitulate the significant past human encounters in his life history in which he somewhere missed the point of existence. He wants to fill the void of *Nothingness* and to clarify the *Absurd*. He senses that this can only be done in a mother/child, God/son, lover/lover relationship of the greatest moment. Reality, and even fantasy, have trapped him so often that he does not easily become a party to such a *commitment*. He must be certain that some human will make the *commitment* he once expected of his mother and he has an extensive testing repertory in which to ascertain this. The schizophrenic wants an intensity of relationship which matches his estrangement—i.e., love of the most unvarnished order. This is the framework within which all therapeutic effort must be set.

It will be said that there is nothing really new here that has not been said by other people in discussions of transference and countertransference. However, with schizophrenics it is necessary *to go beyond the transference*. The transference and its counterphenomena are constructs of the therapist and not the patient. The patient has only the field of the *encounter* and he struggles in this coeval arena. Transference, by definition, is feelings projected upon figures who are surrogates from the past. But the schizophrenic has only the past and no present. His condition is always *to-be-as-before*. But we are two people

[24] E. Weigert, "Problems of Communication Between Doctor and Patient in Psychotherapy," *Psychiatry*, 21 (1958), 241-248.

together in the *here-now* and the transference is not enough, if we accept the conventional understanding of it. It is necessary to *encounter*
the patient in the present (also in the primordial past) with the full
meaning of his humanity. Only then can he test his *being-in-the-world*
by sharing his fate with another who is willing to grow with him. The
therapist is as much on trial as the patient.

This understanding of the patient's needs of course creates problems for the therapist. How many of us can, or are willing, to make such
commitment to schizophrenics? How many of us feel that we need to
grow in our humanity with such patients? It appears that it is mostly
the young or the saints[25] who can carry such a burden.

In such an *encounter* with a schizophrenic all artifice is valueless and
thus the playing of roles counterindicated. Arlow says:

> The tentative, defensive testing attitude of the schizophrenic is a
> necessary maneuver in order to alleviate anxiety by assuring him-
> self the presence of allies in the external world. Because of this
> testing attitude, the playing of roles, or the administering of con-
> trived therapeutic experiences seems to be an ill advised procedure
> in certain cases. Such patients, already specialists in the meaning
> of unreal and inappropriate behavior in their own right, will be
> only too quick to spot such behavior in others, especially psy-
> chiatrists.[26]

The essential ingredient of such an *encounter* may possibly best be
described by Erikson's "basic trust" which, it seems, was lacking to begin with. In many ways such a relationship with a schizophrenic is a
marriage, with all the overtones which this implies but with the sexual
aspects confined to fantasy. Female schizophrenics come to therapy
wearing their wedding rings anew, or shift them from the right to the
left hand and back, depending on the current status of the "marriage."

Prolegomenon to Psychotherapy

This is not the report of the successful treatment of a case. It is rather
the incomplete description of the psychotherapy of a schizophrenic pa-

[25] In a previous paper I noted that historically most of the successful
psychotherapists of schizophrenia were women who were described at various
times as saints. It has also appeared to me that such work is often done in
the enthusiasm of an early career and then tails off as one becomes older.
The number of psychotherapists who have given up treating schizophrenics
is quite startling.
[26] J. Arlow, "Discussions of Dr. Fromm-Reichmann's Paper," in E. B.
Brody and F. C. Redlich (eds.), *Psychotherapy with Schizophrenics* (New
York: Internat. Univ. Press, 1952), p. 117.

tient in transition to an altered form of existence. Whether the patient will ever "be well" I do not know. I am not certain that I know exactly what "being well" means. She has made a number of gains which have been independently recognized by her ward doctor, her husband, her parents, and her peers, but she has not yet completely left the hospital. For Doria I would construe being well as being able to make a choice to be the kind of person she wants to be without the consequent anxiety and conflict which comes from emerging from the tight circle of a homeostatic and pathological family and social situation. When she can make this choice, withdrawal, regression, and archaic cognitive processes will no longer be needed to meet her problems of living. The patient is on her way toward this goal, but the outcome cannot yet be predicted with certainty. It is for the patient to determine how this goes. After years of participation in psychotherapy, I have come gradually, but nevertheless certainly to know that it is the patient's decision to be the way he wants to be, and no one can make it for him. We do not love him less for it!

Approaching Doria's psychotherapy was not done without trepidation. In addition to the usual questions that arise in accepting a schizophrenic for long-term psychotherapy where chronicity and psychotherapeutic failure have been the rule, I was attempting to feel at home with the concepts described in the previous pages (I had employed them in only two previous cases). There was also the question as to whether I could at this time personally offer her the total *encounter* she needed. The selection of such a patient for treatment, I feel, revolves more about the therapist than it does the patient. The traditional indifference of the chronic schizophrenic to psychotherapy is in part a below-conscious awareness of the circumscriptions and limitations set by the therapist's unconscious. If the therapist cannot first reconcile these negative factors within himself—or there is no hope of doing so as psychotherapy proceeds—then he is doomed to disappointment. (The therapist fools himself in this regard more often than the patient.) For these reasons, I most often select people like Doria from my therapeutic group where, in a more limited way, we come to know each other first. It must be noted that the selection of patients for long-term treatment is not a precise thing—in fact, it is something like selecting a mate, where superficial ego factors assume the greatest prominence during the courtship period. On the other hand, sometimes with these patients we know rather quickly that we want to engage them—often in the first or second hour. I look for a kind of *here-now* "presence," or readiness, which I am unable to define but which I very definitely sense or intuit. Of course the patient must have had some form of broad sensitivity to the world, so that the nuances of culture and social living are potentially meaningful. This presumes some cognitive as well as feeling status; but it is not to be identified with positive or negative statements of schizoid or schizophrenic affect so popular in quick psychiatric judgments and not at all related to what I am speaking about.

As is so often true with such patients, Doria was widely read and had even tackled the writings of Kierkegaard (no mean feat for anyone). Her allusions to history, poetry, literature, etc., were often a challenge to the therapist. (She once accused him of illiteracy.) Despite her withdrawal and abysmal social relationships (even in the hospital), the symbolic ferment of idea, image, and archetype was great and this boded well.[27]

She had, of course, been diagnosed in a number of hospitals as schizophrenic. Such diagnoses, however, are cross-sectional and catch the patient in some transitional phase. They are thus only to be interpreted within the longitudinal, observational framework which is the psychotherapy. Because of Doria's rather blatant schizophrenic symptomatology, there was never any question that she was a schizophrenic person—and this was confirmed by my work with her.

Life History

The following life-history material has been gathered from a variety of sources including the patient and her family. It probably has more than the customary reliability for such data for it is cross-validated in many instances by several observers, and was developed longitudinally over a number of years.

Doria Mykonos, as I call her, is a thirty-one-year-old Caucasian female. She is married, has four children, and is Protestant by religion. Her children, all girls, are Jean, Jane, Mary, and Helen, ages nine, eight, two, and one, respectively.

Doria was born in the Middle West in 1928 and moved to still a larger city there nine months later. There she lived with her grandparents as well as her parents. This was the first of a series of moves, until

---

[27] At this stage I cannot conceive of the successful outcome of the psychotherapy of a schizophrenic without the potential for dealing with the primordial and symbolic conflict manifested in this way. Thus Doria says at one point: "Am I really part of Western civilization?" By this she implies that she is really a part of some other epoch.

age six, when she was taken to a large city in northern California where she lived with an aunt until she was twelve. These moves were apparently motivated by a certain restlessness on the part of one or another parent and the inability of the father to earn a satisfactory livelihood during the depression. He sold books, billboards, radio time, and other things, ran a doughnut shop, and participated in a variety of other ventures. During all of this, he demonstrated a singular inaptitude for commercial success yet rather grandiosely believed in his ability in this area. She later lived in several other smaller California towns, finally meeting her husband at a state college which she attended for two years. They moved to a large university town where her husband completed his A.B. in English and worked toward teacher certification. He held several posts as a high-school teacher but rarely longer than one year. More currently he has been unable to find employment in his profession. There were at least six moves in the next eight years, and it was toward the last of these—in 1956—that the patient dates her illness.

The patient describes the years she lived with her aunt (from six to twelve) as happy, but has little recollection of the earlier years, about which she makes a wry countenance. She said she was a "gifted" child, and my independent investigation of her school history revealed I.Q's ranging from 127 up, with an invariable A-minus average in scholarship. (Her achievement tended to drop as she progressed from elementary to high school and college.) She felt that being "gifted" was important since her mother and father valued intelligence. She believed that she had to compensate in this way for the greater love given her brothers— particularly by the mother. She developed artistic interests, but her mother wanted a "happy housewife" type. They encouraged her in sports—which she disliked—and didn't like the people she associated with. She was very attached to her aunt who subsequently died of cancer. Before her death her aunt had started drinking heavily, a pattern which was to be repeated in each instance with her father and her husband.

The records indicate that delivery was spontaneous, normal, and that she was breast fed until nine months. She was a good eater and was easily weaned. However, in family therapy it was disclosed that the circumstances were not always so propitious. She was born after the death of a first child—a son—who was very much wanted, and there were no offspring for four years after Doria's birth—a source of disappointment. She was adored by the father who "spoiled" (*sic*) her. The parents reported that she cried a great deal, was irritable, and became a voracious eater. She reacted violently to the birth of the next sibling. Both siblings—brothers—are successful and apparently well-adjusted persons in professions—law and physics.

While in college Doria worked as a theater cashier, telephone operator, and in a cannery part time. She has not been employed since.

She met her husband in 1947 and they eloped about a year and a half later. She was in love with him but his feelings toward her have not been precisely ascertained. Doria's parents were not fond of him and opposed the match. Mr. Mykonos drank heavily, even during courtship, and Doria was aware of this. When intoxicated, he became physically abusive and sexually aggressive. She would attempt to run away, but her ideals would not permit her to acknowledge his deficiencies. His behavior became more severe as the marriage progressed and he finally sought therapy at the university clinic. Because of this treatment he was able to discontinue drinking.

Mr. Mykonos is a short, dark man with an uncomfortable air, who resembles somewhat the marginal Hollywood male extra. He has an air of weariness and abstraction about him that is chronic. He obviously takes pride in his attire, but his clothes are shoddy and his grooming incomplete, so that the total effect is compromising. Most often he is defensive—and uses his considerable learning in this way— or he removes himself by fantasy in a staring, catatonic-like way. In his own eyes, he is an unsuccessful man. He has not been able to secure and/or retain teaching positions and he drives a taxicab or sells books part time;[28] he is at odds with his parents—he considers his mother exceptionally dominating—his parents-in-law, his wife, children, other authority figures, friends, etc. He apparently expects a kind of homage and recognition from his wife which should substitute for that which the world has failed to give him. He is frankly not interested at this time—and possibly unable—to assume the economic burden of his family (the children are being cared for by the parents-in-law) and he is ambivalent about his wife but is drawn to her. He volunteers that he is neurotic and that he finds it difficult to stay in one place for long. On being queried as to possible treatment goals for his wife, he is vague. He wants her to be as she was during the first two years of marriage—for her to have her "self" back. When pressed, he mentions the stereotype of a "mature woman." Since his wife has been away from

---

[28] It is probably not a happenstance that this was also the sometime vocation of Doria's father.

him for two years, I inquired as to other women. He said he has "catted" around but that they *all want something more.* "Something deeply emotional?" I ask. "Yes," he responds with a shrug.

One of his psychotherapists saw his problem this way:

> The treatment focus was toward clarifying his long-standing dependency needs, his conflict with authority figures, and his erratic acting out with excessive drinking and extra-marital relationships in times of stress and anger. These problems were actively observed in the distorted and difficult relationships that he developed with his wife, his own parents, and in his working relations with employers. His ability to earn an adequate income in proportion to his own skill and capacities to meet the basic needs of his family were seriously affected.

Mr. Bloom, age fifty-five, Doria's father, is a large, bluff man who has a need to make his mark in the world every moment of his existence. He is highly verbal and there is a wide discrepancy between his learning and achievement. He is said to drink heavily and, indeed, became drunk when he had to come to his first family therapy meeting. In 1954 he was a patient in the same psychiatric hospital in which his daughter is now lodged, and he was diagnosed as having schizophrenia, undifferentiated form. The admission note reads:

> This is a fifty-year-old white male who enters the hospital with a commitment history that his condition began suddenly about three weeks ago. He is delusional, not sleeping, overactive, laughing, rambling speech, and is suffering from many financial worries. Patient states that his wife had a gastrectomy a year ago and he has been worried about it. Furthermore, he has had low income. His wife requested that he come to the hospital. His account is very vague and circumstantial. He complains that "he is not equipped for any job"; he blames his failure on the economic situation, and states that things at home are going "both ways." Patient's history of present illness is marked by its vagueness.

Mr. Bloom was the youngest of five children. His father was a brilliant lawyer who died at the age of seventy-nine. He was inconsistent in his discipline, expected more from Mr. Bloom than he could give, and made him feel inadequate. Mr. Bloom's mother was lenient with her children and he was her favorite.

Mr. Bloom has deep psychosexual problems, problems with religion, and problems in interpersonal relationships. He said, for example, "I've had a great deal of sex problems; if I knew about sex I could rule the world," and again, "I'm a lover; I like bad people even, particularly when they don't kick me."

Study in the hospital brought the following additional facets of the father's personality to light:

> Patient has always been a very ambitious person, wanting to succeed in business. He is a perfectionist, wanting everything to work out according to plan. He enjoys organizing and taking over a new business. He becomes overenthusiastic and expands his business beyond its potentialities. He is not very good at managing money. Patient has been upset because of a loss of his business in 1942. He blames himself for his failure, feels he has let his family down. After his business failed, he stayed away from his home for nine months, went to another state and did not correspond with his family. The wife showed considerable understanding, saying that she felt he needed to be by himself if he wished it, and accepted him back when he returned without any comment. He gets along very well with his two older children. He is inclined to argue with the youngest boy, who mother states has a similar personality make-up to that of the father. The wife is a university graduate and taught school. Patient feels inferior to her because of her education, but she feels he is much better informed without a formal education.

Mrs. Bloom seems much less important than her husband in the genesis of Doria's illness. Her perception of herself is of one holding her finger in the dike to prevent an imminent collapse and she has felt this way for many years. Undoubtedly she needs to be masochistic, and many of these needs are served by taking over Doria's children in a suffering way. Physically she is a small, unkempt woman in whose presence I associate a witch. As Doria regresses she comes to resemble her mother in a startling way and improvement can be measured by the visual deviation from this image. There is an antagonism between mother and daughter which is often overt. In parting from family therapy Doria kissed her father on the lips, but she merely brushed her mother's cheek in a most casual fashion. Mrs. Bloom has often had to fill the economic gap in her family, which she has apparently done with little complaint. She herself feels trapped in a set of circumstances which she feels unable to change—like Doria—but she has compromised her existence—unlike Doria—in a set of defenses which she manages at a considerable personal sacrifice.

ONSET OF ILLNESS

Doria's illness came at a time when the family stiuation was better than it had been for some time. They lived in a small town in southern California where her husband was teaching. He brought home a steady pay check and had stopped drinking; their home was nicely furnished and they seemed to be getting on. It was at this time, in March of 1956, that Doria began having difficulty sleeping and became obsessed by the idea that she was dying. She became tense and irritable and finally refused to leave the home. A few days before, while wheeling her child down the street, she had a severe panic reaction and felt that she could not make it home. She had strong feelings of being shriveled up inside and that she was turning into a vegetable. Doria became severely depressed and said at one point, "Now I have everything that I wanted but myself."

Her symptoms continued unabated so that she and the children went to live with her parents while her husband remained at his teaching post. A psychiatrist recommended electroshock, and she received eight on an outpatient basis. Things improved, and in September she decided to move with her husband to a university town in northern California where her husband could work for his M.A. in English. Soon after this her symptoms returned in full flower. Her parents found her house uncared for and Doria in a high state of disorganization. After consultation, hospitalization was arranged at a medical school hospital. This was in November.

Her mental status on admission there was described as cooperative but depressed. She was anxious and tearful, often repeating the question, "Do you think anything can be done about this now?" She needed constant reassurance that her condition was not irreversible, and would frequently break out in tears and repeat that she was not whole and felt all shriveled up inside. It was all her fault and too late to do anything about it, she thought.

Between her admission and discharge her behavior was essentially the same. The following quotation from the medical school summarizes it:

> Since her admission and to the date of her discharge, her behavior has remained essentially the same. The patient's stream of talk is usually coherent, is frequently interrupted by repetitious questions mentioned above, and by repetition of the statement that she feels shrivelled up inside, or that she does not feel whole,

or that she has half a head, etc. Her emotional status was that of
a severe depression with blunted affect. At the time of discharge,
her affect appeared more appropriate and the depression was not
as marked. The only abnormal mental trends noted were the delusions mentioned, which are still present. She is and was well
oriented and seemed to comprehend what was being said to her.
There was no evidence of hallucinations, her judgment was poor,
her past memory is fair, but she has great difficulty concentrating,
and is unable to repeat a simple story recited by the therapist. Her
judgment and insight were and remain poor.

For five months at the medical school she was carried in psychotherapy alone, with the addition of amytal interviews—which revealed
nothing not already known—and methedrine. Following this she was
given thorazine along with psychotherapy. She was unable to make use
of her interviews except for the continuous recital of the somatic delusion that she had only "half a head." Her behavior on the ward was
one of almost complete disorganization: she had to be continually reminded not to smoke in bed and to maintain her personal appearance
and grooming. She improved slightly with the medication in terms of
organization of thinking and behavior.

The husband entered collaborative therapy and as he made progress
Doria seemed to regress. This also operated reciprocally.

> There is much we do not know and understand about this case,
> yet [Doria] consistently uses the interview hour to discuss her
> helpless, hopeless feelings about not being able to get well be-
> cause she only has "half a head." Recently, since she has been
> told she is being discharged, she admits that she still has the
> delusion but she does not talk about it so much because it seems
> to irritate people. She remains a pitiful, helpless, hopeless, margin-
> ally organized female with a sloppily groomed, picked face which
> causes perennial scabs or sores. There are occasional periods when
> Doria seems more motivated to take care of herself and deal with
> her problems in a realistic manner, but these periods of time only
> last for a few days and she again slumps back into her old condi-
> tion. There appears to be a strong element of secondary gain in-
> volved in her hospitalization which makes psychotherapy with her
> very difficult. Recently it has been discovered that [Doria] is
> now eighteen to twenty weeks pregnant, a fact which greatly
> distresses her, but seems to please her husband. Outside of the
> above-mentioned improvements, [Doria] still presents the pic-
> ture of a sloppily groomed, poorly motivated schizophrenic fe-
> male with the somatic delusion of having something missing,
> sometimes a distorted "half a head." Her general clinical impres-

sion has never changed markedly throughout her two years stay in the hospital. It is the general consensus of opinion [staff] that this woman is severely ill, has been, and probably will be ill chronically for a very long time, and that she has not responded adequately to the more permissive attitude of therapy present in this hospital. . . .

So Doria came to the state hospital where the writer first met her. The clinical picture here was not dissimilar from that reported above. However, to give Doria's impact upon the hospital, her ward psychiatrist and a peer—a fellow patient on the ward and in group therapy—prepared a vignette of her as they saw her soon after admission. Beginning with the psychiatrist:

[Doria Mykonos] has been known to me for a year; during the past several months I have been her ward doctor. These rounds should be distinguished from a formal clinical evaluation in that they are candid and less thorough. I first noticed the patient on the admission service. Her face was abraded in many areas; her grooming was careless and unattractive; her walk was fluid and smooth but somehow disagreeable; her manner indicated indecision, preoccupation, and indifference to others; she wept or laughed or looked blank but she communicated no urgency nor was her affect contagious. She impressed me as being unappealing or even repulsive and I wondered at the solicitude others seemed to feel toward her. Later, as her ward doctor, my attitude changed little except that in persistent rule-breaking she became a nuisance, comparable to a low-grade chronic ache. I never felt I could communicate with her, to really get through to her; in contrast to my reaching most other patients. I felt no urgency about helping her. In these ways she stood out as different from other patients.

Now the fellow patient's description:

There sitting on the smoking porch of the ward in the rocking chair, staring out into space with unseeing eyes—yes it's a woman —yet not a woman. More dead than alive. She doesn't care either for herself or the child she carries. Her eyes are dull to this time and place. Now and then they flicker with fires of some other hell—her private hell. The phantoms dance before her eyes in all their shadowy horror, obscuring from sight the world in which she occupies space and time. She digs her face and head until its a bloody pulp. She burns holes in her clothes—slopping ashes and coffee abundantly over herself and the floor until everybody retreats. Minutes later she pulls herself from the chair and slops over to the group—leans over me, takes the cigarette from my hand to light her own—knocking the fire from mine. Then flops on the sofa and commences to breathe down the neck of the girl laying there reading the paper. Minutes pass, the group becomes aware of a vague irritation—it's there again—haunting them—if only it would go away and evaporate into nothingness. If only it was a fly—they could swat it and relieve themselves of further agitation. "What" she repeats. One of the group, suppressing their hostility, explains what has transpired. "Why" she mumbles with apparent disinterest. Hostility mounts within the group— they are tense and mute. They disband, running from their own feelings. She is glad—glad they don't like her—glad that she doesn't like them—glad they are alone now, like she is. She's tested them and they have failed—like she has failed. The world is hate and hate is the world.

I have given my own partial impressions of the patient above and of her impact upon me. Uniquely, I did not feel the repulsion reported by the ward doctor and other patients. I saw only the potentialities for her growth—for an altered existence—and I was willing to make a commitment which would throw us together in an extended psychotherapeutic relationship. Here possibly lies the basic differentiation in her response to me and to the medical school psychotherapist. I have never wavered from this commitment, but I have had two periods in which I became mildly disinterested in her, with, of course, serious but transient repercussions. Such patients, it seems, must also always be treated counter to the hospital's subtly negative and unfavorable prognostications—a pessimism that goes with chronic schizophrenia and the tremendous number of patients to be reached.

No presentation such as this can do justice to the nuances which are the psychotherapy of a schizophrenic patient. My course here will be to sample certain aspects of the treatment which bear most heavily upon my theoretical viewpoints—and which serve to illustrate them. These will involve individual psychotherapy, group therapy, and family therapy.[29] The patient was seen from two to five hours a week for the past year, or approximately two hundred hours, as this is written; and the program continues.

In the analysis of schizophrenic existence the emphasis is on the here-now—on the dynamic interpersonal field. This field comes eventually to mirror all of the facets of the ego in its many layers and in

[29] Co-therapist in family therapy was Arthur Anderson, M.D. He also served as consultant for my other work in this case. I am deeply indebted to him. He is, of course, not responsible for the point of view manifested here.

its cultural boundedness. This is not to ignore the historical or the unconscious, for an ego without its development is meaningless. It is rather that history is put in the service of the *here-now*, so that the *world-design* of the patient can be reformulated on a new choice basis. Regardless of the nature of the schizophrenogenic mother or father involved, it is the patient's life to do with as she pleases and the potential is ever present if it can be freed. Technically, this point of view is subject to several hazards, not the least of which is simplicity. Obviously, the patient cannot make an intellectual *choice* to be different. If she could, she would not need to be treated. This *choice* can only come about through the *encounter* and its transference and countertransference vicissitudes. If one assumes such simplicity then one is doomed to failure. The therapeutic problem, for example, is posed by a quotation from Binswanger.[30]

> The temporality of this world was one of *urgency* [italics his] . . . its spatiality therefore one of horribly crowded narrowness and closeness, pressing upon "body and soul" of the existence. . . . All this could be demonstrated not only in the modes and changes of spatiality, of the hue, materiality, and dynamics of the various world, but also in the modes and changes of temporality, up to the state of the "eternal emptiness" of so-called autism.

The patient must become temporal rather than atemporal; spatiality, that is, object values, must assume new meanings; emptiness or loneliness become pregnant, crowdedness less obsessive and oppressive. This can be done if the basic conflict of the *Absurd* can be resolved—a long and difficult task. Spatiality and temporality are relatives operating within a framework of meaning. Without such meaning they are physical units leading to *Nothingness*, to arbitrary or sick usages. How then do we set about doing this? It must be patent that at our stage of knowledge of the psychotherapy of schizophrenia the relationship between a specific patient and a specific therapist is more determinative than any technique. It sometimes appears as though improvement is actually unrelated to technique. I do not mean to deny technique but to limn its sometime function as a refuge from the highly intimate nature of the *encounter*. In this treatment description there are new departures in technique, but they are secondary to the *encounter* itself.

[30] L. Binswanger, "The Existential Analysis School of Thought," in R. May *et al.* (eds.), *Existence, A New Dimension in Psychiatry and Psychology* (New York: Basic Books, 1958), pp. 206, 209.

The existential analysis of schizophrenia, as I see it, differs from other approaches largely in theoretical or philosophical outlook, which can be exceedingly important in their own right. Thus, in the case of Doria, I talk about transference and countertransference factors, of the analysis of unconscious productions, resistance, interpretation of feelings, and the many other devices which are used in classical psychoanalysis. What does distinguish this approach from others, however, is the emphasis on the patient's world and the need to enter and share it in a way not frequently done; the determinative *choice* the patient has not only of his symptoms but of the world he wishes to make; the valuative and relativistic nature of temporality and spatiality, so that "meaning" assumes a most prominent place in the illness and its genesis; the regressive and symbolic efforts to reconcile *Nothingness* and the *Absurd* not only in the developmental history of the person but in the history of all people and culture. The emphasis is on a new drama of life with the psychotherapist in the *here-now* (with implications of past and future) in which a new mode of existence is found. This does not, in my opinion, exclude contemporary psychoanalytical techniques if these conditions can be met. However, meeting these conditions usually results in some alterations in conventional techniques, or at least in the rigidity with which they are applied.

The transference is only one aspect of the *encounter*, but it is the one we know most about. In the past we have used this concept loosely to describe the entire interpersonal relationship between patient and therapist. This is incorrect, for there is a conscious "living together" aspect of the psychotherapy which is not necessarily transference and, in psychotics, much of the magical-animistic content seems primordial beyond usual transference functions. In fact, it is often difficult to distinguish between these three, since they superimpose and overlap and have a special relationship to each other. Any psychotherapy of a schizophrenic which stops with the analysis of a classical transference will miss both the import of the ego relationship between patient and therapist and the contributions of the deeper past. In the discussion which follows, these separate contributions have not been kept distinctive simply because I could not do so at this time. It is important, however, to be aware of the situation.

In an arbitrary way I divide the transference phenomena into the first, second, and final stages—recognizing that these are not equal in a time sense. The first involves establishing the *encounter* and the clarification of the problem to be solved. This is most often the most difficult phase of all because past therapeutic failure or chronicity have been reinforced and delusional and other defenses set. The manifold and distorted resistances of the schizophrenic to psychotherapy are, of course, now well known. This is the stage where the patient tests the commitment of the therapist to him in diverse ways and where he also tests the "double-bind" propensities of the therapist's *world-design*. Here it is that the therapist must provide a consistent, loving, and open relatedness—a "new" mother prepared to welcome her infant who is much more than an infant. It is in this stage that countertransferences are often maximal, for the demands are exorbitant, the pace slow, and the therapist has a need to cure quickly. His own reality, and what is schizophrenic in him, is challenged so that his anxiety, hostility, and other mechanisms are convenient but troublesome devices. In the most critical moments the therapist re-emphasizes his dedication and this usually suffices. If it is not harmful to the patient, he reveals those feelings or impulses of his own which are blocking the "growth together" of the *encounter*. The work here is often nonverbal.

The middle transference phase is more redolent of the neurotic than the psychotic. The transference has been established and the patient has accepted himself as ill—at least for the purpose of treatment. He gives permission to look at his defenses in a limited way and he will test the reality of the therapeutic hour—as well as hours away from therapy. His anxiety waxes and wanes in degrees in a way which makes it more available for analysis and growth. It is possible now to work with symbols on a verbally interpretive level rather than in the deeper layers. The *encounter* now assumes historical, i.e., mother, father, etc., projections, as well as the *here-now* properties. Implications for the future appear faintly and the patient voices a faint note of optimism. The transference is at its height.

The final phase is the disengagement of the *encounter*. The patient has less and less need of the therapist's ego and is well on the way to *becoming*—an existence in which the *Absurd* and *Nothingness* are assumed as a part of life and do not promote anxiety of a pervasive sort. This phase may be lengthy, for unlike neurotic patients the schizophrenic needs support for a longer period. Practical problems may also arise with his family when he returns to them. This is an area of difficulty for the psychotherapist because he too must experience relinquishment, and the end-points in such a relationship are not so clearly demarcated as are the beginnings in our knowledge. Since our report here deals with a case in progress, not much can be said concerning the termination of psychotherapy.

To borrow an image from Camus, we may say that schizophrenia is "like a plague. One craves human contacts but one never knows when one is infected. It is precisely at that moment when one feels safe or free that one finds his life may be snatched from him." [31] Doria reacted to our opening meetings as though she would be infected with plague. She had invested considerable energy in a system which convinced her that she was unliked and unloved and had considerable family and community support for this. Principally, her scabrous face and insistence that half her head was missing—the thinking, intellectual part—made denial of a relationship easy for her. Indeed, her constant repetition in a whining voice of this "program" made it difficult to love her consistently. I was content to accept her face and delusion for many, many hours, and when crises occurred I reiterated my commitment. If she did not come to me, I went to her. She would come late or not at all, and had the usual repertory of schizophrenic testing behavior: she would oscillate between almost total nihilism and an exuberant giving over to me of complete responsibility for her. Comments such as these were frequent: "I don't know where everything went." "My husband needs me but he can't have me until I have myself." "I don't know how to be useful anymore." "You have to help me. My children are growing up. It is your responsibility."

The turning point probably came when I offered to visit her in a general hospital when she delivered the child she was carrying. Thereafter she would occasionally come to the hours with a slightly less blemished face and with some piece of personal adornment. She became more regular in her appointments and more autobiographical. In the hour, she would need to "destroy" and regularly shredded the matches I made available for her cigarettes. I made no demands on her and gave no interpretations, but I did begin to say that people did have a *choice* about their lives. When she scratched her face in my presence, I offered her my hand to hold—and I did this each time she scratched. After several rejections, she took it and squeezed it warmly and the scratching (in the subsequent hours) gradually diminished. Much later I told her that she did not need to "destroy" and refused to give her the matches after lighting her cigarettes. This limit-setting

[31] A. Camus, *The Plague* (London: Hamish Hamilton, 1957), p. 78.

was salubrious for she was fearful of her own omnipotence and of her possible destruction of me.

At this time I asked her to paint one hour a week and set aside a secluded place for her to work. Later we changed to clay. She was also given a work assignment in the employees' dining room; but the employees complained that the scabs she picked fell into the food and she was sacked. Her creative activity was particularly rewarding because being creative was an important need for her, and her productions were proof of her retained capacities. In addition to making symbolic and archetypal material available, they challenged the vacuum she thought she had in her head. Gradually she began to question the organic basis for her "missing head," discarding chemical, metabolic, and other structural theories. She now talked of a missing "function," but there were frequent regressions. One day she came to the hour without a blemish on her face; and on another day resplendent in a new dress and high-heeled shoes. I was astonished at what an attractive person she really was. Along with this, severe acting-out occurred at the ward level, so that ward personnel became exceedingly unhappy with her and she had to be returned to a closed ward. She seemed to do better for awhile where protection of this kind was afforded her.

At this time she met a male patient in the hospital and began a friendship with him of some intensity. I did not discourage this since it was the first of her nontherapeutic investments in another person of some moment, and it helped to establish her as a person in her own eyes. It served also to provide some "transference distance" [32] at moments when it was needed. But she also attempted to use this man to provoke me by, for example, establishing her meeting place with him under my window.

It was more or less at this point that she began a studied effort to understand her past in terms of its contribution to the present and consented to write her autobiography. The impetus in part was my reading of Walter Lowrie's *A Short Life of Kierkegaard*, which she saw on my desk. She asked to borrow it and read it in the following week. While Kierkegaard has given us the philosophical foundations of existentialism, he himself suffered from unresolved problems of living with which Doria closely identified. This further identification was supportive. At this time, also, a former patient who had been hospitalized

[32] For this concept I am indebted to Helm Stierlin, M.D., of Chestnut Lodge.

here for schizophrenia came with her child to visit me. She met Doria and invited her to her home. This visitor had been in psychotherapy with me for several years and had made a good recovery.[33] Doria wanted to know in precise detail how ill she had been and could not accept the fact that the visitor was now well. However, the example of a new existence for this person was there and frequently referred to in later hours.

Conceptually some of this dynamic material can be organized in limited, threefold way as follows:

1. Mind-bind concept
2. Concept of equality
3. Concept of privacy

1. *Mind-bind concept.* Doria's most prominent symptom was her delusion that she had only "half a head." To this she clung tenaciously and nothing had heretofore budged it. From this stemmed her second prominent symptom. She picked her face to reassure herself unconsciously that her head was still there. Whence came this core defense? Why was it maintained in the face of all evidence to the contrary? Why does the constant reassurance she seeks that her head is still there reinforce just the opposite? I call this the mind-bind problem because in family therapy Doria equated the two by a slip of the tongue, saying *bind* when she meant *mind*.

In the family of every schizophrenic there is one family member who assumes greater importance than all others. If the father or mother, as the case may be, does not have a direct genetic part in the *Either/Or* dilemma then he or she is at least instrumental in keeping it in force. Children have a need to be like and to exceed this parent. The former is possible in ways we now understand, but the latter is fraught with great hazard for the child. The parent we call schizophrenogenic must not be exceeded at any cost although he actually seduces the child into a kind of unhealthy competition. This then provides for his own worth.

The evidence in this case is that it is the father who is most important to Doria. We know that Mr. Bloom was hospitalized and diagnosed as schizophrenic, so there is no question as to his schizo-

---

[33] See A. Burton, "Paradox and Choice in Schizophrenia," in A. Burton (ed.), *Case Studies in Counseling and Psychotherapy* (Englewood Cliffs, N.J.: Prentice-Hall, 1959).

phrenogenic personality structure. Is it far fetched to believe that he has maintained his own precarious existence through Doria's illness? In family therapy he is the most adamant that Doria is ill and needs to be kept in the hospital, all evidence to the contrary. From his own experiences as an ill person, one would expect the reverse attitude to be true. Doria's youngest child is his favorite and he is deeply involved with her—just as he was with Doria. He has found a surrogate for Doria—one close at home—but he similarly has Doria. Because of this child he may yet be able to release Doria; without her it might appear hopeless. It is significant that as she has improved he has found it necessary to find work away from home.

In Doria's need *to-be-as-before* rather than in the "now," she wants to reinstate the seductive and symbiotic relationship with her father she had when she was at one with him and could even exceed him. Then her existence was clear, as was her sexuality. Above all he values the "head," i.e., the intellect, his own tragic infirmity. The "head" is the source of all strength and creation—and it is what makes a man and compensates for his inadequacies. The Bloom family as a whole is distinguished by scholarship despite the paucity of economic resources. Mr. Bloom values just such intellect in Doria's children, but not much else. He is thus following a familiar pattern. Furthermore, this is also the distinguishing hallmark of Mr. Mykonos, Doria's husband. It is the "head" and not the "body" that counts, and when this is missing the inner world collapses. Doria was found to be significantly lacking in body-image conception and body-image language. This occurs also in children whose ego was never given the opportunity of individuation, and the failure to find the "body" is characteristic of those with difficulty in interpersonal relationships.

Through our activity with clay she was able to recover her body to the midsection with significant promise of the rest to come. She is now more than a "head," and for the first time body integration is a possible reality. An image of a Balinese dancer (not illustrated) which she made demonstrated this. Particularly significant for interpersonal relationships in this figure are the prominent breasts and nose, which reveal the maturation described above.

The "double binds" in which children who become schizophrenic find themselves are extremely complex, and no simple formula does them justice. Doria's principal "double-bind" situation was the conflict of *emotion and intellect*, which became the *Either/Or* conflict. She had to give up her existential destiny for the unity with her father, whose adhesive was a kind of perverse love. Later this was sought and perpetuated with the husband. In therapy we have clarified this to the point where Doria has insight into it and recognizes it as one basis for her negation of life.

Since the process of undoing such a "double bind" involves more than Doria herself, the entire family—Doria, husband, mother, father —have been meeting with two therapists—the writer as one—one hour a week as a group. This has been a comparatively late development in Doria's treatment but a very profitable one. Originally, getting the family together seemed an impossibility, so that Doria participated with seven other patients in group therapy two hours a week with me alone. Here members of the group became family surrogates, and she was able to work out some of the "mind-bind" problem in this way. Now direct confrontation of her father and husband is possible in the family group, so that less symbolic and more actual realization is possible. In these groups the undoing of the "mind-bind" problem has begun. They have made it possible for the therapist to determine more accurately the family dynamics and to offer it to the reality consensus of the family. Within this framework, unconscious needs resulting in "double binds" can be clarified in a way not otherwise possible with schizophrenics.

2. *Concept of equality.* Most schizophrenics have feelings that they are being judged. This is not in and of itself unusual since all Western men carry such a sense of being judged. With schizophrenics, however, the judgment is critical and they go through life as what Camus calls judge-penitents.[34] Judgment is a result of the schizophrenic's need to be equal. Thus Doria repeated many times that she wanted to be like others—to be equal—yet she picked her face so that her distinction made her unequal. Equality is a need for a special position in relationship to self and to others. In Western civilization democratic equality is a principal motif, but it invariably assumes a more than egalitarian position of the individual in relationships to others. The schizophrenic is more deeply engaged in life than other people— for example, his need for love, and to offer it—and so the interpersonal is more critical and "basic trust" a matter of the greatest moment. Thus she needs to be *more* than equal—and cannot settle for equality alone. With Doria as with others, fantasy, legend, myth all reveal the need for a powerful position in relationship to people. Humility is a very rare theme in such productions.

A judge-penitent is one who suffers endlessly without either the

[34] A. Camus, *The Fall* (New York: Knopf, 1957).

transcendent quality which suffering brings or the social response of culture to it. It is thus a continuous and meaningless act of self-judgment and punishment. Its senselessness and continuity is such that temporal-spatial values applied to it also become meaningless. It is as though the schizophrenic must continually punish himself *not* for existing—as we formerly thought—but more properly for his extraordinary aspirations toward life. The problem in therapy is to relate the suffering to some personal or interpersonal framework so that grandiosity is given up for the human burden we all share.[35] The style the schizophrenics are after brooks no compromise.

Doria first came to recognize her suffering *qua* suffering,[36] then to relate it to the framework of both of us, and finally to put it into the service of her growing ego.

3. *Concept of privacy.* A common theme with Doria was her need for *privacy*. She felt invaded and had to withdraw to the last cubic foot. This need for *privacy* is often seen in people who have desperate needs for contact and interaction. The paradox occurs because one feels that something is lost or taken away in human contact and that one may go too far with it and be totally lost. Pankow's[37] container formulation seems appropriate here. Schizophrenics do not see themselves as containing anything, i.e., they are empty. This is so because their ego boundaries are ill defined and the personality is at the mercy of the environment, which sweeps in and out like the tide. It can be demonstrated that as the container properties become more fixed and definite, the need for *privacy* vanishes.

In the treatment, the patient's desire for *privacy* is respected and no encroachment is made. The two conflicting needs war with each other and it is a serious mistake for the therapist to take sides too early. A fine balance must be preserved until the patient comes to feel that she can contain something. After the point had been reached where Doria read and discussed Kierkegaard's life with me, she was able to retain more in terms of her boundaries. This was a gradual process but is well measured by the drawings, paintings, etc., that she did. Plate I is a photograph of a vase made by Doria during her clay work. The startling thing about it is the stress on its boundedness, emphasized in lip, orifice,

[35] I believe that culture's hostility toward and segregation of the schizophrenic as a special cultural form is in part due to such pretensions on the part of the schizophrenic-to-be.

[36] Although schizophrenic patients suffer a great deal, their conscious perception of their suffering is most often blunted.

[37] G. Pankow, this volume, Chap. VI.

and form. It resembles to some extent ancient Egyptian vases and I have alluded to her feelings of belonging to the Tutankhamen dynasty. This vase represents considerable improvement in the patient.

Otto A. Will,[38] in describing the psychotic person, says, "The child does not view the world as does the usual adult, nor does the poet. The psychotic person is not a child, and is not always a poet, but he seems at times like both, and we who listen to him feel frustrated as we recognize how bound we are by our conventional frame of reference."

In order to treat Doria it was necessary to know both the poet and infant in her. The former operates on the level of images and symbols; the latter by direct uncomplicated action. The poetic side is probably best revealed by modalities which tap the several layers of the unconscious, unfettered by the rules of logic. Doria made two paintings which she said represented illness and health. These are Plates II and III respectively. Their reproduction here in black and white deprives the viewer of the color dynamics and other nuances, but this will have to serve. Grossly, the two paintings are diametrically opposed in that Plate II is an abstraction and Plate III highly structural. Plate II, representing her illness, has meaning only in terms of the idiosyncratic symbolism involved. Plate III, representing health, is more universal in scope. Since art is a way of portraying existential needs, it is significant that the "ill" painting is typical of the kinds of abstractions painted by leading abstract painters. There is a commonality here between Doria's problems of existence and the avant-garde in what they portray in painting, sculpture, etc. Mental illness in this sense may be closely related to the nonconformist who also copes with *Nothingness* and the *Absurd*. Thus the "squares" in Plate II can represent the four members of her family (including herself) who live a closed existence not in tune with the times. To be a "square" is a most serious condemnation by the Holy Barbarians and means to be out of phase with life. Yet Doria sits (major figure) before the planes of life (parallel lines), dessicated and bonelike, waiting for the flow of life. She is the female principle, but the male essence is kept from her by a "square" who is also male but not adequately so. Plate III is a structure and every inch of paper is richly colored. There is a warmth and reaching out for the richness of life. There are individual blocks in different colors, standing in definite relationship to each other—one, it seems, for each family member (including her children). Instead of a part they are a whole—they have integrity, cohesion, and definite boundaries. Doria is expressing

[38] Otto A. Will, this volume, Chap. I.

PLATE I. A container.

PLATE II.
Painting
symbolic
of illness.

PLATE III.
Painting
symbolic
of health.

here the unity of all human relationships and their melting into a common structure.

These paintings presaged things to come. As her treatment continued she lost more and more of her estrangement, reached out toward other people, and insisted on leaving the hospital. Her improvement was not matched by the growth of her family, who had considerable unconscious investment in the maintenance of her illness. In family therapy she was able, for the first time, to confront her father and husband with her needs as a person and to point out logically the part they themselves played in her illness. At this point the husband told of his ambivalence about resuming his life with her outside the hospital and began drinking again. Mr. Bloom is still adamant that she needs to be in the hospital but is less firm in his position. Treatment continues on all these fronts but less intensively. Doria no longer has the delusion about her head, her face is picked only in times of great regressive stress, and she is ready for what life offers outside of the protection of a hospital.

In the face of earlier therapeutic failure, it seems to me that our significant contribution here was in recognizing in a special way the existential problems in Doria's life and helping her to *choose* a different and better world in relation to time and space. Together the *Absurd* was found to be livable and the flight from *Nothingness* a reality to be faced rather than a chimera.

CHAPTER VIII

Autonomy and Activity-Passivity in the Psychotherapy of a Schizophrenic Man*

Donald L. Burnham

SCHIZOPHRENIA is not a precise term—a fact of which we often are less mindful than Bleuler when he coined it and referred to the *group* of schizophrenias. I regard schizophrenia as comprising disorders in three realms of human functioning: thought, emotions, and social relationships. The thought disorder is featured by disorganization of various types which impair the person's capacity to organize a reasonably accurate and stable view or representation of the world, especially of himself and others, and the relationship between them. In other words, thought and the capacity to employ symbols as a means of testing reality and guiding action are defective. In addition to losing its effectiveness as an instrument for seeking gratification and security in a world shared by others, schizophrenic thought may become a source of gratification and security in itself, and thus contribute to a turning away from the shared reality world.

The disorder of emotions includes faulty emotional control and integration (featured by severe anxiety), "all or none" affective discharge reactions, and inability to delay or modulate such reactions with other than total repression.

The disorder of relationships is characterized largely by isolation

* This study was supported by funds granted by the Ford Foundation to the Chestnut Lodge Research Institute, Inc., Rockville, Maryland.

and withdrawal, based upon such a powerful linkage of intimacy and anxiety that the schizophrenic person deeply fears and distrusts relationships with others.

In thinking about psychotherapy as a process designed to repair these disorders of thought, emotions, and relationships, numerous authors have advanced various types of rationale or theories of psychotherapy. A sample might include: offering the opportunity to establish basic trust; to relive early experiences of great emotional intensity and make a new beginning; to gain insight into faulty behavior and learn more effective, adaptive patterns; to establish greater conscious control of self and interactions with others; to discharge pent-up feelings and thereby relieve their crippling, disruptive effect; to experience sympathetic understanding of the unique personal tragedy of one's life; and to build the capacity for satisfactory social relationships.

Communication occupies a pivotal position in most, if not all, of these theories. Certainly in my own practice it is a useful focus for thinking about my interaction with a schizophrenic patient. In the first place, faulty communication is a major manifestation of the disorders of thought, emotions, and relationships. Second, communication is a primary tool employed by the therapist. Third, one of the prime goals of therapy is to aid the patient to achieve more satisfactory communication with other persons as a means to, and consequence of, better social relationships.

In his effort to facilitate communication the therapist strives to understand the patient's behavior by observing how he behaves and formulating ideas as to why he behaves in that particular way. This requires that he gain some idea of how the world looks to the patient. Therefore the therapist tries by observation, inference, and guesswork to gain a reasonably accurate picture of the flow of thoughts and feelings across the stage of the patient's consciousness, and to grasp the representation of reality which the patient organizes from this flow of conscious experience. Depending on the degree of organization, the patient's representation of reality will be organized along time and space coordinates and will include his self-image or representation, his representation of other persons, and his conception of the relationship he and others bear to each other.[1] It also comprises his view of his life situation and his aims, purposes, strategy, and tactics within this situation. The patient's representation of reality constitutes his context or

[1] D. L. Burnham, "Misperception of Other Persons in Schizophrenia," *Psychiatry*, 19 (1956), 283-303.

frame of reference for his behavior. To the extent that the observer is unable to grasp or imagine the patient's personal frame of reference, the latter's behavior may seem senseless, purposeless, unaccountable, strange, or bizarre.

An especially important feature of a patient's representation of reality is what I choose to term central personal issues. Part of their importance derives from the fact that they are an important focus of the patient's attention, concern, and energy. In fact, they may assume such all-absorbing importance that they threaten to crowd all else out of his awareness, or to draw other data into connection with them. His struggle to avoid, resolve, or relieve these conflicts may absorb every erg of his energy. By this token they deserve the therapist's special attention. In certain phases of therapy he can best reach the patient by talking about these foci of the patient's primary interest and concern, and in practice this often is not such a trite cliché as it may sound.

In the phases of disorganization the patient's total representation of reality and his central personal issues are highly disorganized and obscure, certainly to the observing therapist, and most probably to the patient himself. William James described the infant's mind as probably a "great, blooming, buzzing confusion." [2] Schizophrenic disorganization may entail even more confusion, if only because of the addition of a store of fragmented memory traces, whereas we may presume the infant's mental contents to be largely limited to current sense impressions. In the course of reorganization more clearly defined personal issues emerge as relatively stable features of the patient's representation of reality. Their clarity is one measure of reorganization, and it is likely that the therapist's addressing a portion of his communicative efforts to these gradually emerging issues facilitates the reorganization.

I wish to illustrate something of this process as it has occurred in the course of nearly seven years of psychotherapy (four hours a week), as yet incomplete, of a schizophrenic man. The issues which have emerged as centrally important with him are those of autonomy and activity-passivity. Here I refer to concepts which recently have received considerable attention from psychoanalytic theorists, notably Rapaport[3] and Hartmann,[4] although for the most part I shall use the con-

[2] W. James, The Principles of Psychology (New York: Dover, 1950).

[3] D. Rapaport, "Theory of Ego Autonomy," Bull. Menninger Clin., 22 (1958), 13-35.

[4] H. Hartmann, "Ego Psychology and the Problem of Adaptation," in D. Rapaport (ed.), Organization of Pathology and Thought (New York: Columbia Univ. Press, 1951).

cept of autonomy in a somewhat more limited sense than does Rapaport, by referring more to the issue of autonomy of the self or self-representation than to autonomy of the ego or central cohesive organization of mental processes of which the self-representation is only one part. It probably is accurate to say that the degree of autonomy in one's image and appraisal of self is positively correlated with, and therefore an index of, the degree of relative autonomy of ego from stimuli and demands from two sources: internal drive forces, conceptualized as id; and the external environment. Activity and passivity are behavior modes highly relevant to the appraisal of whether the self is relatively autonomous, separate, and independent or relatively dependent and helpless. I hope further to clarify the nature and scope of the phenomena thus labeled as I proceed with clinical illustrations. I certainly do not mean to indicate that the issues of autonomy and activity-passivity were the sole focus of my therapeutic attention nor that they represented the total of this patient's personality and illness. Likewise it is impossible to determine the exact proportions in which these issues are common to all humans, specific to schizophrenia as cause or effect, or unique concerns of this individual patient. However, they have been useful in viewing his central personal issues or core problems, and a useful focus for our communicative efforts. In his thinking about himself and his life situation these issues have at times assumed an almost all-pervasive significance. Occurring initially in the form of scattered fragmentary threads, they have gradually emerged as a broad strand running through the stream of his life experience.

BACKGROUND HISTORY

The patient, Jack, now forty years old, is the son of wealthy Jewish parents and grew up in a large Midwestern city. His mother was rather flighty and suffered from periodic nervous upsets requiring rest cures but never hospitalization. His father, now retired, was a successful, highly reputable businessman. His only sibling, a sister two years older, died when he was twenty, and two years later his mother died. After about two years his father remarried.

The patient's childhood care was largely by nursemaids, the most significant of whom reported him as having been very stubborn and self-willed. He concealed a shy, sensitive nature by a "devil may care" attitude and numerous reckless escapades. He is described as taking after his mother, but also showing some social dependence on his sister by attaching himself to her circle of friends rather than cultivating his own. After a year at a prep school in another part of the country, he attended a college near his home. He managed to graduate but several times narrowly averted expulsion for breaking college rules, auto accidents, and unauthorized absences. College was followed by reserve officers' training and, with the outbreak of World War II, active service in the Army.

He served successfully for nearly three years as an officer and was promoted twice before being hospitalized overseas for "a mild manic excitement." In retrospect, the two most significant life-situation events in the months preceding his psychotic break had been: a more independent command, whereas previously he had been a subordinate officer; and his father's remarriage. After return to the United States and discharge from military service, he worked briefly as a laborer, sought psychiatric treatment, soon became disturbed and depressed and was hospitalized and given electric and insulin shock. Hospitalization has been continuous for the past thirteen years in a series of veterans' and private hospitals. In the earlier of these he was reported as deeply disturbed, attempting to castrate and kill himself, and requiring tube feeding. During that time he received many electric and insulin shock treatments. Two previous therapists died while or shortly after being in charge of the patient's treatment.

EARLY PHASES OF TREATMENT

When I first saw him, Jack was gaunt, toothless, and disheveled. His clothes were torn and twisted into strange disarray, and he assumed bizarre postures and appeared older than his actual age. His teeth had been removed at a previous hospital after they had become badly eroded from acid stomach contents repeatedly regurgitated and held in his mouth. He still did this and often would spit a mouthful on the floor, furniture, or even on another person. He also urinated and defecated wherever the urge of the moment dictated. Although his speech was badly disorganized, fragments of his talk were responsive to me from the beginning, and he said something about having come here to learn how to get along with men.

His talk was vague, rambling, and disjointed and his thoughts seemed largely a whirling maelstrom of constantly shifting fragments of sense impressions, memory traces, and hallucinations. The instability of his thought structure was paralleled in the sphere of action by incessant indecision, vacillation, and conflict—whether to sit or stand, which chair to use, which clothing to put on or take off, upon which side of the road to walk, and especially whether to swallow, regurgitate, re-swallow, or expectorate food. His speech was pervaded by indecision, with sentences begun, broken off, restarted, and interrupted by, "No—not that—oh—no," etc. It was possible occasionally to pick out coherent thought clusters of apparently enduring or repeated concern to him. These pictured him principally as a victim of external influences which for the most part were vague, abstract, and nonpersonified, such as electrical influences, connected in some unspecified way with big business, power and telephone companies, politics, and Washington, D.C. He believed that these influences were mediated via his clothing, especially his shoes, which he made active efforts to "treat" by dunking them in water, urinating on them, and breaking down the backs so they resembled slippers in shape. When an aide purchased a particular type of shoe he had requested, he became furious, threw the shoes aside violently and said he hadn't really wanted that type. This incident also illustrates something of his conflict between urges to seek the help of others and fears of domination by them. He also indicated that he believed the furniture and walls of the room and the food were sources of bad influences.

The effects he attributed to external influences were mainly body ruination, especially of his penis, and loss of ability to defecate or urinate properly.

There was some personification of the bad influences. He spoke angrily of women being too powerful and controlling everything. When in the vicinity of nurses or women patients he usually taunted and insulted them or increased his display of bizarre, unconventional behavior. Occasionally he said that he could hear the controlling voices of his dead mother and sister, and that he was being used as a martyr for his family.

He sometimes spoke of me as secondary mediator of bad influences but not as a primary source, saying, "Get off that wall panel—don't sit on that chair," implying that there was magical influence on both of us via the furniture. Occasionally when he made such a complaint, he winced as if from pain and either rushed from the room or came toward me to attack me.

He strenuously asserted that he wanted no part of me and that I had no significance for him. When I came to see him, he either ignored me or asked with bored irritation, "What do you want? You're a nuisance, I have no wish to see you." There were several contradictions of his denial of me. For one thing, he occasionally stated that he had known me and my family under other names in previous life situations. He also betrayed interest by objecting that I was too young, excessively interested in clothing, and associated with certain business interests. Especially relevant to his own problem of lack of autonomy were his doubts about my autonomy: "You're a stooge of Jones" (the doctor who accompanied him on his transfer to this hospital), "Don't use that tone of voice—use your own voice—talk for yourself." Somewhat later, instead of vehemently telling me to go away and refusing to stay with me, he might say with a touch of humor, "I suppose you're here to have your hour now. I don't know why I have to allot you time, but I suppose it's all right if you feel you must have it." The connotation of reversal of the roles of active giving doctor and passive receiving patient was typical of his keen sensitivity to implications of dominance and submission, activity-passivity, and social-status differences.

Occasionally he complained that I was better equipped by training or the clothes I wore to resist bad external influences, and a few times he fairly realistically said that my having a wife, children, and other interests gave me more with which to keep myself actively occupied than he possessed. The theme of activity as a solution to problems later became recurrently prominent.

During the first two years I went to meet him rather than having him meet me for the therapy hours, in part because I was convinced that he needed such a concrete demonstration of my willingness to meet him at least halfway, and that this was vastly preferable to having him escorted to my office. Although I briefly considered placing him in a wet pack for the therapy hours to afford him relief from the disruptive fear of his assaultive impulses, I chose instead to permit a wide range of geographical movement during our sessions. This entailed trips to the hospital canteen and walks over the surrounding countryside during which he could literally put distance between us when he became more upset. This, I believe, averted the serious threat to his precarious sense of autonomy which restriction of his movement would have been.

In my communicative efforts I usually referred to the form of his experience—its instability, unpredictability, conflict, indecision—rather than to specific items of verbal content. Much of his concern about unpredictability stemmed from his fear of sudden, uncontrollable murderous impulses, which I commented must be very frightening to him.

There was further softening of his defensive denial of my significance. When I arrived on the ward to see another patient, Jack often hastened to the nursing office to request a watch with which to time my appointment with his therapeutic sibling. Previously he had been seemingly uninterested in and even fearful of the watch. Somewhat later he began to show a clearer awareness of the time of our appointments and a less disguised wish for them to last the full sixty minutes. A few times he greeted me with a smile, and even permitted himself to touch my shoulder and say, "Let's go out for a walk." Usually such friendliness was followed the next day by sullen indifference or angry castigation with the statement that he had no use for me. Sometimes he was able to tolerate periods as long as a half hour in my office before he punctuated them by jumping up and walking rapidly to the canteen where he anxiously crammed down food, often grabbing it without waiting for it to be served. After ten minutes or so I would suggest that we return to my office. He usually complied, once or twice initiating the return himself. Another landmark was his direct acknowledgement of my significance, "You're the best non-Jewish friend I have, but of course you ought to get a razor strop to sharpen yourself up a bit." Or, "You're all right, but God damn it, I don't want to get attached to anyone, least of all to a man."

Meanwhile, his delusions of influence changed from the telephone or power companies to far more personal references to persons from the East or ambitious young doctors eager to exploit patients and gain prestige. Such remarks were likely to be sandwiched into a stream of disjointed talk. Now and then he abruptly and directly accused me, "You're an incestuous bastard—you're a Jew—you just want to suck my cock." Such accusations I often met by the statement, "So what? What's so terrible about that?" on the assumption that I was dealing with a projection. This assumption was borne out by other statements that I was causing him to have incestuous thoughts or trying to make him into a fairy by forcing him to associate with people here who were part of a male harem.

He believed that people in the sanitarium were acting and masquerading, especially that women were posing as men and vice versa. Once he hit a student nurse without apparent provocation and later explained that her short haircut proved that she was a man dressed as a woman.

His complaints of external influence all seemed to contain an implicit statement that he lacked autonomy. At this phase of treatment he emphasized the strength and malignancy of the external influences rather than his own sense of weakness and vulnerability to them.

The theme of independence and freedom was prominent in his

talk, with repeated loud protests regarding social injustices in general, and specific hindrances to his freedom—being led, directed, and controlled. Often he was defiantly nonconforming and negativistic. There was evidence that some of his assaults were triggered by situations in which he felt especially helpless and at the mercy of others. Complaints that he was being exploited or experimented upon were coupled with angry statements that he was going to leave and go elsewhere. I acknowledged his wish for a sense of greater freedom and commented that I hoped he would stay here until he was well, that we did not intend to make him leave, and that I often wished we had longer than one hour to spend together at a time.

I hazarded the open implication that he felt attached to me and others partly because his adamant denial of need for others had softened considerably with several brief but open acknowledgments of feeling lonely. He voiced fear of his father dying, and the consequences to himself, since his father was the only person he had. He intermittently spoke of needing a woman, with the implication that this need was more in terms of mothering than sex. A direct expression of dependency urges was that rather than a psychiatrist he needed an engineer to teach him engineering. In this way he not only made a rare acknowledgment of my identity as a psychiatrist but also showed his deep need for model objects for identification purposes, a need which later became much more open and prominent, as it became clear that on the other side of the fear-of-domination coin were strong wishes for advice, instruction, and training.

Gradually it became possible to discern a phasic activity pattern. Periods of dull lethargy, in which he sat staring blankly or dozing, alternated with periods of agitation (pacing, and talking in loud, disjointed, and often angry fashion). His eating habits fluctuated from ravenous stuffing of food to nearly total refusal to eat. Conflict between active aggression and passive submission was manifest when he assaulted others, only to stop and invite them to strike him. If an aide struck a token return blow, Jack often said, "Hit me harder—there—now I respect you." Fear of both activity and passivity were evident in his attitude about shaving as he alternated between protests that he was unable to shave himself, fearful refusals to allow an aide or a professional barber to shave him, and relatively docile acceptance of being shaved by others. In retrospect it appears that much of this fluctuating behavior related to vicissitudes in his sense of autonomy and that the alternating phases of activity-inactivity might be regarded as rather gross caricatures of helpless passive resignation and aggressive active independence.

Further indications of the central importance of activity and passivity were contained in his fears of the latter: fear that the food might turn him into a pervert or a woman, and that women generally exerted too much influence on him. At the same time he voiced a wish for me to be more active: "Do something. I need action—take me to a ball game—get me a woman." His ambivalence regarding activity-passivity as well as his lack of a solid sense of personal competence and autonomy were obvious in these pleas that I supply the action.

MIDDLE PERIOD OF TREATMENT

During this period Jack was given reserpine, the decision to use the drug being made jointly by myself and Jack's administrative physician. We were influenced in this decision by favorable reports in the literature regarding the drug and because Jack's periods of disturbance, although somewhat less frequent and prolonged, were discouragingly unmitigated in intensity, which seemed to perpetuate a discontinuity of his subjective experience and his personal relationships. The daily dosage of the reserpine was 6-9 mg. for the first three months; 4 mg. for another three months; and subsequent maintenance dose of 2 mg. for sixteen months, reduced to 1 mg. for a final four months, comprising a total period of two years.

Several distinct changes became evident within a few days of initiation of reserpine therapy. He showed improvement in his personal hygiene and dress; was more sociable and participated more successfully in a broader range of activities on and off the ward; wore dental plates, which he had stubbornly refused to use before; and began venturing to the dining room for meals instead of eating from a tray on the ward. He stopped eating with his fingers, a habit which had been coupled with a phobic avoidance of silverware and vaguely expressed fears of contact with persons named Silver. On the first day that he used the dentures, he greeted me with, "How do you like my new smile?" This incident also illustrates the not uncommon and not insignificant experience with schizophrenic patients of being treated to glimpses of their potentialities for great warmth and personal appeal. Experiences such as these are a major factor in bolstering the therapist's interest and perseverance. Diminished destruction of clothing accompanied an interest in such new purchases which he carried through with much less indecision and disruptive upset than before. Greater constructive interest in clothing did not entirely postdate the reserpine, for in the previous month he had repaired his shoes in the craft shop, an accomplishment of which he clearly was proud.

The processes of communication and psychotherapy were distinctly facilitated by changes apparently attributable to the drug. Although there was minimal change in Jack's thought content, there was substantial improvement in his ability to communicate his thoughts and to sustain a topic without lapsing into incoherency and cryptic fragmentation. Several times he explained ideas previously expressed in incomprehensible fragments. For instance, he elucidated previous vague persecutory references to a clothing store by saying that the initials of this store, prominently displayed in newspaper ads, were identical with the designation of the last military unit with which he had served prior to his first hospitalization, and that this was associated with shame and humiliation. Occasionally he was able to add that he felt a deep sense of failure about his discharge from service, especially because he regarded this as the one phase of his life in which he had been on his own without the auspices of his family, and thus touching pertinently on the theme of autonomy.

Such statements were part of a generally increased ability to stand back a bit, as it were, from an immediate disorganized flow of experience, to observe himself and report some of his observations. Clear indications of this improvement in the self-observing function of his ego were apparent within days of beginning the drug. He spoke almost as if a veil of fog had lifted, so that he suddenly could picture his life situation in clear detail and perspective. "I'm in terrible shape. I've been mentally ill for eight years. I don't know what I can do to get well." This was accompanied by a wave of acute depression and a sprinkling of suicidal talk. His ability to maintain the observing function of his ego was by no means constant, nor is it accurate to say that he had shown no such ability prior to reserpine. However, further presumptive evidence of the drug having an effect was provided when, unknown to patient, therapist, and nursing staff, the administrative physician substituted a placebo for a brief period and the patient showed distinct reversion to greater disorganization.

Another aid to psychotherapy in this period was an increase in his capacity to delay and control sudden violent affective discharge, notably rage and assaultiveness. There was by no means a total flattening of feelings and even the assaults did not entirely disappear. When they occurred, however, he showed more capacity and a greater concern to account to himself and others for the event. For instance, while talking with his administrative physician, without apparent provocation he suddenly turned and struck an aide who was standing nearby. The next day when asked if he had any idea what had prompted this he replied, "Yes, all of a sudden I was jealous of him because I thought he was better off than I am." This ability to discuss an event the following day also illustrates the greater continuity which gradually became manifest in his behavior and presumably in the flow of his subjective experience. It was as if events and experiences, rather than occurring in small blocks, disconnected and discrete from one another, now were at least partially woven into a fabric of some continuity and stability.

Greater continuity was noticeable in his relationship with me. More frequently he openly showed pleasure when I arrived for appointments, and occasionally at the end of the session checked with me the time of the next. His recognition of me was just that; instead of seeing me variously as a number of different persons, he more consistently and openly recognized me as the same person: a doctor and a psychiatrist. Sometimes he ostensibly complained: "You're the worst psychiatrist. If I had set out to find the worst one in the world I couldn't have found a worse one." More often he implicitly denied mental illness with recurrent complaints of physical illnesses: cancer, tuberculosis, heart disease, bladder trouble, kidney disease, muscular dystrophy, and others. Most consistent were complaints about excessive intake of food and defective elimination: "I can't shit. It's piling up inside me—all through my body. How can I get rid of it?—I shouldn't eat so much." For him the word *consumption* was a key one in its various connotations as a synonym for tuberculosis, eating, processes of devouring or being devoured by feelings or persons.

Although still interwoven with fears of external influences via food, clothing, or proximity of other persons, it was noteworthy that some of his concern was now focused inward on himself and his actions.

His complaints about internal physical problems usually were accompanied by statements of needing an internist and physical treatment, and requests that I be more active and take him to a general hospital where active treatment such as the use of "shit-removing machines" were available. Such requests contained strong overtones of helpless submission and relinquishment of autonomy. Sometimes I responded quite bluntly, "You seem to be saying that your troubles are all physical and not with your feelings, thoughts, or relationships with

people. It might be a hell of a sight easier if this were so, but it isn't
and I for one think we can do something about these other troubles."
At other times I questioned his conviction that talk was useless, saying,
"You don't seem to think that talking does much good. Maybe you
fear that it will only stir up memories which you wish to forget or feelings which you're afraid you can't control. I know that sudden strong
feelings can be very upsetting. However, I think one of the best ways to
achieve better control of feelings is by telling your thoughts to another
person. As a matter of fact, I've noticed that in recent months as you
have communicated more you are more able to control your feelings."
In actual practice I didn't say this *in toto* but repeated portions of it
at what seemed appropriate times.

His pleas for more action by me sometimes were associated with
statements of his own need to be more active. "I need to keep busy.
There should be more things to do. I want a job, like driving a bull-
dozer or a tractor. Where can I get a job like that? How can I get a
driver's license? I need exercise." He suggested that keeping busy
would keep his mind away from troublesome thoughts and drain off
energy which might otherwise lead to assaults or other explosive outbursts of feeling. The wish to be active was far from pure and consistent but involved many layers of conflict. As previously described,
there were periods in which action was so fraught with danger for him
that massive indecision, hesitancy, paralysis of effective action, and a
pervasive sense of frantic desperation resulted. Impulses toward action
were countered by a welter of doubts. For instance, he might say, "I
want to go to a trade school—no—people of my class don't go to those
places; they are for delinquents."

The connection of conflict about activity and ambivalence toward
advice, guidance, or direction became more clearly defined. Continued
protests against domination and influence were intermixed with more
frequent remarks about need for training or direction. Despite previously repeated loud requests to leave the closed living unit, when he
actually was transferred to a semi-open unit, he was extremely uncertain. He was permitted to enact his indecision by spending part time
on each unit, until one day he was heard by the charge nurse of the
semi-open unit to mutter something about uncertainty of laws. She
responded, "So it's laws you want. Well, we'll take care of that. Here is
a daily schedule of what you are expected to do when you live here."
When handed this schedule he read it, crumpled it in a ball and threw
it down, saying, "You don't want me here." The nurse replied, "You're

wrong. I do want you here but I want you to be more comfortable." Thereupon he picked up the schedule, reread it and placed it on the dresser in his room. Despite continued protests that he hated people telling him what to do, he seemed appreciably relieved and decided to stay on that unit.

During this period it also became clear that Jack's struggles over autonomy and activity-passivity were closely linked to the vicissitudes of identification with others, especially me. He indicated uncertainty regarding his own identity in its personal, occupational, and other aspects and, as part of his struggle toward a more stable and autonomous personal identity, he repeatedly expressed wishes for a more satisfactory model with whom to identify. His posture and clothing had taken on noticeable similarity to mine; but he seemed to feel that he required a clearer and, in some respects, different image of me, complaining that I did not tell him enough about myself, that I was not old enough to merit his respect, or that I was not active enough, especially in giving him leadership, instruction, or advice. He reiterated wishes for therapy featuring something more than talk, saying that he required advice, should get more exercise, a job, attend drivers' school or reform school, or find a mentor or proctor whom he could emulate.

He also complained that I did not speak for myself, but was controlled by someone else or a vague "them," and was just a tool. In other words, he complained that I lacked autonomy. He also protested my unreality by saying that I was acting, and this was all a big act with other persons using assumed or stage names. At such times he often said, "I don't play these games."

At other times he bemoaned his inability to emulate me, saying that I possessed various sorts of training, background, mental and physical equipment, clothing, group affiliations, more opportunities for activity, or other advantages which he did not.

His wish for a model for identification purposes might be regarded as a form of interpersonal strategy in which his goal was more the emergence of a clear image of the other person than revelation of himself. This is to be contrasted to some patients whose central striving in therapy seems more a confessional type of self-revelation in the hope that the therapist will accept all that is revealed. In response to Jack's implicit plea, "Show me yourself; then I can become like you and leave behind my bad self," I did make myself more visible to him by maintaining distinctly less therapeutic anonymity than is my practice with neurotic patients. Almost from the beginning of our relationship we had done things together such as taking walks, playing catch, and shoveling snow. Later our joint activities included auto rides, shopping trips, restaurant meals, sports events, and an alumni luncheon of his college. At the same time I let him know that I did not agree with the thesis that our relationship was to consist only of his getting to know me to the relatively complete exclusion of his revealing himself to me.

We clarified as a source of resistance to self-revelation his reluctance to accept or acknowledge the role of patient with its connotations of sickness, need, and especially craziness. Bearing this sensitivity in mind it was useful for me to phrase my comments about personal problems either in terms of people in general or my own personal experience, and thus remove from him some of the onus of being the patient.

Jack's wish for an identification model was ambivalent; although he viewed identification as a means to achievement of autonomy, it also threatened his autonomy. Partly related to this threat were his loud complaints of being dominated and controlled, which became more specific and personal. He regarded physical proximity to others as dangerous because he might take on their qualities and said that he must get away from this place because it had the wrong kind of people. He complained that a particular suit would be wrong for him because it was too much like one of mine. After shaving with a borrowed razor he was fearful that he would become similar to the owner of the razor. At times he was fearful of my office and car on the same basis. He expressed the concern that being around persons who wore glasses would cause him to go blind. Noticing a nurse who limped from a residual poliomyelitic paralysis he said, "They're trying to paralyze me." Fear that proximity to Negroes would change his skin color was still another indication of his extreme sense of vulnerability to influence by his surroundings. Fear of loss of his separate autonomous identity also was contained in protests that he didn't want to become an Elk, Rotarian, Mason, or member of any lodge, Chestnut or other, while simultaneously complaining that he was not a member of any group.

Fear of influence via food became more definitely connected with other persons, with intense conflict over whether a given food was "male or female," and reluctance to eat in certain restaurants because they were "for children." One day I said that he seemed almost to think that eating the food was equivalent to eating another person's body and becoming like that person. His prompt response, "But that would be cannibalism; I don't go for that!" indicated that the thought was not new to him. Subsequently, cannibalistic desires and fears came even more obviously to the forefront of his thinking. He talked of being a "consumptive," while saying that he preferred to associate with strong persons, with the obvious implication that he had urges to cannibalistically incorporate their strength.

The connection between oral incorporative conflicts and identification was further corroborated by sequences of events such as the following: at the end of one therapy session I invited him to accompany me on an errand to the bank, which he did after initial hesitancy and vacillation. The next day he said he wished to open a bank account, which also after initial uncertainty he accomplished. The following day he was quite upset and kept complaining that he was too full: consumptive, piggish, and likely to be killed.

The complaint of being too full, accompanied by concern over inability to eliminate urine and feces, often coincided with his phases of agitated activity and was likely to be followed by a period of morose lassitude associated with subjective feelings of boredom, monotony, and emptiness. The schizophrenic dilemma of interpersonal closeness versus distance seems highly correlated with literal sensations of fullness or emptiness. This correlation has been observed by several authors, perhaps most notably Guntrip,[5] and seems clearly connected to the intense wish-fear of incorporating the other person.

For Jack, as for many schizophrenic patients, body feelings are a very important mode of experience. When Jack spoke of having heart disease (or no heart), low blood pressure, no circulation, too few corpuscles, and of being aged, there were multiple determinants and meanings including similarity to attributes of his father, but perhaps most importantly a symbolization of weak, feeble, helpless passivity. References to loss of his teeth were related to object losses in general, especially loss of his mother and sister; loss of his personal equipment, including loss of mental abilities; and self-derogation for being so passive as to have allowed his teeth to be removed. The equivalence of "I have a cancer inside," to "I am filled with hatred" was demonstrated when he half-apologized for an angry outburst by saying that it had been caused by cancer. This outburst had been noteworthy in itself because instead of assaulting me he had limited it to a vehemently shouted, "I'd like to kill you," following which he had been visibly shaken and made the remark about cancer.

Statements of concern about aging referred to discouragement over

[5] H. Guntrip, "A study of Fairbairn's Theory of Schizoid Reactions," *Brit. J. Med. Psychol.*, 25 (1957), 86-104.

the number of years he had been ill and hospitalized, and fear that it was too late for him to ever get a job, marry, and have children. He spoke with near anguish of developing bumps on his skin, gray hair, and baldness, all of which he regarded as signs of aging.

Castration sensations were a common preoccupation with him. Earlier it could be inferred that he was extremely fearful of castration when he walked about holding his pants away from his genitals. He complained that belts and other constricting clothing were bad, or said that the tightness of the blood pressure cuff had ruined the bones of his arm. Now he expressed his fears explicitly, and also reported the sensations as occurring in specific situations rather than as something which just seemed to happen in a generally malevolent environment.

In addition to trying to clarify the context for the bodily experiences which he reported, I sometimes said that he seemed to experience many of his feelings in terms of strong sensations in his body. When he replied, "What about *your* body?" I answered that certainly I too noticed certain of my feelings in terms of body sensations; for instance, when tense I might notice a tightness in my chest. When I suggested similarity between us he seemed pleased and reassured but was also made anxious by possible loss of autonomous identity. Once, ten or fifteen minutes after I had commented that I didn't think we were so terribly different in our ways of feeling, he began to complain that we were too different in temperament and that he should get a new doctor—one who would be more like him and who also would have the arguing abilities of a good lawyer, thus denying the similarity between us which I had emphasized. Perhaps he valued ability to argue as a means of maintaining a sharp distinction and individual autonomy between us.

Regarding body experiences, it seems especially pertinent to his problem of autonomy vis-à-vis the environment that Jack focused much preoccupation and concern on mouth and anus, which are vital zones of interchange with the environment; in this interchange either extreme of activity-passivity, strength-weakness, or of autonomy-slavery, was dangerous. These same issues figured centrally in the first dream he reported to me. He said, "I dreamed that I was driving a car and was approaching the top of a hill. There was another car coming in the opposite direction. I tried to put on the brakes suddenly but wasn't able to do it. Then the man sitting next to me was going to do it. I think maybe the dream has something to do with your not letting me drive the car the other day." In addition to this reality day residue, the dream clearly seemed to concern such issues as fear of loss of control, competition, dependency, and lack of autonomy.

Gradually expressions of guilt, self-blame, and criticisms became more frequent, in contrast to his previous nearly exclusive assignment of blame to the environment. Some of his earlier expressions of guilty responsibility were in a magical delusional form ("Eisenhower depends on me. If I make the wrong move, millions of people will be killed.") and at other times a more realistic concern that he might harm the family reputation or be the end of the family line. There also were fragmentary expressions of guilt regarding the death of his mother and sister. Later his self-criticism also clustered around feelings of inactivity, weakness, and lack of assertiveness: "I'm not active enough—I'm lazy —I just lie around—you shouldn't let me sleep so much—all I do is eat—yellow—a coward—lack will power—can't make decisions." Without using exact words he often seemed to lament having no active role in society. Cryptic allusions to harming certain business organizations by buying or not buying their products seemed partly determined by his viewing his only significant social role as that of a consumer.

In his self-denunciations for inactivity and indecision he betrayed his ambivalence about activity and passivity by saying that others should tell him what to do. Thus his remedy contained the very passivity of which he complained. This was especially clear in his many complaints of inability to defecate. The well-established significance of bowel training experiences and achievement of self-regulation of this function as the core of an individual's sense of autonomy, self-control, and assertiveness was amply corroborated by this patient. For him, inability to regulate defecation symbolized his problems in achieving autonomous self-assertion and control in all realms of functioning and was accompanied by the wish-fear that others direct and regulate him. He said, "How can I get rid of the shit? I need instruction in how to shit." Or with an even more submissive masochistic tone, "Give me an enema. Can you knock the shit out of me? I need to have it shocked out of me—I should go to a hospital where they have machines to remove it."

Similar conflict over activity-passivity and autonomy was apparent as he criticized his eating: "I eat too much. I lack self-control. I should be led. I shouldn't be allowed to eat so much. I'm a pig." He continued to alternate between voracious engorgement and ascetic refusal of food. Regurgitation and reswallowing of food, although much less frequent, still occurred sporadically.

Although in his dilemma over autonomy versus regulation by others he had shifted from "others run my life and use me" to "others don't give me strong enough direction," he still quite frequently clamored that he was a prisoner and needed freedom and independence. At the time that he chided himself for not being obedient, he was stubbornly negativistic. He lamented being unclear as to what was expected of him, but when offered a suggestion he growled that he would not be dominated.

I offered interpretative comments that a person early in life may encounter conflicting expectations. He once had said, "This place is controlled by the moon. I need a place controlled by the sun." I also said that trouble with decisions and a wish for clear directions might be related to experiences of excessive criticism at every turn. One such comment evoked from him, "Have you ever heard of psychotherapy being able to get rid of bad stuff from the inside of a person?" I answered that I was certain that it could help with a person's low opinion of parts or aspects of himself which because of early experiences he had come to regard as bad, unspeakable, or unacceptable. I added that sometimes a person tries to avoid what he regards as bad parts of himself by trying to become like some other person.

Some minutes later he said musingly, "I suppose I should acknowledge the superiority of others and emulate them—but—doing that means desertion of yourself." I commented that he expressed this very well indeed. Soon, thereafter, he began moaning that he had no ability to talk, his tongue had grown too long, and he should find a place where he could get training in sign language. My response to this was first to say that he was doing himself a disservice by so grossly underestimating his ability to talk when just before he had expressed something as clearly and succinctly as I had ever heard it. Then he grumbled, "You're always repeating yourself. Don't you get tired of it? I suppose, though, you don't listen to yourself." After laughing and commenting that many things can stand repeating, I said, "I gather you felt very uncomfortable at being complimented and it sure is a hell of a note that you can't stand a bit of praise." After a pause he said, "I haven't noticed any of the girls praising me lately."

I cite this interchange because it illustrates so well Jack's anxious dilemma regarding autonomy. His anxiety and self-derogation following a good performance and praise illustrate his dual fear of independent assertiveness on the one hand and on the other the closeness and dependence implicit in enjoying acceptance and confirmation from another person. His statement of lack of praise from women indicated additional strong fearful overtones of homosexual attachment contributing to intolerance of closeness to me, as if he had said, "I should get close to women rather than to you." His own eloquent statement of the danger of loss of self in identifying with others can hardly be improved upon.

Gradually it was possible to link some of his fear of closeness to fear of his own destructiveness aimed at himself and others. Viewing himself as an agent of destruction rather than always the victim was in itself an advance. I commented that destructive urges when near others must be very frightening, and related this to occasions when he had fled my office in the face of an upsurge of anger. I said that he seemed caught in the dilemma of being terribly lonely when away from people but upset when near them. His response to this was a startling, "Well, I have schizophrenia, and that's not easy!" This was startling partly because he usually denied mental illness and partly because neither of us customarily used the term *schizophrenia* in our talks.

LATER PHASES OF TREATMENT

The beginning of this period was marked by two to three months of increased disturbance during which problems of autonomy and activity-passivity were very prominent, especially in his relationship to me.[6]

The disturbance began in the weeks immediately preceding my vacation, always a critical time of separation for any schizophrenic patient, but even more so for Jack now that his denial of my significance had so considerably lessened. In these prevacation weeks he showed sporadic recrudescence of conflict over attending therapy sessions, arriving late, sometimes after the whole hour had elapsed. Greater body preoccupation and occasional regurgitation of food also recurred, with complaints that he was being turned into a "two." This term had connotations of a synonym for "queer," or some other personal identity which he eschewed, perhaps that of being a duplicate of another person rather than himself. The context for its use one day was as follows. He complained to a male aide that he had never had a friend in his life and the aide replied, "I'll be your friend if you like." The patient then said, "Oh, no, I don't want to turn into a two." His body and identity concerns were accompanied by an outcropping of phobic anxiety regarding clothing,

[6] A possible contributing factor was the discontinuance of the maintenance dose of 1 mg. per day of reserpine. However, this may be largely, although not entirely, discounted since there were some prior signs of increased disturbance and this disturbance subsided without resumption of the medication.

especially shoes, his false teeth, electricity, and magnetism. The last was clearly related to the attraction of objects to each other, with quite obvious general interpersonal and sexual implications.

In one therapy hour in which he was especially distressed and blocked I asked whether he might be thinking some about our having only a few hours before my vacation. He promptly asked whom he would see for his hours then. I was startled and, I suspect, somewhat anxious; I do not know whether this was because of his fairly direct acknowledgment that I was significant enough to be missed and require replacement, or because I was hurt by the implication that I might easily be replaced. I replied, "Well, I'm not sure. Do you feel you want a substitute?" With this he quickly said that he ought to be returned to the closed ward where he had lived earlier and which he had been visiting more frequently during this more disturbed phase. Then he talked disjointedly of eating too much, self-destruction, needing a real sanitarium, and having no air in his lungs (only in his head because there was no opening between his head and chest). Then he rushed from the room. After a brief pause I followed him, and he offered no objection to my walking with him. When I later asked whether his leaving the office had been prompted by intense discomfort and perhaps a fear that he might slug me, he answered that it had just been an impulse to leave. It appears in retrospect that the transference-countertransference situation at that point was full of separation anxiety, and that his question regarding a substitute therapist, simultaneously an acknowledgment and denial of need for me, had uncovered unconscious levels of my wishes for him to need me and to miss me in my absence, as well as fears at the possible depth of his attachment and needs. It is difficult to say to what extent his flooding with anxiety and self-derogation, and fleeing outdoors were a response to his acknowledgment of needing me, his denial of that need, or to my anxiety-toned reply.

In the next few days after only partially satisfactory attempts to discuss further the question of a substitute therapist, I decided against it, partly because Jack was indefinite about it and partly because of the risk of confirming his fear of complete dependency and inability to get along without a therapist.

During my absence Jack commented on this fact occasionally to the nursing staff, something which to my knowledge he had not done during previous vacation periods. Upon the day of my return, Jack was in the throes of indecision as to whether to make a few days' trip to a beach cottage with a group of patients and aides. The idea of asserting his autonomy by actively leaving me seemed both appealing and dangerous to him. He finally decided to go and was reported to have enjoyed it. However, at our first therapy hour after his return he was disheveled, barefoot (shoes in hand), fumbling with his other hand about his neck, chest, abdomen, and genitals. His talk was blocked and fragmented and contained references to guilt as well as the need for control and direction. "I'm all filled up—I need instruction in how to get rid of it—All I did down at the beach was eat and drink— I shouldn't be around people here—I don't control my urges." When I asked whether he thought his urges were so different from those of other persons, or whether he thought he had less control over them, he replied, "I have lost all control. I need instruction and reform school."

In the succeeding six weeks there was a resurgence of now quite stereotyped body concerns, influence phobias, and tortuous indecision. Running through this welter of influence fears were conflict over closeness to and identification with me and fear of passivity. One day while on a drive, he said, "You're just trying to show me your ability to go along with your arms turning the car. I can't do that. My arms don't work." In the same hour, he complained, "I don't want to be an Elk. You are an Elk. You're trying to make me into one. You have an Elk's ring" (actually a wedding band). "I've got to get away from this place. I'm not good at handling . . ." (Patient blocked here.) Three days later he said, "I need driving lessons. I want to learn to drive as you do." Another three days later, "I'm too full—too much food. I need to get away from women—you're all right. I like you." The following day, "I want to be myself. You're trying to make me something else. Using nails in my shoes and rings—you work for him."

His fear of passivity was expressed in increasingly frequent complaints that he didn't want to be around women or elderly persons, both of whom apparently symbolized weakness and passivity to him. His fear of a passive recipient role was further demonstrated when he was with an aide at a local tavern for a few beers. When the aide ordered the beer, the patient complained that it was "female beer"; but when he himself did the ordering, he seemed content with the beer and the total situation. This was similar to an earlier complaint that he didn't wish to eat at restaurants which were "for children." Similar indications of the linkage of fears of passive influence and femininity were contained in his concern after riding a girl's bicycle, for he felt this might have weakened him. Or he had moderately severe anxiety about being first in a cafeteria line because "women should be first in line."

These observations have distinct relevance not only to individual psychotherapy but also to ward administration and total hospital organization, which traditionally allocate a largely passive-recipient role to the patient as well as stripping him of many aspects of his personal identity and autonomy. Recent studies by Kai Erikson,[7] a group research team at Austen Riggs Center,[8] and Goffman[9] bear pertinently on problems which the traditionally defined patient role creates or compounds for the patient, especially the schizophrenic person who already is deeply conflicted regarding passivity and autonomy.[10]

Although eating was strongly linked to fears of passivity and influence, it also was an expression of activity and assertiveness. Twice during this upset phase he seemed to break out of a mire of indecision by an eating spree in which he gulped down a conglomeration of food and which was followed by a wave of guilt in the next few days.

I tentatively inquired whether his guilt stemmed from feeling greedy or that he wanted much more than he deserved or than others could provide. I further speculated aloud that perhaps in childhood he had been made to feel that his wishes were too much for others. At times he used food as a "peace offering," often wanting to "treat" me on the day following vehement hostility toward me. Usually I accepted this offer without interpretive comment because I thought that the latter might spoil his active assertion of ability to give to another.

I did interpret some of the sequences of his oral assertiveness as relating to a fear of loss of control, especially of his body and what he might do with it, and that his wish to go to a general hospital was partly a desire for someone else to take control of his body. Following one such statement he seemed relieved and expressed a wish for driving and flying lessons which seemed to represent active, potent mastery over sexual urges and body motility.

[7] K. Erikson, "Patient Role and Social Uncertainty—a Dilemma of the Mentally Ill," *Psychiatry*, 20 (1957), 263-274.

[8] N. Polansky, R. White, and S. Miller, "Determinants of the Role-image of the Patient in a Psychiatric Hospital," in M. Greenblatt (ed.), *The Patient and the Mental Hospital* (Glencoe, Ill.: Free Press, 1957).

[9] E. Goffman, "Characteristics of Total Institutions." Presented at the Walter Reed Army Institute of Research Symposium on Preventive and Social Psychiatry, 1957, pp. 43-84.

[10] Also relevant is an unpublished paper from Chestnut Lodge Research Institute on observations of changed social structure and patient behavior at a summer cottage: R. W. Gibson and Gloria George, "Environmental Change and Patient-Staff Relationships on a Psychiatric Ward." Presented at the APA meeting, Philadelphia, May 1, 1959.

Some months later, after a period of relative quiescence, he began showing a distinct increase in sexual interest and assertiveness. In contrast to previous seeming indifference or insulting taunts toward student nurses he now made several friendly overtures and enjoyed small talk with them. One evening with his eyes closed he wandered about the women's section in an apparent dramatization of his conflict over interest in women. On other occasions he followed a young woman patient about at group recreational activities; once he started to strip before her, and another time went to her room, stripped himself and was fondling her breasts when he was discovered by staff, who hustled him to his own room. Immediately following this he was acutely anxious and said in anguish, "I'm totally insane—criminally insane—I want to drown myself—please get a gun and shoot me." In the week preceding this episode, as evidence of increased sexual interest mounted, he had made remarks such as, "criminal insanity, sexual weakness, no good for mankind, and should be jailed." During this same period, he took an unattended police car and drove several miles into the country. I strongly suspect that this act of boldness was not without phallic significance to him. Also during this time he urinated on the furniture and floor in a seemingly deliberate bid for censure by the staff. Behavior designed to provoke punishment was a rather frequent pattern for him in general. In his therapy hour the day following the episode in the female patient's room, he suddenly swept an armful of books and papers off my bookshelf and almost before I could voice my anger he said, "Go ahead, eliminate me!"

His declamations of guilt and need for control and punishment also related to oral aggression. He requested that he be taken to court for sentencing to protect others from harm by his eating habits. Evidence that this fear was rooted in primitive cannibalistic urges became clearer and more frequent. He said that probably "they" had removed his teeth because of the way he ate, and on another occasion said, "I'm really not an alligator." One day in the midst of agitated expressions of guilt about oral activities, I asked whether he perhaps feared that he had injured his mother by wanting too much of her breast. He abruptly became quiet and replied in an even direct tone, "Yes, that is right. She is dead," following which his talk became very fragmented and incoherent.

Coinciding with these various indications of increased assertiveness were several statements by the patient that his father was dead, and it is tempting to speculate that this semidelusional idea was directly related to the patient's upsurge of aggressiveness.

At this point the patient suffered what at first appeared to be a bout of flu which then was mildly epidemic in the hospital, with mild fever, body aches, and prostration. However, in a few days the clinical picture changed and he refused all nourishment, regurgitated and vomited, with some of the vomitus having the appearance of blood. These symptoms subsided after several days of intravenous feedings and parenteral compazine. Gastro-intestinal X-rays taken soon after revealed a gastric ulcer. It is, of course, impossible to know whether the ulcer had been present in chronic form for a long time or whether it was a relatively acute development. It is tempting to speculate that it might have been a response to the conflict stirred by his surge of assertiveness, in particular his cannibalistic urges. In this regard the reports by Garma of the role of an internalized orally sadistic mother figure in the development of peptic ulcers are intriguing.[11]

Jack's ulcer was treated by a medical regimen, and in several months it healed completely. His reaction to the strict diet and various antiulcer medications was very interesting in terms of his conflicts regarding autonomy and passivity. Despite initial loud protests that he would not be dominated and controlled, he soon became quite tractable and co-operative about the regimen. This was reminiscent of his response to the issuance of a set of "laws" when he first moved to the semi-open unit. Fairly frequently he objected to being given the medicines by women, and usually preferred to take them from a male aide. For the most part his eating in the past year had been quite regular and not subject to the earlier swings between engorgement and starvation, or to regurgitation. Other than periodic reiteration of the complaint of being too full (and this seems to refer more to a general feeling than specifically to his stomach) he has had no symptoms referable to his stomach.

The past year has seen a number of other encouraging developments which are pertinent to the issues of autonomy and activity-passivity. His statements of wanting greater activity have become more specific, realistic, and backed by fairly effective work on the grounds maintenance crew. He has been able to discuss the various meanings of the wish to be active, such as relieving guilt and a sense of uselessness, having an active contributing role in society, keeping his mind off problems by staying busy, and overcoming feelings of weakness and passivity.

Ambivalence toward independent activity still is prominent. His talk of wanting a job often is accompanied by the idea that someone else

[11] A. Garma, *Peptic Ulcer and Psychoanalysis* (Baltimore: William & Wilkins, 1958).

should arrange this for him. Although he speaks of wanting freedom from the sanitarium and a car and a home of his own, in the next breath he is likely to complain of too much freedom, the need for more direction, a more organized environment, and greater obedience on his part. He has said, in so many words, "I want more responsibility but I am afraid of it." Whitehorn has written perspicaciously of the meaning of freedom for the schizophrenic patient by describing how ostensible complaints about external authority often represent complaints against a sense of dependency and pleas for permission, direction, and support.[12]

Although some of his expressions of desire for freedom have the quality of defensive denial of attachment and passive yearnings, he also manifests genuine hope when he talks of wanting a job, marriage, and children. As yet, when he refers to the latter two he usually abruptly lapses into laments of his incapability and anger at interfering external influences, or says that he hates women anyway. Scattered among continued expressions of self-derogation and victimization have been sporadic half-humorous, half-serious references to himself as the best athlete or the most popular and personable person here. He also has shown periodic efforts at general reorientation and restitution of his interest in the outside world, reading newspapers, listening to news programs, reading maps, books, and dictionaries and then discussing this material with me in a manner which seems clearly to indicate that he is eager to fill in memory gaps of which he has recently become aware. For instance, he will review who the presidents of the United States have been during the past fifteen years, the period of his psychotic illness, and will inquire whether Willkie ever became president.

Concurrent with these indications of increased hopefulness have been increased ability and lessened reluctance to discuss matters which previously were laden with such overwhelming anxiety that he could not, or would not, make more than the briefest mention of them. Most noteworthy among such topics are the deaths of his mother and sister, his father's remarriage, and the failure of his Army career. Insistence that his trouble is all physical is less frequent and he now more often refers to himself as mentally ill. Some of these references are in the form

---

12 J. C. Whitehorn, "Hateful Self-Distrust: a Problem in the Treatment of Schizophrenic Patients," *Am. J. Psychiatry*, 3 (1954), 420; "Problems of Communication Between Physicians and Schizophrenic Patients," in P. Hoch and J. Zubin (eds.), *The Psychopathology of Communication* (New York: Grune, 1958).

of self-castigating epithets: I'm crazy—I'm a homicidal maniac." Others are quite realistic and discriminating self-criticisms and appraisals of his mental difficulties: "I have trouble with my thinking—I can't concentrate—I can't think long range—can't stick to a subject—I get confused—I have trouble controlling my feelings—I can't make decisions—I'm awfully impatient." Such remarks illustrate a shift from concern with external forces which disrupt his autonomy to internal disruptions. Concurrently he has shown a much greater interest in and capacity for discussion-type therapy sessions in my office.

As he communicates more of his thoughts he shows lack of cognitive autonomy on two fronts: the environment and his id. Much of his thinking is too readily permeated by and bound to raw primitive sexual and aggressive drives, and at the same time is ready prey to cues from the environment resulting in excessive distractibility and suggestibility. This dual interference with relative autonomy of his thought processes seems to be one basis for his complaints that he is at the mercy of outside influences and inside chaotic forces.

Along with his flashes of hopefulness and interest in greater activity, Jack has achieved a greater measure of success in several spheres of activity, including work on the grounds, bridge games, athletics, dances, and dramatics. Each increment of successful activity is likely to be followed by a wave of doubt and fear, sometimes in the form of self-recrimination for having been active. For instance, the day following a number of bold assertions and criticisms of his family he said, "My tongue is not my own, I should shut up." Successful activity frequently triggers fear of competition, talk about various other persons winning, and dominating or even killing him. At times he fears enslavement to the person with whom he had the successful activity. Playing bridge with skill and evident enjoyment may be followed by concern that he now is "hooked up" to his bridge partner.

Another revealing type of sequence consists of a self-derogatory response to friendly overtures. For example an aide said one afternoon, "Jack, I have to walk to the canteen to get Ed some cigarettes. Want to come along with me?" Jack accompanied the aide but almost immediately launched a series of self-depreciatory remarks, "I'm a second-class guy, a Jew, worthless—I should get more exercise—need to find a way to exercise." This response, which has been repeated almost automatically in similar contexts, seems to contain the latent thoughts: "I am really not worth this fellow's friendly interest and this makes me feel weak, helpless and worthless. However, exercise might be a way of strengthening and improving myself."

Jack's work experiences on the grounds crew have been very valuable in strengthening his sense of personal worth and competence, but also have been fraught with autonomy conflicts, especially the wish-fear of identifying with Andy, the grounds superintendent. While repeatedly protesting dislike for Andy, Jack has developed a deep attachment to him. After great indecision he purchased work clothing similar to Andy's, only to grumble then as he returned to the ward, "O.K., Andy wins now." He has showed a fear of total identification with Andy, saying, "I don't want to become a gardener," implying that if he associates with Andy he may take on *all* of the latter's qualities. Work in the greenhouse and seed beds has the additional taboo of being "feminine," whereas Jack vastly prefers active "masculine" jobs such as tractor driving. An additional problem is dependence on Andy's literal and continuous presence because as yet he lacks sufficient autonomy to sustain his work performance when Andy turns to assist another worker or to attend to another job.[13] Similarly, on a rainy day which prevents outdoor work Jack is all at loose ends. Awareness of this degree of dependency and vulnerability to separation is in itself an additional source of anxiety and protest that he doesn't wish to become Andy's slave or toy.

This is similar in quality to Jack's reactions to separation from me on week ends or my vacations. As a matter of fact, the development of his attachment to and identification with Andy seems to have made him more able to acknowledge and register complaints about separations from me. At the end of a week, to my "I'll see you Monday," he may respond, "I'm not sure. I may be killed before then." He recently has said, "What I need is a constant companion," a wish which he is more able to voice now that he has two major relationships upon which to draw. Furthermore, there is evidence that when he feels especially comfortable with Andy he shows greater assertiveness with me, sometimes by inquiring what he can do for me and suggesting that he buy me a meal or help me in some other way. These have the ring of a genuine shift toward greater autonomy rather than simply denial of his own

[13] Freeman, Cameron, and McGhie termed this phenomenon primary identification in distinction from the later-developed secondary identification which the patient is capable of maintaining in the absence of the identification model. T. Freeman, J. L. Cameron, and A. McGhie, *Chronic Schizophrenia* (New York: Internat. Univ. Press, 1958).

problems, needs, and passivity. This also is true of recent expressions of concern for other patients, and urges to help them.

As Jack's relationship with Andy has developed, there occasionally has arisen the question of whether his identifications with me and Andy would conflict and whether he would experience divided loyalty—problems for which there has been some precedent earlier in his life. As yet these conflicts have occurred only in a form leading to useful and insightful resolution rather than constituting a block to further therapeutic progress.

In summary, as I look back over the arduous seven years of therapy with Jack and the modest but definite degree of reorganization and resocialization which he has achieved, the issues of ego and self-autonomy and activity-passivity occupy central positions. They are highly relevant in the three spheres of disordered functioning—thought, emotion, and relationships—which I regard as characteristic of schizophrenia. In all three spheres autonomy may be threatened by inside forces and by outside forces, and the two sources of threat are intertwined insofar as lack of internal stability and control may cause a wish-fear of external control, and vice versa. At first primarily preoccupied with fear of external influence, Jack gradually began to desire external regulation and control as a means of achieving control of fearsome inner forces, impulses, and drives. Activity was desired as a means toward greater autonomy, but also feared because it might possibly lead to loss of impulse control. Passivity or submission to external control was likewise both feared and desired; feared because it meant weakness and vulnerability vis-à-vis the environment, desired as a means to greater autonomy vis-à-vis id forces. Clarification of these issues has been a generally useful communicative focus throughout the course of therapy, especially as they appeared in deep conflicts surrounding identification processes.

CHAPTER IX

Activation and Symbolization of Delusions in Schizophrenia*

Igor A. Caruso and Edmund Fruehmann

OUR VIEWS ON SCHIZOPHRENIA and its therapy are based, at least up to a certain point, on the Vienna Clinical School, of which the applications are similarly represented in the Vienna Working Circle for Depth-Psychology. We are not of the opinion that schizophrenia is primarily a psychogenic illness in the sense of a quantitatively intensified neurosis. In addition to a somatic basis governed by genetic factors, a psychical primordial conflict leading to a weakness of the defense system seems to be the nature of the illness.[1] The fluctuations in the individual history of the somatic and psychic aspects overburden the personality's already weak system of regulation, and this state is followed by a breakdown of the personality. It now depends on the historical situation of the person concerned whether a somatic illness or a "somato-psychosis" will develop.[2] In the second case presented here we will find a specific disturbance of the psyche in correlation with a basic disturbance of the enzyme apparatus.[3]

* Translated from the German by Maria Tortschanoff.

[1] O. H. Arnold, *Schizophrener Prozess und schizophrene Symptomgesetze* (Wien–Bonn: Wilhelm Maudrich, 1955); H. Hoff, *Lehrbuch der Psychiatrie* (Wien: Hollinek, 1957).

[2] H. Meng, *Psyche und Hormon* (Bern: Hans Huber, 1944).

[3] O. H. Arnold and H. Hoff, "Synthese in der Schizophreniefrage," *Med. Klinik,* 53 (1958), 1, 8-12; O. H. Arnold, "An Attempt to Form a Bridge from the Schizophrenic Manifestation to Heredogenetics," in *Chemical Concepts of Psychosis* (New York: McDowell, Obolensky, 1958).

This is a very complicated situation. Does it mean that the psychic facts cannot be influenced by physical means, or that the somatic situation cannot be altered from the psychical side? The question of how the organism is to be treated is a question of the best possible results and the expediency of the proceedings. It is, for instance, not advisable to treat a real neurosis solely with medicaments because the basic process is primarily (but probably not solely) caused by psychic events. It is also not advisable (and not safe) to treat an appendicitis or a tonsillitis psychologically because they are radical and dangerous somatic reactions. (They may also, of course, be an expression of a psychic situation.)

An objective judgment of the prognosis and course of the illness is essential for a relevant therapy of schizophrenia as well as for the delineation of the present stage of the illness.[4] In making such judgments, the "actual" process, the delusional state, and the defective state have to be evaluated. The "actual" process is beset by limitations and seems—at the present stage of science—not suitable for psychotherapy. In certain cases (e.g., acute catatonia) a delay in somatic therapy can be catastrophic.[5] Psychologically seen, the "actual" process appears as a breakdown of the relationships to the world: the mediating faculty of symbolization is lost and life becomes strange and cannot be accepted. The schizophrenic delusion is no longer the touchstone of schizophrenia; on the contrary, this delusion is an attempt to regain the relationship to a strange world, and is actually an affective state reached at this affective pathognomonic phase, but an inflexible and only partial solution.[6] The delusion is an attempt to find new symbols, i.e., new possibilities to encounter the world; but these symbols are poor and appear as a reified reality.[7] The delusion, therefore, is a misleading pathway to self-realization. At this stage psychotherapeutic effort might possibly apply by using

[4] R. Schindler, "Über die grundsätzliche Stellung der Psychotherapie der Psychosen," *Acta psychother.*, 5 (1957), 148-155.

[5] O. H. Arnold, "Untersuchung zur Frage der akuten tödlichen Katatonie," *Wien. Z. f. Nervenheilkunde*, 4 (1949), 386-401, and 2-3 (1951), 235-258; O. H. Arnold and H. Hoff, "Die Therapie der Schizophrenie," *Wien. klin. Wschr.*, 66 (1954), 345-352.

[6] R. Schindler, "Über gesetzmäzige Beziehungen vom Erlebnisinhalt zur Erlebnisform in der Schizophrenie," *Wien. Z. f. Nervenheilkunde*, 10 (1954), 195-230.

[7] I. A. Caruso, "Symbol und Welterfassung," *Jahrb. f. Psychol. u. Psychother.*, 3 (1955), 66-74; "Über die Symbollehre als psychosomatischen Beitrag zur Erkenntnislehre," *Z. f. psycho-som. Med.*, 1 (1955), 307-311.

these affective phases and giving them adequate recognition. Finally, the defective state[8] means a constant but limited relationship to the world; psychotherapeutic efforts might be able to alter this stage to a more dynamic phase of delusion, but this could be dangerous and is probably not economical. In any case, however, the psychotherapeutic treatment must acknowledge delusion in the transference and must operate within this fluctuating relationship.[9] As a whole, the treatment of schizophrenia must avoid any one-sidedness and bias.

As we have already mentioned, the optimal method of treatment should be found, but it is not limited to one exclusive method. Under the social, cultural, economic, and scientific conditions of Middle Europe as they influence life of both patient and therapist, any single psychotherapy would be the exception. In any case, the complete treatment of schizophrenia should be under the responsibility of a physician who should be a specialist in psychiatry. But this does not exclude non-medical psychotherapists, who under the supervision of the psychiatrist may apply the difficult and long-term psychotherapy and may be more experienced in these cases than the physician with whom he is working on the team. Our knowledge of Mrs. M. A. Sechehaye and her method of "symbolic realization" [10] carries the conviction that the psychotherapy of schizophrenia requires specific talents and specific abilities. Under Middle European conditions, however, the individual psychotherapy of schizophrenics can only be a rarity, as it requires too much of the time and energy of the psychotherapist. A significant addition would be such forms of treatment as "bifocal group therapy." [11] This kind of therapy means the greatest engagement of the patient by active analytical transference through a therapeutic group, paralleled by another group which unites the members of the patient's family. The transferences of the pa-

---

[8] We speak not of "defective process" but specifically of "defective state." This is a pathological stability that results after a schizophrenic process and can—but must not—be characterized through certain mental deficiencies.

[9] R. Schindler, "Übertragungsbildung und Übertragungsführung in der Psychotherapie mit Schizophrenen," *Acta psychother.*, 3 (1955—Supplem.), 337-344.

[10] M. A. Sechehaye, *Symbolic Realization* (New York: Internat. Univ. Press, 1951); *Introduction à une psychothérapie des schizophrènes* (Paris: Presses Universitaires de France, 1954).

[11] O. H. Arnold and R. Schindler, "Bifokale Gruppentherapie bei Schizophrenen," *Wien. Z. f. Nervenheilkunde*, 5 (1952), 155-174; R. Schindler, "Bifocal Group Therapy," in J. Masserman and J. Moreno (eds.), *Progress in Psychotherapy*, III (New York: Grune, 1958).

tient depend upon the collective structure of his family, and bifocal group therapy makes it possible to influence therapeutically the original family bonds and focus the permanent conflicts.[12]

In this chapter we shall deal only with the *individual* psychotherapy of schizophrenia. This will enable us to stress one important dynamism, namely, directing the revived delusion to the analyst by means of the transference. We will find that this problem is connected with facilitating the acting out in an optimally symbolized way.

The Case of Astrid Nevran[*]

Astrid Nevran came to us because she suffered from anxiety during the night and had several other "vegetative" complaints (heart stitches, paresthesias, shortness of breath, etc.). She was thirty years of age and a rather robust woman with a dysplastic habitus. Her hairy face ("lady's beard") was remarkable. She seemed restless and strained, and at first walked up and down the room. Only at the end of the first interview did she calm down a little.

Astrid's grandparents and great-grandparents had been farmers. Psychotic or nervous illness was unknown in the family. Astrid's father was a very handsome man, the second of four children. He worked at a hardware factory and was very diligent in his work. He had many affairs with women; he also occasionally liked to drink. He guarded his daughters jealously and was able for a long time to prevent their having love affairs. In the mother's presence he was harsh to Astrid, but otherwise he spoiled her. He died at fifty-seven of heart disease. For Astrid his death was accompanied by intense guilt feelings because she had caused him considerable trouble.

The mother was the fourth of seven children, grew up under poor social conditions, and did not have much parental love. She married her husband more for social reasons than for love. She was reserved throughout her life, never tender or kind, and always anxiously looked after her possessions. She suffered from undetermined irritabilities and in such periods was aggressive and quarrelsome.

The marriage was unhappy from the beginning. There were frequent quarrels and then the mother would run away from home for one

[12] R. Schindler, "Ergebnisse und Erfolge der Gruppenpsychotherapie mit Schizophrenen nach den Methoden der Wiener Klinik," *Wien. Z. f. Nervenheilkunde,* 15 (1958), 250-261.
[*] In all the case histories, the names are pseudonyms.

or two days. Astrid would go with her because she was afraid her mother might harm herself.

Astrid was the third of four children. Her brother was four years older, a sister two years older and another sister one and a half years younger. This sibling position (girl in the middle) is unfavorable for the relationship of child to mother as well as in terms of group position in the family. Astrid was not the nestling nor could she identify with the mother as did the oldest sister. Astrid very soon developed an ambivalent relationship to her brother, who left the family early (he went to the grandparents at the age of six). The elder sister soon began to play the role of the mother of the family. She is now a happy and resolute woman who is always helpful to Astrid. She chose a husband similar to her father: a slightly older, very handsome man who is not always faithful to her. The youngest sister had always been spoiled by the father. Astrid came rather early into a hopeless rivalry with her which Astrid has even now not overcome.

When Astrid was a child the mother was rather exhausted and never had much time for her. The early childhood was shadowed by continuous quarrels between the parents; Astrid always feared they would kill each other. She remembered quite well that because of this fear she once went to her mother's bed, from which her father turned her out with a beating. She reported a frequent occurrence: the mother stood in front of the sleeping children with a knife in her hands shouting, "I'll kill you all and hide you in the dunghill."

In school Astrid was at first a very aggressive and malicious child but later on made good social contacts. She was intelligent and her school achievement was good. When about six or seven years old, she adored an elderly, strict, but correct teacher about whom she still speaks with enthusiasm. One year later she developed a relationship to a female teacher who wanted Astrid to tell her about "forbidden play" (as playing doctor, the nude swimming of the children, etc.). Astrid resisted at first, but later agreed when this teacher wanted to do "funny things" with her. Her ambivalence for sex is supported by an attempt at sexual violence when she was thirteen years old (normal menarche at age twelve). In the following years Astrid was shy and encountered many difficulties in making contacts with other young people. In this she was also hindered by her father. She met Donato (twenty-one years of age, a clerk) when she was seventeen, but she was disgusted by sexual intercourse. One and a half years later she met Donato again. She would have liked to marry him but her father interfered and broke up the relationship. Astrid thereupon fell ill with "influenza." Sometime later she met a "tall and handsome man" in the street who glanced at her with "glowing black eyes." She felt she was hypnotized and was forced to think of him continually. Astrid grew very anxious and she avoided the street in which she had seen the man. She also suffered from alienation experiences, and for a short time from sleep disturbances too. All these events were reported as dreamlike and "magic."

When she was twenty she met a man who became the father of her son Elmar. Without any difficulty Astrid broke this relationship when she learned that he was already married and had a child. Five years later she made the acquaintance of Aram, her present husband. This modest-looking man, fifteen years her senior, offered his assistance, which she gladly accepted in the difficult days after the war. When he offered to marry her, she could not refuse; but she consented against her convictions and against the wishes of her family.

Her husband was the older of two children, but he never could assert himself against his stronger and more vital little brother. He was ambitious, diligent, and became a favored employee. Because of his relative impotence (ejaculatio praecox), and Astrid's aversion to sexual relationships, the marriage was frigid.

Everything went well as long as they were busy equipping their home and attempting to attain a certain standard of living. Astrid felt a void and they often quarreled. Aram did not care for her any more and she began to masturbate. By this time she developed a hysterical-like syndrome for which she went to see one doctor after another. For several years she was treated for a heart neurosis, vegetative dystonia, stomach neurosis, vessel disturbance, and phlebitis migrans. She had a new attack when she consulted Dr. Emo, whom she found, from the beginning, most attractive. One day when she went to see him because of one of her vegetative attacks, the following happened (taken from the patient's protocol): "The doctor was preparing the injection when I suddenly was certain that this was a particular experience which is not allowed. Then I felt funny, began to tremble, and everything was changed. My body was glowing and red all over. My arms did not belong to me and I touched them to feel whether they were still there." Astrid was brought to a psychiatric hospital with the diagnosis of a schizophrenic attack. After discharge some weeks later, she again had attacks of anxiety and fear. Astrid moved to her sister's house. There her brother-in-law took an interest in her and later tried to approach her sexually when the sister was not in. Astrid reacted with vegetative attacks and again came to the clinic. After the second discharge the patient came to us in the state described.

When we first saw Astrid the diagnosis was a schizophrenic defective state (subsiding attack) with the appearance of a hysterical neurosis. Astrid's view of life was a dangerous one because of the neurotic fixations which produced a permanent stress and which included the possibilities of new attacks. It was not our task to remove the neurosis because it may have protected her from a psychosis. It was our aim to get to know her special life attitudes and biases. Knowing this might enable us to correct her wrong view of life. Therefore, we began an analytical therapy (couch, free associations, interpretation of dreams). After an affective crisis had been reached, a somewhat modified technique had to be used.

The Therapy of a Schizophrenic Defective State

In the following we want to give a short sketch of the course of the therapy. In the first four sessions only sexual problems were reported. Rather remarkable was the form in which they were given. She got up, sometimes jumped up, ran up and down, screamed, etc. This acting-out seemed to be demonstratively hysteric, but actually was caused by real fear. In the sixth session she doubted whether she would come again because the therapist had been silent. The content of the interviews became more and more aggressive, revealing the typical fear of psychosis. She was of the opinion that schizophrenia means to kill children. She was unable to think clearly, and depended absolutely on a nurse.

Beginning with the thirteenth session we found a certain transference. Astrid reported that even her mother, who up to then was always seen in dreams and fantasies as "a negative, devouring mother," had been good to sick children. Astrid wanted the protection of the therapist against this evil power; he became the sign of the good mother. In this phase the following observation seems to be important: Astrid used to purse her lips and, turning up the lower lip, she made movements as if she were suckling and gulping. Such movements should be given attention in these cases, where they seem to arise in connection with certain events. In regard to the psychotherapy the "symbolic realization" of Mme. Sechehaye can apply here. In our case it was essential first to relax the neurosis. Therefore the therapist remained consistently passive and, because of this, the patient did not succeed in making a real contact in this phase. She still made attempts but in other ways. She called the therapist "the man of her dreams" (but she also mentioned that she loved him as a son). The expected reaction to this did not occur. His question, "What do you remember in this connection?" became simply another block. In the following hour she compared the therapist with a strict teacher. Then Astrid wanted to know more about her illness. She asked for medical terms, explanation of medical reports, etc. At home she was calmer and able to do more work in the house. Sexually she was still frustrated. Since she had several times said that her doctors looked at her in a "funny way" and invited her "by secret sign" to have sexual relations, it could be expected that this tendency would somehow become manifest in the therapy.

Beginning with the thirty-third session the associations became nearly exclusively sexual. Astrid's reaction to frustration by the therapist was that she felt hypnotized (that she also had the hallucination of genital sensations was discovered only much later). It was a large field within which Astrid was attempting self-realization in a symbolic as well as in a parasymbolic way. (Symbols are signs of real relations of an intersubjective kind—on the same or on a different level of signification. Parasymbols are more subjective signs which do not have the function of creating a real subject-object relation, but serve to maintain a coherence of experienced intrasubjective events.) At the same time Astrid had a "repetition of experience," i.e., the guilt feelings following the hallucinated orgasm caused the therapist to be seen as aggressive and refusing. This father position of the therapist, followed by his being the bad mother, was the reason that Astrid verbalized many indirect aggressions, bringing a certain relief as, of course, the therapist did not react to the hostility. We asked the patient to interpret her behavior; this demand caused a feeling of isolation in her. She felt forsaken by the therapist and went to a doctor who had treated her before. But the same day she telephoned us anxiously, asking for an extra session. In this session she seemed excited and restless. While the therapist was adjusting the table lamp, the shadow of his hand fell on the wall. Astrid stopped talking, had a helpless expression on her face, her respiration became rapid and anxious, and her whole body was stiff and strained. Full of fear she asked: "What was that? I have to find myself." She sat up, looked at the therapist, and said, "What have you done with me? You know that I am willing today, and that is what you have been waiting for." In her protocol of this session Astrid wrote: "I looked at the doctor and felt weak. He finally was succeeding. It could have been world-shaking. He had hypnotized me."

Here we have to stress the following. It was the question of a short event, "an experience with open signification," which could be understood only by her expression and behavior. But it was not followed by a real coherence between subject and object; it had become a delusion. It was important for the therapist not to show fear and, also if possible, not to have fear. In this critical session the patient could be calmed by discussing the occurrence in a relativistic way (it was brought up in relation to other real experiences). The therapist's fear could be found in the protocol of the next session: "He is very active and tries to keep Astrid out of numerous sensitive associations." Contrary to the therapy of the neurosis, it is most important in a psychosis that the ego of the therapist assist as an "auxiliary ego" in cases where the id becomes too powerful and threatens the historical (not the biological) integrity. The transference in the following period swung between positive (the unattainable lover) and negative (the bad and dangerous mother). The primary conflict was thus clarified. The hysteric mechanism disappeared at that time. Astrid said: "Since I have to think so much I have no more complaints." At home Astrid was absolutely calm, a situation produced by the "transference psychosis." But she resisted all endeavors to analyze the transference and reacted to this demand with great fear. The always passive behavior of the therapist made Astrid doubt her hallucinations and enabled her to correct her relation to reality. Beginning with the fifty-sixth session she became more active; she took part in social gatherings and had no more fears of staying alone at home.

In the protocol of the fifty-ninth session she wrote: "The illness is now really left behind. But it is not good that my thoughts are too much engaged with the doctor." In fact she was of the further opinion that the therapist was hypnotizing her and causing "feelings" which kept her away from the illness. It was now most important to get Astrid to abandon this psychotic conviction. As important as the symbolic acting out might be, it was just as important that it be eventually reduced through relating it to other experience. It was essential that the patient find a system in which the reality could be arranged and the fear-provoking occurrences lose their danger. This would enable her to put distance between her and the field of fear and aggression. A further step would be to bring the subjective system to relationship with reality.

After the eightieth session Astrid began to get a certain insight into her own reactions: "I have learned something during the sessions. I am not as good as I thought I am. Probably I have loved myself too much." A little later she wrote: "Probably I love my second self when I love you." The transference became more transparent and certain projections were withdrawn. But the ego was still too weak to bear the whole reality of the id. In the eighty-ninth session she remarked aggressively: "Probably I myself am causing these feelings." Again she wanted love tokens of the therapist. She was not able to renounce her pathological defenses and to use those which were reality oriented. This situation became critical when at this time she gave up all social relationships (to husband, children, friends) and all her libido was directed toward the therapist.

In the ninety-fourth session Astrid seemed to be nervous and highly excited when reporting her nightly occurrences. The protocol of this session noted: "It is awful what happened last night between 11 and 1 o'clock . . . it is not normal. If I had not been wide awake before as well as afterwards I would take it for a dream. It was as if you were with me. One event came after the other in the right order: falling in love, marriage, children; and I was happy. I stood up and lay down again, happy, and immediately went to sleep." The details which Astrid related without much resistance can be omitted. It obviously was a state between a hallucination and daydream. However, it was a fulfillment of wishes that cannot be seen symbolically in its subjective reality but has to be taken as pseudoreality. Psychiatrically this occurrence can be interpreted as an affective illusion because the patient did not have the conviction "you have been with me," but said "it was as if you were with me," and this "as if" means the separation of the process from the personal reaction in the libidinal breakthrough.

After this session Astrid was allowed to sit during therapy. This seemed to us to be necessary because the patient's ego was too weak to stand the pressure of the transference and therefore always attempted to escape into delusion. Astrid explained the above occurrence as the "emanation of an immense desire," but still clung to the conviction that the therapist was transmitting these feelings by hypnosis. In this case the affective illusion was on a delusional basis. Sitting and discussing her problems enabled the patient to rid herself of her fear. The therapist became a real vis-à-vis, although she still misinterpreted his reserved and quiet behavior. But the patient gained more self-reliance. Now the situation at home became more difficult as Astrid gave up her masochistic, pampering attitude toward her husband. He had an operation for ulcus ventriculi eight months after the manifest recovery of Astrid. After the 105th session Astrid had no more complaints and was able to read books, which had not been possible before because of difficulty in concentration.

The son of the patient also reacted to the mother's new-found health by aggression against her and the stepfather. It was now our task to analyze the "altered libido." Eventually it was possible to bring up feelings toward the family. Astrid now became able to verbalize "hypnotic events" and sometimes she even laughed about it. Because her son became more and more difficult she wanted him to be treated by the therapist. Although this request was refused she remained quiet and understanding and sent the boy to another therapist. Beginning with the 110th session the patient began to talk of her new interests. Also her sometimes rather poor social relationships (friends, neighbors) improved. There were now difficulties with the husband, who became frustrated in many of his needs (out of the protocol of the 112th session: "My husband behaves awful. He says: 'Give the good things to the doctor to eat, not me.'"). The sado-masochistic nature of the partnership was now more transparent to Astrid and she offered her husband fewer possibilities for releasing his aggression. His oral sadism turned inward toward himself and in the following months he had to have surgery. But this brought him again close to his wife, who had to provide for an exact diet.

After the 130th session Astrid only came occasionally to talk about problems she was not able to solve herself. In spite of her defect she now was the stabilizing element of the affective and labile family. At this time the children (two in puberty, one younger) began to show psychogenic disorders. But Astrid managed it in a relevant, calm way. She arranged for a better working place for one of the children, and helped prevent the failure of the other in school. She was busy the entire day and realistically handled the deficiencies of her marriage and her goals.

Federn[13] put the question whether it would be possible to start a process and then to cure it psychoanalytically. We don't believe so. Psychoanalysis and analytical psychotherapy are based on the biological sphere but operate on the level of social relations. The technical relation in the therapeutic transference activates the displaced social and individual reactions (and most of all sexuality is—biologically seen— the center of all possible social relations). It seems to us—at least in the

[13] P. Federn, *Ego Psychology and the Psychoses* (New York: Basic Books, 1952).

present case—important that the symbolic and parasymbolic (delusional) events lose their threatening aspects by means of the therapeutic situation. (Fear is caused by the unknown.) Astrid Nevran learned that the existing possibilities for self-realization could not destroy her real world, and in this way the "delusion" could be "related by experience" and the fear disappear. The seeming hypnotic events and the pseudohallucinations became irrelevant. We could not cure Astrid's schizophrenia on the hypothesis of a somatic basis, but she learned to live with it, and her ego became strong enough not to be destroyed by the fear which earlier had followed emotional outbursts and frustration. We don't believe in curing schizophrenia by psychotherapy insofar as schizophrenia is the nosologic totality of a somatic process. But we are of the opinion that analysis and analytical psychotherapy can regulate, through its personal contacts, the subject-object relations. We believe that the ego psychically represents the function of these relations. But being free of fear means also relief of the vegetative and somatic mechanism from the psychical side. Here we have touched on the major point regarding the treatment of the psychoses psychosomatically seen: the totality of the human organism, and of the humane relations, which ultimately means a personalistic anthropology.[14]

THE SYMBOLIC ACTIVATION

In the case reported above, a technique was applied which is largely the technique of classical psychoanalysis. Only with the ninety-fourth session did the analyst change this technique to a more active face-to-face therapy.

We are of the opinion that the technique of treating a psychosis has to be adapted to each specific case, although it is always based on the concepts of psychoanalysis. The psychoanalytic therapy of psychosis should never be applied irregularly or accidentally. Paradoxically, the frustrating reality can be accepted by the patient initially by giving him satisfaction, i.e., he will be able to accept frustration only if he has the possibility of satisfying his needs. We also know quite well that the classical psychoanalysis of the neurosis means a delicate combination of an optimal permissiveness (the verbal release of all pretensions) and an optimal frustration (prohibition of acting out). We find the com-

[14] By "personalistic anthropology" we mean the science of man in his dialectical totality (*Ganzheit*) as physical, social, mental, and psychical being. Eventually one might say instead in English, "science of man," but we are not sure of this.

bination of these two procedures in the analytical psychotherapy of psychosis. Here the possibility of verbalizing is not only provided for but also a certain acting out, in so far as it can be accepted interpersonally. The frustration produced by the psychotherapy is circumscribed by directing the wishes for acting out into a suitably transferred symbolic form. The situation of the therapeutic frustration is to replace a "not possible" acting out by a symbolic and suitable acting out. For example, the patient shall not kill himself or the therapist, or have sexual relations with him. If this is understood it can be seen that the paradox of the treatment of the psychosis is principally a certain "symbolic realization," according to M. A. Sechehaye. It depends upon the knowledge and experience of the therapist to dose the symbolic acting out suitably. Melanie Klein[15] feels that verbalization is the actual aim of all psychoanalytic treatment, even for little children. We don't want to take sides in the differences between the schools of Melanie Klein and Anna Freud, but we have to agree that any activation of psychotherapy (children or psychotics) must consider the specific human ability to understand one's own behavior and to objectify it by verbal definition. But as the libido-pretensions of psychotics are based upon a preverbal state it might be suitable, up to a certain point and for a specific length of time, to refrain from verbalization and to look for a symbolic form of acting out.

To demonstrate such individual exceptions we want to report a case here treated with a less classical technique than was applied in the case of Astrid Nevran.

Mr. Marc Gauss was a diplomatic officer of one of the Allied forces that had occupied Austria in 1945. He came to us in 1946 and was treated until 1957. (There were several interruptions in the treatment.) When the therapy began he was twenty-seven and had been sent to us from the psychiatric clinic of a university with the diagnosis of "schizophrenic defective state." This clinic had proposed electroshock therapy, which had been refused by the patient. It seemed that the patient had his first episode when he was twenty-three years old. (He had always been individualistic and an odd person.) At this time he had to take his final law examination and was also called into the military service. After an ostensible hepatopathy—the diagnosis was hepatitis sine ictero—he was in an acute delirious state, and had hallucinations several times. The center of these hallucinations was his mother and other mem-

---

[15] M. Klein, *The Psychoanalysis of Children* (3rd ed.; London: Hogarth, 1949).

bers of his family. It seems strange that this was diagnosed as cyclo-
thymia in another country and no specific treatment for schizophrenia
was given. The patient soon recovered but became shy and was unable
to work. He felt persecuted and unfavorably influenced by his family
(who lived far away from him). Although he was ambitious and intelligent he had great difficulty in his field of work because he transferred his family difficulties to his professional situation.

Marc Gauss was very inaccessible to psychotherapy. He came regularly to the sessions, but it took months until a somewhat satisfactory relationship could be established. He was silent for hours and although
encouragement was given, he did not speak beyond reporting his past
life briefly. Several attempts to activate the therapy failed. He would not
bring the paintings which the therapist had asked for. One day the therapist proposed that he draw his family, and this was a great success. He
then brought numerous drawings which totaled 7,000 sheets of both
drawings and doodlings. On about 300 sheets there was, seemingly stereotyped, the signature of the patient. This became important during the
treatment, for the patient said that he became related to his own ego by
means of his signature.

There is not the possibility here of giving the details of the long-term
therapy, which actually consisted of the discussion and interpretation of
the paintings and drawings; reporting this would fill a book. In nearly
3,000 of the drawings the patient used his mother as a theme. The second most important person was his father; then came the patient himself; and finally his sister. These persons were not always represented as
they actually were but appeared symbolically as a witch, a prostitute, a
foreign woman, a matron, an officer, a priest, the president of the re-
public, a stationmaster, a little child, a pupil, and so on.

The following may explain the activation of delusional representations leading to the symbolic form of the drawing. In the middle of the
treatment Marc was occupied for months with fantasies about the
"bad" or "poisoned" or "stinking" milk he thought he drank from his
mother's breast. At this time he was exclusively interested in oral fantasies. Hundreds of times he drew the flat breasts of the witch with the
suckling child and, as compensation, the chubby, round, big breasts of
a good mother. He made complicated diagrams involving pseudomathe-
matical formulas to explain the milk supply and its quality. How did
the transference go at this time? First it was dominated by the bad
mother. Marc was particularly aggressive against the analyst, whom he

accused of not sufficiently explaining the psychological situation, etc. (The "milk" of the therapy was bad and scanty.) But eventually the transference imago of the good mother developed. After an especially capricious period Marc became attached to the therapist in an enthusiastic and somehow slightly homosexual way. He was grateful for the patience of the analyst, seemed to be rather dependent on him, and enjoyed every opportunity of talking with him about paintings, etc. By and by a real ambivalence developed. In the therapy Marc began to accept an ambivalent world—a world which is not only bad, but also good. After this he very soon accepted the vicissitudes of the analysis. For example, he now was happy when he found a satisfactory interpretation for a painting without the assistance of the analyst. Several times he even became impatient when the analyst tried to assist in the interpretation.

We can only report a small fragment of the analysis of Marc Gauss. This fragment, however, lasted several months and then only comprised 5 per cent of the painted material. It was a sometimes dramatic period, but only a small part of the immense work that had to be done with him. Activating the delusional representation of the rancid and insufficient milk of the mother seems to us not to be a real redintegration of an event that may have happened analogically during the first months of Marc's life. But we take this activation for an adequate fantasy which represents the psychic reality in a mythological way. It would be naïve to think of it as a causal discovery in a mechanical sense. But actually it is *a symbolical restructuring of a thema which contributed to the development of a psychotic disease.* This symbolization did represent for Marc Gauss a pathogenic frustration which at the same time could be compensated by the symbolic "food" he got from the analyst. Eventually the patient came to realize that his fantasies—there were several others—represented a mythological system. For instance, the remaining oral fixations found their expression in his conviction that the "nourishment difficulties of his early childhood later produced his liver problem," and "the lack of his mother's love caused his fear of reality."

We do not know how this patient went on in life, but there was a remarkable change. When we saw him he had left the subordinate post in the diplomatic service and found an important position of considerable leadership in which he has been successful for five years. Up to a certain point he is still an introverted person, but he finally made contact with women and was able to overcome all complications following his rather late regressions. He is now engaged to a very intelligent and vital woman. The relationship to his parents is, though distant, normalized.

If someone would say that all this could have been attained through a spontaneous remission, we would take exception to it. We can only see how a person actually develops and never know how he would have been developed under other conditions. But we are of the opinion that the knowledge and experience he found by psychoanalysis never would have been attained without it—at least not in such a favorable combination and frequency.

The Optimal Symbolization of Acting Out

As can be seen, our method of psychoanalysis is connected with a certain "activation" of the delusion. The risk of activating the schizophrenic process can be found in both of the above cases and especially in that of Astrid Nevran. Provoking the delusion and leading it to the transference regresses the current conflict with reality to the primordial conflict which originally stimulated restriction of self-realization.[16] Fixation of the delusion on the therapist (transference of the delusion, i.e., "transference psychosis") offers the possibilities of "symbolic realization" with the effect of diminishing fears and feeling of security.

Activation of the delusion supports the acting out up to a certain limit. This seems to be the essential difference to the psychoanalysis of neurosis. But when one looks closely into the matter the difference will not be found to be as radical as first supposed. *The quantitative difference becomes dialectically a difference in quality,* because the rule in a strict psychoanalysis is to cause the projection of the "transference neurosis" to the analyst. Certainly the same rule requires that the patient not be allowed to act out but to *verbalize* his transference (as well as his resistance).

But does verbalizing not mean a kind of symbolic acting out? If I tell a witness all my fantasies—and if I just have to tell everything—this verbalizing contains, as well as compensates for, the acting out in an altered way. But verbalizing merely means keeping the acting out in an optimal state—limited to the verbal situation—suitable for the analysis. And this situation is optimal for the analysis of neurosis because the neurotic transference deals satisfactorily with the reality, and the neurotic

[16] Schindler, "Übertragungsbildung und Übertragungsführung in der Psychotherapie mit Schizophrenen."

person learns to appreciate the reality by the contradiction between the verbal acting out and the actual frustration caused by the deprivation. It therefore *cannot* be said that the strict analysis of neurosis does suppress the acting out from the very beginning. It is a paradox, dialectically seen: the acting out has to be supported in a new, symbolic way by the verbalization. The direct acting out is replaced by the verbal acting out. The symbolic contents of the direct acting out become transferred into words and will be interpreted.

This is the qualitative difference between acting out and verbalization. The interpersonal relationship of the psychomotoric acting-out type is much more unreflected than the verbal relationship. It remains, as Pavlov said, in the stage of the so-called second system of signals. This indirect function is most important for the development and improvement of the ego. Verbalization means that the highest indirect function—that leading to concepts, and which means nearly pure symbols—is applied to express impulsions instead of the more primitive realization through psychomotor patterns. Indirect functions also need energy, but they are a way of getting distance from one's own affect.

The analytical psychotherapy of *psychosis* has the same aim; but here verbalization cannot be obtained as easily as in the therapy of the neurosis. The acting out has to be supported by activating the delusion, but has, if possible, to be led to a symbolic form. This symbolic form need not always be verbal: the psychotic person needs more archaic symbols than concepts. *But any behavior is already a symbol and means at least some confrontation with the world.* The affect can be symbolized by different behaviors, and it is the task of psychotherapy to provide the most suitable and constructive symbolization. We are of the opinion that the basic methodology of M. A. Sechehaye; namely "symbolic realization," means an acting out compared to verbalization, but is still a symbolization and the first step towards verbalization.

In an analysis of a neurotic person an acting out with a symbolic wish fulfillment is possible. Certain motoric expressions, gestures, weeping, and others go in this direction; but sometimes there are also more indicative behaviors. A neurotic patient (with schizoid features) who was treated according to a strict analysis brought the analyst three or four presents, such as an apple he took out of his pocket when he came, or a magazine from abroad (in which the analyst was not at all interested). The analyst each time thanked him briefly and put the gift aside without looking at it. Afterwards, while the patient was lying on the couch the analyst asked him to interpret this behavior. It was, viewed strictly, a real acting out. But in this specific situation the analyst was of the opinion that this acting out did not make the analysis impossible. In fact these simply symbolic actions (they were examples of acting out but in a symbolic way) brought it to the conscious awareness of the patient that for the first time in his life he was fully accepted and that the analyst could be grateful for his gifts.

Such a situation is exceptional in the analysis of neurosis (although we are of the opinion that, contrary to "orthodox" dogma, certain nonverbal activities such as, for instance, painting of unconscious motivations may assist the actual verbalization). Such a situation is not, however, an exception for the analytical psychotherapy of psychosis; there it is the particular rule. But it is important to find the optimum transference of the acting out. The reaction should be the most *suitable* symbolic form and should be made conscious for the patient by its symbolic contents.

The greatest difficulty with acting out is that it can never be "solipsistic"; both the patient and the analyst take part in it. Because analysis means an interpersonal relation, the acting out cannot be purely one sided; acting out means making contacts and altering the situation. For example, our patient Marc Gauss could not tolerate the demands of his military service, which seemed to him intolerable (although they were not so); he asked the analyst to write a letter to his chief requesting amelioration of the delusionally seen difficulties. The analyst promised to write such a letter. For four weeks this letter was thoroughly discussed and interpreted, but after this the patient did not need the letter any more. He now attempted to meet the difficulties involved in his duties in a more realistic way. The acting out that the analyst was asked for in this case had been realized in a symbolic form (the analyst was prepared to protect his patient in the role of the good father against the bad father).

We are not able to discuss in this chapter the specific engagement of the analyst in such a treatment situation. The countertransference in the psychoanalysis of the psychosis, especially in the periods of acting out, is much more profound than in the strict analysis of the neurosis. With P. C. Racamier, we are of the opinion that through the countertransference a great deal of the analyst's anxiety becomes mobilized.[17] As in

---

[17] P. C. Racamier, "Psychothérapie psychanalytique des psychoses," in S. Nacht (ed.), *La Psychanalyse d'aujourd'hui*, II (Paris: Presses Universitaires de France, 1956).

all active therapies it is most important to have the countertransference under control and much more so than in a "normal" analysis. We hope this necessity has been clarified since we insist on the interpersonal essence of the confrontation between analyst and patient.

CHAPTER X

The Evolution of the Mother Transference in Psychotherapy with the Schizophrenic Patient*

Harold F. Searles

RECENTLY I PRESENTED A HYPOTHESIS that deeply denied positive feelings are the most powerful determinants of the relationship between the schizophrenic and his mother, and of the development and maintenance of the patient's illness.[1] To condense that extensive theoretical discussion, I described the mother's poorly integrated personality structure, her fear of her own love for the child, her low self-esteem, and her transference to him of a welter of feelings, consisting basically in thwarted love, from her own childhood relationship with her mother. I traced the consequent frustration of her child's—the patient's—need to give love openly to his mother, and his expressing this love in a therefore disguised, but nonetheless wholehearted, fashion. He sacrifices his potential individuality in a dedicated effort to preserve her precarious integration, through introjecting the dissociated components of her personality, components which become distortedly personified, and in a sense crystallized, in the schizophrenic illness.

The mutual love in the mother-patient relationship is early subjected

* This research was supported by a grant from the Ford Foundation to the Chestnut Lodge Research Institute.
[1] "Positive Feelings in the Relationship Between the Schizophrenic and His Mother," *Int. J. Psychoanal.*, 39 (1958), 569-586.

to so rigorous and unconscious a denial in each participant that its presence is difficult or impossible to discern through history-taking from either of them; nor is it easy to detect in their interaction with one another. I became aware of the presence, and striking intensity, of this love only in the evolution of patients' mother transference to me in the course of intensive psychotherapy conducted in each case over a period of several years.

This chapter is intended, first, to take advantage of the opportunity to present two more case descriptions, buttressing the earlier paper's single case, in support of the above hypothesis, which I regard as the most important insight I have reached in ten years of work with schizoprenic patients, and which stands, as the earlier communication showed, in marked contrast to a voluminous literature on the relationship between the schizophrenic patient and his mother.

Second, these two case descriptions will serve to highlight a number of theoretical and technical points concerning the dynamics and therapy of schizophrenia. Third, they will demonstrate the marked involvement of the therapist's personal feelings, which I regard as an essential component of the recovery process and which, despite younger therapists' guilt and anxiety on this score, is *relatively* infrequently based preponderantly on countertransference in the classical sense. I by no means wish to imply that the therapist can dispense with personal analysis; on the contrary, the degree of feeling involvement required by this work necessitates, in my opinion, that his own analysis be at least well under way before he undertakes intensive psychotherapy with patients of this degree of illness.

These case descriptions are not intended to do justice to the multiplicity of factors which go into the development, maintenance, and resolution of schizophrenic illness. They trace but one theme among many which are of significance and which would have to be included in any comprehensive report of my total experience with either of these patients. For example, I do not attempt to show fully, in either case, the importance of the father transference (although this will be touched on, more than passingly, in the second case); I omit data concerning transference from other early-life figures; and I shall make only a few remarks, at the end of the paper, concerning the *new* interpersonal experience which the therapist brings to the patient, experience which must be of great significance, otherwise the transference could not evolve as I shall describe, and eventually be resolved.

THE FIRST CASE

A twenty-seven-year-old woman, the mother of two children, had been overtly ill with paranoid schizophrenia for at least five years at the time I undertook intensive psychotherapy with her. There was much evidence that she had suffered from latent schizophrenia since about eight or nine years of age. At the age of twenty-four she had finally been hospitalized in a nationally famous institution near her home, but over the course of a year there failed to show even symptomatic improvement, despite psychotherapy, sixty-five insulin coma treatments, and twenty-five to fifty electroshock treatments. She was then transferred to Chestnut Lodge where another therapist on our staff began intensive psychotherapy with her. But he discontinued working with her after fifteen months, discouraged by her adamant opposition to treatment and by the steadily mushrooming, rather than lessening, development of her paranoid delusional system.

At the beginning of my work with her, I found her verbalizing a luxuriantly delusional experience of her life, both past and present, as being saturated with external malevolence. She was genuinely unable, evidently, to recall any experiences of fondness with anyone at any time in her life, and she spent the great bulk of each therapeutic session in paranoid tirades directed toward everyone around her—but, increasingly as time went on, focusing more determinedly upon myself—as being the same malevolent figures who had surrounded her all her life. She incessantly poured out accusations that we were raping her, performing surgical operations on her for various weird purposes, extorting money from her, and maddeningly frustrating her own efforts. She repeatedly vowed murderous revenge; she subjected me to verbal abuse of truly battering intensity; and, as the months went by and she became increasingly sure that I was the malevolent mother who was primarily responsible for the whole venomous "master plan," her aggressiveness had to be met very firmly to dissuade her from physical attacks upon me and other persons. This was her predominant mode of functioning for about the first eight months of our work, and it remained the more or less persistent matrix of the therapeutic interaction for more than two years after that, long after the favorable changes which I shall describe had begun their development.

I acquired from her during those initial eight months, as well as from the history given to us by her youngest sister, a picture of her relationship with her mother as having contained nothing but hostility, fear, and rejection. The sister had told the admitting physician, with considerable shame, that up until the patient's late teens, the mother had beaten her so brutally that it sometimes made the sister nauseated to hear the blows. A younger brother informed us that the mother had "loved to dominate" the patient.

The patient repeatedly described in her therapeutic sessions her mother's having many times punished her by beating her or by locking her in a closet, and having incessantly blamed her for myriad occurrences, telling her harshly, "You're evil!" or "You're crazy!" Whenever the daughter was physically ill, she was given to feel that the illness was a sign of her own sinfulness. Whenever she revealed some of her own confused thoughts, in a search for clarifying information, she was turned away, by others in the family as well as by the mother, with an abrupt "You're crazy!" Innumerable times in her presence her mother would say to one or another member of the family, "She's hopeless—she'll never make it!"; and the patient tried desperately, but always unsuccessfully, to find out from the mother what it was that she, the daughter, was supposed to try to carry out. Whenever she would be taken to a movie by the mother, she would be told at the beginning of the picture, "Now, *think!*" and would then feel herself to be a hopeless failure for not succeeding in perceiving in the picture the same hidden meaning which the mother, who evidently suffered from at least a latent schizophrenia throughout the girl's childhood, perceived in it.

The mother, as I got the picture at this time, incessantly rejected the daughter's femininity and her efforts to identify with the mother. When as a small child she would try to get into her mother's bed the mother would tell her harshly, "Go and get in bed with your father; he can love you," whereas she would accept the patient's siblings. The mother arranged a birthday costume party for the child to which her little girl friends came in dancing costumes, but the patient, as she described it bitterly, had to get her hair cut short and go to the party dressed as a stagehand, in overalls. When one morning the patient awoke to find that she was menstruating, she immediately assumed that it represented the "issue of blood" which the Bible describes as the mark of a guilty person, felt that she literally bore a "curse," and hid in the bathroom all morning and thought of committing suicide.

Much more convincing to me than all this content—not so different, qualitatively, from that which one may obtain from hysterical patients—was the psychotic intensity of the mother-daughter relatedness as it was revealed in the transference relationship. I found every evidence that the often extremely upsetting tirades, of a blaming, hostile, threatening nature, with which the patient castigated me were an accurate sample of the manner in which the mother had treated her throughout her upbringing.

In the ninth month of my work with her, the patient gradually began uttering, especially toward a fellow patient whom she misidentified as the mother who had beaten her in childhood, murderous threats which seriously worried the ward personnel, and in the tenth month, after she had rushed up to this woman and had begun to choke her violently, she was transferred to the maximum-security ward. She was showing a more than usually murderous hostility toward me, also, as a malevolent mother figure in the transference, at that time, and for a week or two I thought of this administrative move as having been necessitated by an intensification of murderous feelings in the transference which had partially overflowed to her ward life.

But then, in reviewing my notes, I found that it had been only eight days before this incident that she had revealed intense tender, solicitous feelings toward a third woman patient on the ward. This woman had just been readmitted to the ward from outpatient status one evening, and the next morning I found my patient red-eyed and on the verge of tears throughout the session, as she had rarely if ever been previously in my experience with her. She told of having stroked the head of this (gray-haired) woman as the latter was lying on a couch in the living room. Although she disclaimed, with great anxiety, that she had felt any fondness or solicitude toward the woman, such feelings permeated her voice as she described the incident. I now realized in retrospect that the increased disturbance which had necessitated my patient's transfer to the maximum-security ward had stemmed not from a purely de-repressed murderous feeling alone, but rather from de-repressed *ambivalent*—tender and solicitous, as well as murderous—feelings traceable to her early relationship with her mother.[2]

She remained on the maximum-security ward for slightly more than one year. During this period a great deal was achieved in the therapy, in terms of further de-repression of her ambivalent feelings—about, most importantly, her mother—with the consequent releasing of intense,

---

[2] R. C. Bak, "The Schizophrenic Defence Against Aggression," *Int. J. Psychoanal.*, 35 (1954), 129-134 states that schizophrenic regression is a defense against aggression. On the basis of such clinical experiences as that described above, I have developed the impression that it is a defense against not aggression alone but overwhelming *ambivalence*.

long-repressed feelings of grief and loss.[3] A few weeks after her arrival on that ward a nurse's report contained the following item about this woman who had long been bellowing her denial that any such thing as love exists in the world: ". . . told Dorothy [another patient similar in age and similar, also, in being a mother] about 'love' tonight. Then abruptly ended by saying, 'There is no such thing as love. What am I talking about?' "

For the first time, now, since her admission to the hospital she began crying openly and wept a great deal both during her sessions with me and at other times. Her insults toward me now took on, at times, a friendly, teasing quality. During one hour, near the end of the tenth month of our work, we laughed together at her joking, not entirely inaccurate characterization of me as a "Briggs ham"; and at the end of the session, as I walked up the corridor, she called after me in the friendliest departure we had experienced thus far, "I must say, Dr. Searles, that your sense of humor is improving." During the course of this same hour she had reminisced about "one of the fathers" in unprecedentedly friendly terms, saying at one point, "That one really is my father," definitely and with much feeling.[4] Heretofore she had denied ever having any real parents, and she continued for years to think of her parents— as of all other individual persons in her past and present life—as being multiple persons. It is noteworthy that it was to require years of further therapy before she could become aware of equally clear-cut feelings of fondness toward her mother.

For many months, however, her overt emotional expressions were more often than not ones of intense hostility. But I counted it a landmark in therapy when in the thirteenth month of our work she became able to regard me, for whole sessions at a time, as being a thoroughly malevolent mother; the therapeutic relationship had not been strong enough, before, to withstand the degree of hostility which she now ventilated. My therapeutic conception of such a development was, and had long been, different from that of many therapists who feel it necessary in working with a paranoid patient to try somehow to avoid getting into the position of an evil delusional figure in the patient's eyes. Hand in hand with this development came equally intense and evidently newly

[3] I have presented elsewhere ("The Psychodynamics of Vengefulness," *Psychiatry*, 19 [1956], 31-39) data showing that paranoid vindictiveness is founded, in part, upon repressed grief and separation anxiety.

[4] This reference to her father, and the accompanying hints of a positive father transference at this point, show how artificial must be my present endeavor to trace the course of the *mother* transference alone.

de-repressed depths of fondness, tenderness, and solicitude toward me as well as toward various women patients on the ward whom she often regarded as being, like me, literally the "mothers" from her past. It became more and more obvious now that her hostility, no matter how intense and at times genuinely dangerous, was in the nature of an unconscious denial of fondness. For example, in this same month, after she made venomous threats for weeks toward a patient named Alice, whom my patient seemed particularly to fear and hate, she became able to confide to me, "There is one Alice that I like." During this same month she brought out in the sessions many touching, indirect expressions of her dependency upon me and her unconscious wishes to marry me.

In the fifteenth month there came for the first time a description from her of some childhood interaction with her mother which clearly revealed a deep fondness between her mother and herself; fondness which she as a child had concealed behind an insolent kind of defiance, and which the mother had concealed behind harsh and scathingly condemnatory words toward the daughter, and the existence of which the patient had still to deny unconsciously. The content of the dialogue she quoted was much like that which I had heard from her many times before, but this time the feeling-tone was one of obvious fondness. At the end of the hour, she demanded, in her usual paranoid fashion, why she was having to cry all night long. "Is it because the [Baptist] Church requires it?" she demanded loudly and castigatingly. I replied, gently, "No—it's because you miss your home and your mother so much; you've made that clear to me today beyond a doubt." Whereas a few months before such a statement would have brought a most venomous tirade from her, she now did not deny what I had said.

By the eighteenth month, our relationship had become predominantly one of intense, mutual fondness of a mother-child sort. I consciously adored her, perceiving her varyingly as an adorable childlike person, and as an omnipotent mother. For her part, she evidenced toward me a comparable adoration, which she always denied and expressed somewhat indirectly. Whether exhibiting deeply dependent or maternal fondness toward me, she had to pooh-pooh the existence of such feelings in herself. She revealed her loneliness in a most touching way: she had long voiced the delusion that "they" literally turn people into bugs, but now she went ahead to make out a case for the desirability, instead, of "their" turning bugs into people. "Then," she said poignantly, "a person could take a bug and turn it into a person and then they'd have something to call their own."

This same period yielded many useful results in terms of her realizing how intensely she had yearned to be literally at one with another person and, now, how impossible of fulfillment is such a desire. In spontaneously ruminating about the possibility of her ever having someone of her very own, in this sense of genuine psychological oneness, she said that even though one turned a bug into a child and brought the child up and married him, "there would still be hatred." As she was saying these things, she was extending her arms as if embracing a beloved person. She listened with open interest to my response, "Yes, if you try to hold anyone too close, they will hate you, and you will hate them as well." She was able to tolerate a good deal of exploration of her fantasied omnipotence, a broad subject so integrally related to her long-held conviction that a mother and child can be truly at one with each other. Whereas earlier she had threatened me with physical assault when I had tried to question some of her concepts of mothering, now she listened with interest to my views.

In this same month and in the following (nineteenth) one, I had the impression that she was very near to being *conscious* of her fondness for me, as being—so she evidently perceived me at these times of apparent conscious fondness—literally her own beloved child. She berated me a great deal in a bellowing voice, called me a "degenerate," "stupid," and complained loud and long of having to do this "baby sitting"; but there was so much fondness in her tone that many times I could not help laughing happily, basking in this fondness while she was ostensibly insulting and browbeating me. She interpreted my laughing as a sure indication of my unrepentant malevolence, and found in it food for more of this ostensible vilification. There were times when I felt nearly overwhelmed by the intense fondness, with sexual components, which the interaction with her called up within me, and I found abundant evidence that what I was experiencing at her hands was a precise replica of much that she had experienced in childhood at the hands of her mother, who had untiringly "castigated" the daughter in just this same way. It was in this (nineteenth) month that we reached a consensus that she had long felt, and still felt, required to keep a kind of steel wall around her fond feelings; previously, she had denied adamantly that any such feelings existed within her toward anyone.

But I could not long forget that her intense *ambivalence* had yet to be resolved.[5] Later in this same (nineteenth) month, for example, on

[5] It is not only theoretically sound but technically useful to conceive of ambivalence as a primitive defense against the overwhelming intensity of the

one occasion she subjected me to such a prolonged, savage raging that I became filled with panic lest, if I did not get out of the room and if she kept up this raging much longer, I lose control of myself and kill her. I managed to hold on until the end of that session, and before our next session took place she had succeeded in temporarily decompressing our relationship by getting into some relatively harmless acting out, in a way which enabled her to release a good deal of this steam.

Late in this (nineteenth) month, I saw unfolding, in her previously malignant, pathological delusional thinking, a charming, playful quality. For example, concerning another female patient whom she had previously misidentified as being some really sinister person, now in a spirit of childlike pretending she termed this woman a Vietnamese soldier. This was at the time of the warfare in Indonesia, and the patient revealed, here, a healthy, childlike pretending that she was in the midst of this exciting, much-publicized situation. Over these same several weeks I heard from her unprecedentedly realistic and friendly descriptions of her marital family life with her husband and children, and of her psychotherapy, during the first year of her hospitalization elsewhere, with a female therapist. She made clear to me that her mother had imbued her with the conviction that she—the patient—had a life mission to fulfill, of some indefinable sort, as a lieutenant of the mother;[6] and she made clear that in her own experience as a mother she had felt it necessary to protect her children from her own genuine maternal love feelings. I found, also, a number of extremely moving indications that she had felt it necessary to remove herself, via hospitalization, from the lives of her children in an effort to protect them from the psychosis-transmitting effect upon them of her presence in the home.

In the twenty-first month, for a period of about two weeks, there reappeared in full force the hostile side of her ambivalent feelings toward me as a mother figure in the transference. She literally reacted to me as

---

love which characterizes the preambivalent phase of infancy—overwhelming, in these abnormal instances, to the mother and, as a result, to the infant also.

[6] I have found evidence, not only here but in a number of other cases, that the paranoid patient's "mission" consists, basically, in a striving to convince the world that his mother's distorted and largely dissociated (or at least poorly integrated) views are valid. This is all part of his effort to protect both her, and himself, from the recognition that these views are tragically inappropriate, "crazy." (For an extensive theoretical exposition along this line, see L. B. Hill, *Psychotherapeutic Intervention in Schizophrenia* [Chicago: Univ. Chicago Press, 1955]).

being a murderous woman who had killed my husband and was determined to kill her, and she showed such a terrible fixity in her paranoid delusions that, for the first time, I felt deeply discouraged as well as anxious in the face of her tirading. But then, when we had weathered this, unprecedentedly intense grief emerged with regard to rejections which she had suffered at the hands of her husband; in this, he was described in terms which were identical with those she had employed in telling, earlier in the therapy, of her mother's rejections of her.

And so it went, in the subsequent many months of the therapy, with the ventilation and exploration of her ambivalent feelings toward me as a mother figure constituting the most important thread in the continuing work. The fondness became gradually more sustained until the hostility which for so long had been the predominant theme became limited to briefer and briefer episodes. For a long time still, however, this hostility was a formidable element. There was an occasion in the thirty-seventh month when, in response to her raging insults, I again felt great anxiety lest I lose control of myself and kill her; and there was more than one occasion late in the therapy when I felt beaten by her verbal battering to a kind of hurt and helpless pulp, much the way she may have felt after the physical beatings she had received from her mother. On the occasion of the incident in the thirty-seventh month which I mentioned, the intense ambivalence between us again spilled over to her "extra-analytic" life: she became disturbed in the evening and bit one of the nurses on a breast; then, while in a cold wet sheet pack later that evening, she twice asked for, and received, a kiss from another nurse. The latter nurse, telling me of that incident, had been amazed at the tenderness and dependency which the patient had revealed, and enthusiastically termed the patient "a different person" from the hostile and suspicious person she had been a year previously.[7]

By the end of the third year of our work, I was finding myself deeply moved at seeing how full of love this woman was, not only toward me (as, predominantly, a mother figure in the transference) but also to-

---

[7] H. Stierlin, in a paper to be published entitled, "Psychotherapy of Schizophrenics and Its Repercussions in the Hospital Structure," has pointed out that such a temporary splitting (or diffusion) of the transference, such a diverting of it to persons other than the therapist, has a constructive aspect in terms of the preservation of the patient-therapist relationship. Ideally, perhaps, such occurrences should never transpire; but any therapist's tolerance of anxiety has some limit, and the schizophrenic patient's ambivalence may be, at times, too intense for him—the therapist—to bear in a persistently sharply focused state.

ward people in general, including various patients whom she had long vilified.

At the end of the third year, also, I began to see evidence that her long-standing and severe ego splits were in part a function of a powerful striving on her part to help other persons to become better integrated, even at the expense of her own psychological wholeness. For example, in one session, the patient, who had long been exercising her ability as an artist, set about helping me to draw in an uninhibited, imaginative way. Finding me more than a little inhibited, she spoke of the efforts she had made in childhood to help "one of my so-called brothers" to become "integrated" so that he could express the artistic talent which, from various indications, she knew that he possessed. She let me know that she had felt great distress and frustration at finding herself unable to help him overcome his "pathetic" inability to give free rein to his imagination. She did not demur when I commented that I had never realized how hard she had tried, probably all along, to help other persons become integrated. I began to get the hunch that her highly imaginative delusions, involving an extreme degree of ego fragmentation, had been partially in the service of an effort to help other persons whom she perceived as being tragically inhibited, helplessly cut off from *joie de vivre* (a phrase she herself used), to become at one with themselves and thus more participative in living.

Three months later (thirty-ninth month), there emerged further data along this line. When I came to her room for the session, I found her weeping, clutching her chest, and shrieking in unmistakable agony. She demanded to know whether we had taken her heart out. To my great relief, she was able within a few minutes to bring out some data which helped to explain what this was about. She told me that she had just come back from a trip to the local drugstore with a student nurse. While she was eating a sandwich at the lunch counter, "There was a man sitting nearby who looked as though he needed a heart. What did they *do?* Did they take me outside and take my heart out?" she demanded, in great anxiety and pain. She had noticed that next to the man sat a woman whom she considered to look like an utterly unfeeling, social-climbing clubwoman, and the patient evidently had more than half suspected that this woman had somehow taken out the man's heart. She told me, further, that while on the way back from the drugstore, "I thought, 'Don't I have a heart?'" Thus the chest pain had been precipitated.

Although there are clear hints here of unconscious guilt, what had impressed me particularly had been her tone while describing, in some detail, that suffering man in the drug store: she spoke with deep compassion in her voice, giving me to understand that she had regarded him as a fellow sufferer toward whom she had experienced a helpless, anguished yearning to bring him relief. Although she scoffingly dismissed my suggestion that her "heart had gone out to" the man in the drugstore in his suffering, I noticed that at the height of her agonized weeping and shrieking she said, "This is just the way I felt all the time I was at Twin Elms Farm!" [during her childhood]. She went on, with encouragement from me, to say that there had been a person there who had complained of heart trouble and would take a drink to relieve it, but that she knew all along that he didn't really have heart trouble—knew that he was really "a hard-boiled wool-puller" like the woman in the drugstore. The impression I developed was that she had had to repress, and was still having to repress, much of her desire to dedicate herself to the welfare of that person in childhood. As nearly as I could determine, that person consisted in the mother whom she loved, and the hard-boiled person was the mother whom she hated. I had learned long ago that she referred to her mother, more often than not, as "he."

Further confirmation of this reasoning came during the forty-fourth month when there came to light a long-hidden (genuinely repressed, I believe) loyalty to her first therapist, a woman whom the patient described in terms identical with those she had used to describe "the so-called mothers." I now realized something of the extent to which she had been carrying the torch for that therapist and for, at a deeper level, her mother. Also, she now described aspects of her mother's personality of which I had not heard before: she gave me a picture of the mother as being not so much a malignantly powerful figure, as, rather, an insecure recluse with many naïvely inappropriate conceptions of the outside world. This description tallied rather well with that given me by an older cousin who had lived near the patient's home during her upbringing; he described the mother as being considered by all who knew her an eccentric, socially withdrawn person. In this same (forty-fourth) month she expressed for the first time memories of having suspected that her mother was psychotic: "I thought she was hallucinating, and she'd tell me, 'You're evil!'" And when she referred to "the people who used me throughout the Hoover Administration and the Second World War [periods coinciding, respectively, with her early childhood and with the onset of her overt psychosis in adulthood] to represent the confusion of ideologies, to amalgamate thinking," she was revealing, I felt, that her delusional thinking was based partly on an unconscious *effort to* foster the amalgamation, the personal integration, of the other family members in a home which was indeed full of personality difficulties and paradoxical behavior.

In one of these sessions she, who for years had been convinced—and for many months yet was to remain convinced—that trees are persons who have been transformed, tragically, into trees, recalled a childhood incident which constituted one of the sources, I felt, of this particular delusion. The family was living on a farm, and they needed some firewood. The patient, as she recounted it, had made a simple and practical suggestion to her mother, "Why don't we get a power saw and cut down the trees [which had died long before] in the orchard?" At this, the mother had gasped and said, "Good heavens, no!" and had shown every indication of being utterly horrified. This reaction of her mother had made the child suspect that the trees must really be persons, for only through some such interpretation could she find her mother's reaction to be a sensible one. This proved to be the first of several detailed accounts of childhood experiences with her mother's highly eccentric and inscrutable reactions which had fostered delusional thinking in the child, who had not been able, and still in the psychotherapy was not fully able, to face the fact of her mother's psychosis. Soon after this it became clear that the patient's own psychosis had been precipitated, in adult life, in a setting in which she was re-experiencing, vis-à-vis her husband, the same kind of intense anxiety, ambivalence, and confusion which she had felt in childhood in her relationship with her mother.

Meanwhile, the patient had been showing impressive progress in other ways. At the end of the second year of our work she had been able to move, for the first time since her hospitalization four and a half years previously, to an unlocked building. By the thirty-seventh month, although still having to maintain denial mechanisms against her dependency upon me, she was clearly revealing, through misidentifications of myriad persons as being me, that she unconsciously felt me to have a godlike importance to her; it was as though she succeeded in avoiding a sense of missing me desperately, between our sessions, only by perceiving me all about her in the guises of various persons on the hospital grounds and in the village. And in the thirty-eighth month, having maintained previously the most adamant resistance against any frank and acknowledged collaboration with me in the psychotherapy, she asked me to give her a schedule of our weekly sessions. It was in the same month that for the first time she used the phrase "my friends" in recounting some incidents from her past—used it in a tone which made me realize beyond doubt that this woman who for years had violently denied that she had ever known the friendship of anyone, had really had friends. Now, too, came clear-cut evidence that she had been her mother's *favorite* child to such an extent that she had always feared her siblings' envy and had therefore had to stress the black side of her trips to the movies with her mother—trips which, it now became clear, had been by no means devoid of pleasurable aspects.

In the forty-fifth month she began reacting to me as having a head which was not my own and expressing this in such a way that I felt intensely anxious. In a session a few days later, she expressed a confused, anxious semiconviction that the building in which she was housed consisted, in actuality, of the disjointed fragments of a human female body, and I found that she had packed all her belongings to flee "this place" which "is dying." It became clear that she had experienced an identical sense of threat as a child in the family home. And she made known that her fear was that if she did not flee she would be "turned into this building." In this same session she spoke of "smelling a rat" in such a context that it conjured up in my mind the concept of a rat deserting a sinking ship. She continued for several sessions to express her conviction of my being, in essence, anatomically unintegrated; the conviction still concerned the identification of my head.

This was a crucial time in my work with her. I felt that the dying building symbolized her crumbling illness system, but did not realize until later that both the perception of myself as being anatomically unintegrated and of the building as being an anatomically fragmented human being had to do with her coming closer to an awareness of the full depth of the ego fragmentation which had prevailed earlier in her mother and which had long prevailed in herself partially as a result of her having introjected that ego-fragmented mother.

In response to her intensely threatened feeling that she must leave, the administrative psychiatrist suggested that she move to a different room in the same building. Her moving out of the room which she had been occupying for nearly two years to this new room coincided with a marked diminution in her anxiety and an increasing ability to relate to other persons, including myself, on close and friendly terms. Within the first few days after this move, I found her expressing the conviction that she was now in a different building, one in which she felt relatively secure. She asked me in puzzlement, "What is this building? Is this building supposed to be my sister Lucille?" and went from this into fond recollections of pleasurable experiences she had had in past years with this (youngest) sister. Several times in the next few sessions she expressed a puzzled semiconviction that the building, or the room itself, was composed literally of the body of this sister, and the patient evidently felt warm and sheltered in proportion as she was convinced of this. Not until a week or two later did it dawn on me that this move had symbolized a shift from her identifying, heretofore, with her loyally-clung-to, but considerably ego-fragmented, mother to her identifying now with this sister, who in reality was a much better integrated person than the mother and whose visits, letters, and gifts were playing an increasingly valuable part in the patient's recovery.

Six weeks later (forty-fifth month) there emerged from her almost incredibly intense feelings (though still indirectly expressed and denied by her) of cherishing and adoring me, and simultaneously came a marked shift in her self-regard, from a former self-loathing to a perception of herself as genuinely precious. All this was expressed in bodily terms. She asked, looking at me, "Is that my body you have?" in the intimately possessive way in which a person regards a beloved sexual partner. She went on to express an almost complete conviction that my body had indeed once been hers, and went on to say that "back when I had a [i.e., that] healthy body . . . they could make rubies out of my blood, and amethysts out of my saliva. . . ." All this was said in such a tone, and with such additional verbal communications, that I felt admired in the most glowing way one could imagine. There was much evidence that she was reacting to me here again as a mother figure—but a mother figure now who was not threateningly fragmented but adorably and beautifully whole. Later in this same day a colleague expressed to me his amazement and enthusiasm at having found during a hospital party that morning how warm and friendly and relatively rational this woman had been while having a lengthy conversation with him.

Space does not permit me to describe the subsequent and increasingly favorable course of her psychotherapy. In essence, with the transference evolution which I have traced here, she was now solidly on the road to recovery from an illness which at the beginning of our work had presented, by reason of its depth and chronicity, an unusually formidable therapeutic task.

THE SECOND CASE

One of the points of incidental interest in this second clinical example is the unusually clear role of displacement of positive feeling on the part of the patient—from mother to father. The case reported in my earlier paper also showed this phenomenon conspicuously, and it has been frequent in my experience that the schizophrenic patient's deeply repressed love for the mother is hidden thus, behind an openly expressed adoration for a father who prides himself upon being both father and mother to the patient, while the actual mother remains—to *outward* appearances—rather off the scene.

This woman, thirty-five years of age at the time of her transfer to Chestnut Lodge, had been suffering from overt schizophrenia, with paranoid and hebephrenic features, for five years. She had been hospitalized on four occasions during this period, for time spans of a few months to one year; had received a total of 175 insulin coma treatments and an indeterminate number of electroshock treatments; had been engaged in sporadic psychotherapy throughout these five years; and had been sent to the Lodge for a two-month trial of intensive psychotherapy as a last measure to avoid her being subjected to a prefrontal lobotomy which had been recommended by a number of psychiatrists. She had failed—primarily because of her insidiously developing mental illness —to complete high school and her background was grossly deficient, too, in the acquisition of ordinary social skills. A battery of psychological tests given upon her admission here showed evidence that schizophrenia had "engulfed very large areas of the personality," with unusually great—even for this hospital—impairment of her intellectual functioning. Her full-scale I.Q. (measured by the Wechsler-Bellevue) was only 77.

Her relationship with her mother seemed, at the outset of my work with the patient and for several months thereafter, to have been devoid of love on the part of either person toward the other. Her father, who was indicated by all the family members (including the patient's only sibling, a sister two years younger) to have always been the patient's idol, told the admitting psychiatrist, "Her mother never knew where she stood with Martha; I always felt I did." He told me later that his mother —who had lived in a nearby village throughout the patient's upbringing—had warned him that if Martha's mother didn't stop treating the girl so strictly and critically, "she will wind up in a mental hospital." He obviously blamed his wife for Martha's illness, telling how punitive his wife had always been toward her, for example, by not letting the girl go to the movies for a week when she had done something which had displeased the mother. The sister, in a visit one year after the patient's admission, told me, "There has always been some antagonism between my mother and Martha," going on to describe the patient as having been always disrespectful to the mother.

Throughout her childhood and adolescence the girl had been much attached to her father, to her paternal grandmother, and to a nursemaid, while treating the mother with open antagonism and disdain. When she would repeatedly taunt her mother with the question, "How did *you* ever manage to get a man like Daddy?" the mother would slap her face; but otherwise the mother seemed to accept a thoroughly scorned, Cinderella role in her own household, being treated with open contempt by Martha and the husband and finding only one ally: the younger daughter. This sibling, who had evidently adopted many of her mother's views and personality traits (as I saw in successive interviews with the two women), fared much more successfully than the patient—attended college, had a number of boy friends, worked capably at a job, got married and had children, and never became mentally ill.

As the patient went into her teens her open antagonism toward her mother increased, and she now became violently competitive with her sister, toward whom there had earlier been at least a fair measure of fondness. As her psychosis became overt, she finally picked up a hammer and threatened to kill her mother with it, and repeatedly made murderous threats to her sister ("I'll get you in the back when you're not looking") which the sister found reason to regard very seriously. Even some years after the patient's hospitalization here, the sister frankly expressed her fear of the patient's aggression, and the mother similarly continued to react in an acutely threatened fashion to any indication that the patient might be considered by the hospital staff sufficiently well to attempt a visit at home.

Throughout the first two years of her stay at the Lodge, the patient acquiesced to see her father during his periodic visits, but flatly refused to see her mother and showed intense fear and agitation at any suggestion of her mother's visiting her. During this time, although she referred frequently to past experiences with her father and her sister, she seldom spoke of her mother. In a psychotherapeutic session six weeks after her arrival here, she said, "I don't care for my family. I liked my grandmother. I used to care for my father," without mentioning her mother or sister.

Within the first two months of our work, she made clear that she had become disillusioned with her father upon finding unmistakable evidence that he had coached her in golf—the one area of living where she had achieved really notable success—not primarily as an expression of genuine interest in her but rather so that she would serve as an instrument to his own greater glory. She spoke of him still at times, however, with respect and even adulation. For many months, though, she devoted most of her time to ruminating about two men with whom she was autistically in love: a young man in her home city, Eddie Wilson, whom she had been idolizing for years, and, secondly, Dr. Jones, the psychiatrist on our staff who had admitted her here and who served as her psychiatric administrator for the first few months of what proved to be her unusually long hospitalization.

Concerning each of these three men (her father and the other two) she spoke in much the same terms, evidently perceiving each as being an omnipotent father figure, and she frequently wrote letters addressed to a composite delusional figure comprised of all three as well as various additional father persons.

Within a few weeks she had settled into a pattern which endured for nearly four years—a pattern of idolizing Dr. Jones and, to a lesser extent, her father and Eddie Wilson; and treating me and the nurses and her mother as though we were the dirt beneath her feet, or as though often we simply did not exist.

There were occasional hints, even within the first few months of the hospitalization, that she was reacting to me as a mother figure whose importance to her was not insignificant but rather was being subjected to a vigorous unconscious denial, and that her so-conspicuous infatuation with the father figure, Dr. Jones, was at least in part a function of this need to deny the importance of the mother. Despite this I was cold-shouldered by her so persistently that my own feelings for her became, as I realized subsequently, subjected to a reactive denial. After the first few months of our work I mainly felt a sense of chronic irritation, dissatisfaction, scorn, and disinterest toward her, and tolerated with Olympian detachment her so conspicuously preferring my colleague to me.

It was in the eighteenth month of our work and at a time when she was now practically mute, disheveled, and continuing to exhibit the extremely bizarre behavior which was to keep her on a disturbed ward for a total of four years, that I suddenly became aware, with astonishment and very considerable anxiety, of feelings of adoration toward her and fantasies of being married to her.[8] With considerable anxiety and embarrassment I reported these personal feelings in a staff confer-

---

[8] I have discussed such aspects of the patient-therapist relationship in a recent paper, "Oedipal Love in the Countertransference," *Int. J. Psychoanal.*, 40 (1959), 180-190.

ence which took place about two months later, and was relieved and strengthened to find that my colleagues did not abhor or despise me because of my having such reactions to the patient, and a few months later still (at the end of the first two years of the work) I began seeing with increasing clarity that I was far more important to the *patient* than either of us had been able to acknowledge previously. The nature of the patient's transference now became quite clear to me so that, although this transference denial of my importance was still far from resolution, I could now consciously invest much deeper feelings in our relationship without loss of self-esteem or intolerable jealousy when she conspicuously continued to show a doglike worshiping of my colleague and to act as though I were of less importance than a dog to her.

We had a long road yet before she became able to acknowledge consciously either my importance to her or her mother's importance. In the twenty-fifth month of the therapy, for instance, when I made some mention of her mother, she replied with utter coldness, "I have no mother . . . ," referred to her mother still only sporadically and impersonally now as "Mrs. Kennedy," [9] and on one occasion in this month while using my telephone to call her mother (her first conversation with her mother, to my knowledge, in about three years), spoke to her mother in a loud, flat, impersonal voice as if to a maid who has the status of a nonperson in a household, ordering her to go out and buy and send to her *"three dark red, seductive-looking* dresses." I had stepped out into the corridor and closed my door before this conversation started, but could not avoid hearing the patient's strident voice and getting every impression, as later information from the parents substantiated, that the mother meekly acquiesced to—and actually solicited—this kind of scornful treatment from the patient.

By the end of four years of work, when she was finally able to move to a ward for undisturbed patients (though still in a locked building), she had become appreciably freer in revealing fond feelings toward me, toward certain of the nurses and some of the other female patients, although not able as yet to divulge any fond memories about, or fond interest currently in, her mother. A little less than one year later (now at the end of four and three-quarters years of work) my patient, who throughout these years had been manifesting deep confusion as to her sexual identity—she had consistently referred to herself as "a girl" but had misidentified other persons on innumerable occasions in terms of a projected male-female unconscious image of herself—referred to her-

[9] The patient's surname (pseudonym).

self for the first time in all my experience with her as "a woman." Intense feelings of dependency, loneliness, and grief were now emerging from her in the hours as she began expressing fond memories of transitory acquaintances with various girls and women in the past both at school and in hospitals. Although still maintaining her letter-writing to the tenaciously-clung-to Dr. Jones, she was now addressing these letters in such a fashion as to make clear that they were directed as much to me as to him. In a fit of pique at feeling snubbed by Dr. Jones, she expostulated, "Why, I'd rather be married to a woman!"

By now (just one month short of five years) we had become so consciously, but as yet very shyly, fond of one another that we could not look at each other during the session without our faces revealing this fondness. I recall that I fantasied now, and continued to fantasy for many months thereafter on innumerable occasions during our highly productive hours together, that I was giving suck to her from my breast. This was a highly pleasurable experience free from either anxiety or guilt.

She came to express glowingly libidinized memories of various girl friends, expressive of feelings of adoration and sexual desire which were at least as intense as those she had long expressed, earlier in our work, with regard to various father figures. These included long-repressed feelings of intense interest in the female breast. The nurse in charge of her ward reported that she and the other nurses could now deal with Martha much more constructively than ever before; heretofore, every one of a long series of charge nurses had been in Martha's view a thoroughly rejecting mother figure with whom she had locked horns in endless, unproductive power struggles, maintaining a haughty, demanding demeanor toward the nurse.

By the beginning of the sixth year she had established an obviously friendly pal relationship with another young woman patient, and reported a dream in which they were living together. Her erstwhile offensively grandiose delusions had now come to be expressed in charmingly childlike terms, like the pleasurable fantasies that little girls have of being princesses, and the nurses commented to me upon her looking like a little girl who is trying so hard to be grown up.

In the first month of this sixth year, at a time when she was bringing out evidences of both small-child dependency feelings and genital-sexual feelings toward me, I had, one night, two dreams which show something of the personal pressures I underwent in the course of this derepression of her warm feelings toward me as a mother figure. As a background, it should be mentioned that during her upbringing, whereas there had been an abundance of physical contact between the patient and her father, she had rarely had physical contact with her mother except at times when she succeeded in provoking the mother into slapping her. Similarly, whereas she had literally thrown herself around the neck of Dr. Jones or certain other male colleagues of mine, she was extremely intolerant of any physical contact, however slight, with the nurses or me.

In the first of my two dreams, Martha and I were stroking one another in a free and sexually exciting way. In the second dream I was preparing to have intercourse with my infant daughter; at first I felt some guilt and hesitancy, but then overcame these and was, when the dream ended, in a state of going ahead with this in a conflict-free spirit. I immediately felt, upon awakening, that these two dreams belonged together, and realized that Martha was inspiring much this same combination of feelings in me; one might well term her, at this time, a very sexually exciting infant. I have every reason to think, from subsequent data, that this extraordinary combination of feelings was a measure of the earliness, in Martha's relationship with her mother, of the time at which their fond feelings for one another became subjected to a mutual, rigorous, unconscious denial.

In the next month, Martha made clear in a communication which I found extremely moving that she had long been anxious lest I "drop" her "like a hot potato" because of the embarrassment which she had been causing me over the years by her publicly flaunted contempt for me. This fit exactly with the fact of her mother's having threatened, in indirect ways throughout the patient's upbringing, to "drop you like a hot potato," completely and permanently. In the same session this young woman, who had been hospitalized off and on for the past ten years, and constantly for the past six years, and had shown, of course, a most deep-seated hopelessness for long periods of time, said determinedly, "Some day I'm going to get out of here; I'm going to get people's recognition; and I'm going to be a worthwhile person again!"

Two months later (the fourth month of the sixth year) for the first time she reported a dream in which her mother appeared; also, in her description of this dream she used, for the first time in our work, the phrase "my mother." In the dream her mother was rejecting her, treating her as being of lesser importance than a father figure who also appeared in the dream, and in so doing, Martha said, "She was not a friend of mine." But I clearly felt that this content emphasis on the negative side was of far less significance than were the two positive aspects which I have mentioned. Over a period of several months, in several different sessions she supplied data which clearly portrayed her competitiveness with men for the mother's favor, and I learned that she regarded even the long-idolized Eddie Wilson with basic antagonism as an interloper in her earlier, more deeply cherished relationship with a girl friend whom Eddie had taken away from her. In the middle of this sixth year she reported a dream which symbolically portrayed her having rejected her mother as a person with whom to identify, and her having identified instead with her lonely, isolated father in a way which had been dangerous to herself—processes which, as I by now knew on the basis of abundant information, had actually taken place.

In the first month of the seventh year she moved to an unlocked building. She had become much surer of her identity and was able to be healthily assertive, in a basically unhostile way, toward me as well as toward other persons.

For example, in one session she was reminiscing about one of the several brief jobs she had held, as a salesgirl, between her early hospitalizations. She told of having been informed at the beginning of a week that she was to be fired at the end of that week. "So," she said, matter-of-factly, "I worked to the end of that week." I replied, in an effort to encourage her to express feelings of rejection which I assumed that this incident must have aroused in her, "That must have been tough." She said, "No, it wasn't," in the same matter-of-fact tone. To this I responded with unusual heat and insistence, "Well, *I* should think it must have been *tough*, working there the rest of that week, knowing you'd been fired." At this she pointed out to me, emphatically and directly, "*You're* not *me*," and went on to make clear that she had felt "relieved" while working there the remainder of that week, feeling that the next job she obtained would probably not require her to work as long hours as this one had entailed.

Not long before this I had been surprised to find on awakening one morning that I had had this dream: she and I were riding a tandem bicycle; the bicycle broke down, and Martha took command of the situation, fixed the machine and assumed the driving of it. I had been surprised, that is, at seeing her in a new light, as a competent, self-assured person; this dream had occurred at a time when her confusion, which I have not tried to describe here but which was a most prominent factor throughout all these years, was still very much in evidence.

She also began revealing a rich sense of humor. She showed this, for example, in the course of an hour in which she began doing some quite practical, verbalized ruminating as to how she could obtain a livelihood in the future—commenting that probably she will inherit enough money from her parents so that she won't have to work (quite true), but that the money might not last her all her life (conceivably true), and that, in this latter event, she might then go to a state hospital. I pointed out with some amusement, "You'd have to have a psychiatric illness to get into a state hospital, Martha." To this she replied, emphatically, "If I were in *that* situation I'd *have* a psychiatric illness!"

In the fourth month of the seventh year came relatively clear-cut evidence of her feeling reproachful toward me, as a mother figure, for my having failed to stop her from "running to"—identifying with—the father figure Dr. Jones, and she told in the same session of a motion picture she had seen long ago in which a little girl, out walking in the care of a nursemaid, starts to run across the street to her father and is killed by a passing car; she expressed her feeling that the nursemaid should have stopped the child. There was steadily developing a picture of the father as a remote, isolated, socially insecure individual with whom the patient had identified herself in an attempt to rescue him from his isolation, with, of course, disastrous consequences to herself.

It was becoming clear, too, that the father had long reacted to this girl as being a mother figure, and that he clung to her by, among other methods, undermining her self-confidence by treating her in a chronically belittling way; and undermining her relationship with her mother by showing a chronic derision toward that relationship. I learned, now, of his long-standing fondness for uttering such "witticisms" as "A woman's only a woman but a ten-cent beer's a drink," and "You can tell a lady by the way she picks her nose." Martha had become able by now to show a little of her fondness for her mother—to give a little acknowledgment of her mother's importance to her—by more frequent phone calls in which she asked the mother to buy various sweets and other items of food and send them to her. In an interview which I had with the two parents together and in which the mother sheepishly but fondly spoke about doing these errands for Martha, the father broke in with a cynical laugh, "I know what Martha's up to—she just wants to save allowance money!"

A few months later, during another of their visits to the Lodge, I found that despite Martha's showing (in her diminished confusion, in her improved grooming, and so on) solid evidence of impressive progress, the father expressed an awareness only of the fact that she had refused, on this particular occasion, to go out to dinner with them. He be-

haved exactly like a very small boy who has been disappointed and enraged by a frustrating mother, and it became painfully clear to me that
he was not primarily interested in his daughter's becoming genuinely
well, but rather in her developing to a point at which she would satisfy
his infantile dependency needs. It was in the fourth month of this same
year that Martha provided historical data which clearly indicated that
her own psychosis had become overt just as she was beginning to realize that her father, in whom she had been maintaining such a deep emotional investment after having forsaken her mother very early in life, was
himself a person ridden with fragility and behavioral eccentricities.

As her disillusionment with her father became worked through—
primarily in the transference to me as being a "crazy," depressed, withdrawn father person—there was a further freeing of constructive identifications with her mother, and the development of increasingly positive
relationships with women about her in the hospital.[10] For the first time
one of the nurses found this young woman, who had for so long been
cold, haughty, and demanding toward the ward personnel, to be "sweet"
—as I had often seen her to be in the therapeutic sessions, beginning
about one year previously. Martha now revealed solicitude toward a
woman patient of about her mother's age, and poignantly told of how
at the time of one of her hospitalizations she had been planning to "go
to California to stay at a hotel with my mother [who had been born
and reared in California]" but that—because, she hinted, of the father's
interfering possessiveness toward her mother—she "was sent to ———
[a psychiatric sanitarium] instead." The long-standing displacement of
her transference love for her mother, from me over to Dr. Jones, had
now shifted to the extent that, after telling me of some home-town girl
friend who had blue eyes, she commented, "like your eyes," and then
added, *as an afterthought*, "—and like Dr. Jones' eyes."

Halfway through this seventh year she began revealing feelings of
self-reproach for not having taken better parental care of her mother,
for having let her mother go out dressed in such a fashion as to amount
to her committing social "suicide." Martha recounted this in terms very
similar to those in which she had told me in the first few months of the
therapy of herself having destroyed irretrievably—as she then felt—her
own social standing through indiscreet (actually, psychotic acting-out)

[10] The resolution in the transference of her still more deeply ingrained
introjection of comparably "crazy" aspects of the mother's personality came
much later in our work, at a time when a basically positive mother transference (the achievement of which marks the end of the period covered by
this case description) had long been established.

behavior toward young men. This dovetailed with evidence, which I found in my own contacts with the mother, that the older woman had an astonishingly small-child orientation toward her daughter, reacting with a kind of helpless dependency upon Martha and feeding on the daughter's mother-hen kind of picking at her about her grooming and manners when the two were together.

But there came up in the therapy now, too, feelings of warm admiration on Martha's part toward her mother as displaying a kind of vigorous absorption in earthy, practical things, with an obliviousness toward what Martha and her father regarded as essential niceties of high-society living. In quoting some bluntly outspoken critical assessment which the mother had made about someone outside the family, Martha laughed in a warm, merry way (for the first time in all my experience with her) and said, not with ridicule but with warm admiration, "My mother— she's something!" A few days later she expressed the same kind of admiration for her sister, laughing in this same fashion, and now expressing a regretful wish that she herself could be as uninhibitedly "catty" as her sister (and, I knew also, her mother) had often been. She described her sister's making the "catty" remark in question "with all the vermilionish-ness of life!" Martha, whose liberal use of neologisms I have not tried to describe here, was showing an unusual degree of "vermilionishness of life"—of vigor and *joie de vivre*—in saying this, as a result of this freeing of a constructive identification with her more spontaneous sister and mother.

Over all these years, the most powerful pathological dynamism, or unconscious ego defense, manifested in me as well as in the patient, proved to be the denial of fondness in the mother-child relationship. This denial was predominantly a transference phenomenon which resulted from the mode of relatedness—the mutual denial of fondness— existing in her childhood relationship with her mother. To a lesser extent it was based upon countertransference phenomena traceable to my having experienced a qualitatively similar childhood relationship with my own mother. My personal analysis, which had been completed prior to my work with the first-described patient, had been only half completed at the time I started with this particular woman. This countertransference element was undoubtedly a relatively great hindrance in the first two years of my work with Martha; but for years after my fondness for my mother had become powerfully de-repressed, the denial of mother-child fondness loomed up formidably, time after time, in this particular therapeutic relationship as a measure of the remarkably intense denial which had characterized the relationship in childhood between this profoundly ill woman and her mother. Each time this denial was broken through, I found in myself new depths of fondness for her, and she moved into a stage of fondness-toward-mother which was still a bit deeper than any she had reached before.

Near the end of the seventh year she came to a poignant realization of the finitude of life.[11] She expressed this at first with a kind of child-like, puzzled, protesting refusal-to-believe—not very different, probably, from some of the feelings which any human being finds in his heart as he comes face to face with this transcendental fact of his existence. But the most memorable thing of all was her expressing this—as I was both astonished and deeply moved to find—in terms of a readiness to sacrifice herself, to consecrate herself, so that scientists could overcome this barrier which, she now realized, stood between her fellow human beings and immortal life. I am paraphrasing her own words which in actuality were doubly moving because of the groping, fragmentary, neologistic manner in which she expressed them. She wondered why "they don't take blood from me" for this purpose—expressing this wonderment not in a tone of guilty self-reproach, not in any spirit of atonement for past sins, but in a genuine eagerness to dedicate her life's blood toward this supremely worthy human cause.

At one point in this first session in which she began expressing such sentiments, these feelings had clearly to do with her beloved paternal grandmother who had died a few years before Martha's first hospitalization. Seven weeks later—weeks in which the sessions were devoted primarily to this same theme—she brought out these feelings in clear reference to her father, who for many years, during her childhood, had suffered from anxiety about his heart. She asked now, "Why does a person die?—their heart wears out, is that it?" and went on to express a child-like puzzlement and protest as to why "they" don't do something about this problem, why they don't "duplicate" the heart; "a mirror duplicates things," she pointed out. "I *can't* understand it," she said protestingly and frustratedly, and then added something which made me feel like crying: "Why don't they take a child's heart . . . [and, in essence, use that to keep the person alive]?" I asked, as calmly as I could, for I had long ago come to realize that she could express herself relatively freely only if I responded in a calm way to her communications, even the

[11] In a recent paper to be published, "Schizophrenia and the Inevitability of Death," I have discussed schizophrenia as being a defense against—among other types of anxiety—this form of existential anxiety.

most surprising and deeply moving of them, "Wouldn't that be kind of tough for the child, Martha?" She explained then, in a tone of whole-hearted acceptance of the subjective fact of life which she now stated, "It would be born for that purpose. Otherwise it wouldn't be born, I guess." She made clear, further, that she felt that since the child owed its existence to the parent, there would be no reason for the child to feel any protest about this.

In ensuing months she went on to express similarly deep fondness, adoration, and dedication toward her mother, referring to her in a warm, fond tone as "my mother." At times her admiration for the mother was interlarded with expressions of her viewing her mother as be-ing a delightfully impossible or idiotic, endearing child. From my own contact with the mother, I had no doubt that she felt much more com-fortable at being responded to in this latter fashion by Martha than in any openly admiring way. These feelings came, as usual, through the medium of the transference: Martha would laugh in amusement at statements and behavior traits of mine which she evidently found amus-ingly naïve, and at other times let me know, indirectly, that she admired and appreciated her mother-figure therapist as being "very helpful" and "handsome." Interestingly, such open expressions of fondness came in a context of her overtly pressing the Director of Psychotherapy for several weeks for a change of therapists—something which I met with an open-handed, genuine readiness to relinquish her if she were determined to bring this about. Over the years evidence had appeared, recurrently, that her great anxiety was that a fond relationship with her mother would be tantamount to the annihilation of her own individuality; so I thought it no coincidence that these new fruits of psychotherapy were to be won only in a setting of my being able to brave the very real possibility of her leaving me for another therapist.

She had become sufficiently well, near the end of the seventh year, to move to outpatient status, and during the three years which have passed since then she has not required readmission to the hospital.

Discussion

Difficult though it is to discern the nature and progressive evolution of the patient's transference to the therapist, it is even more difficult to conceptualize that which is *new* which the therapist brings into the rela-tionship, and which, as J. MacK. Rioch[12] has emphasized, is crucial to

[12] J. MacK. Rioch, "The Transference Phenomenon in Psychoanalytic Therapy," *Psychiatry,* 6 (1943), 147-156.

the patient's recovery. Rioch is in my opinion quite correct in stating, "Whether intentionally or not, whether conscious of it or not, the analyst does express, day in and day out, subtle or overt evidences of his own personality in relationship to the patient."

I surmise that there is a companion evolution of *reality* relatedness between patient and therapist, concomitant with such a transference evolution as described in each of the above cases. In my work with patients I have repeatedly had the impression that it is only when the reality relatedness between patient and therapist has reached, finally and after many "real life" vicissitudes between them, a depth of intense fondness that there now emerges, in the form of a transference development, a comparably intense and long-repressed fondness for the mother.

Presumably a point which Freud [13] made concerning projection also holds true for transference. He stated that projection occurs not "into the sky, so to speak, where there is nothing of the sort already," but rather onto persons who in *reality* possess an attitude qualitatively like that which the projecting person is attributing to them. So it is with transference; we may presume that when a patient comes to react to us as a loved and loving mother, this phase—as well as other phases—of the transference is founded upon our having come to feel, in reality, thus toward him. M. B. Cohen[14] stresses here the importance of the therapist's inevitable feeling response to the patient's transference; and I am suggesting that a second and equally healthy source of the therapist's feeling participation is the evolving reality relatedness which pursues its own course, related to and paralleling, but not fully embraced by, the evolving transference relatedness over the years of the two persons' work together. Of a third root: namely, countertransference (which I showed to be a significant factor in Case 2), much literature has already been written; but as I indicated at the outset, there is a great need for us to become clear about the sequences which the *recovery process* in the schizophrenic adult, very roughly analogous to the growth process in normal infancy, childhood, and adolescence, tends innately to follow. When we have become clearer and surer about this, and particularly about the reality-relatedness element necessary to this, then I believe that frequently—though by no means always—various manifestations of feel-

[13] S. Freud, "Certain Neurotic Mechanisms in Jealousy, Paranoia and Homosexuality," *Collected Papers*, II (New York: Basic, 1959; paper first published in 1922).

[14] M. B. Cohen, "Countertransference and Anxiety," *Psychiatry*, 15 (1952), 231-243.

ing participation by the therapist which in the past have been regarded as unwanted countertransference will be seen to be inevitable, and utterly essential, components of the recovery process.

What are some of these new ingredients of relatedness which the therapist brings into the situation? I shall mention only those which are of most immediate relevancy to my main theme. These lie in the realm of the therapist's acceptance of the deep dependency,[15] including even—at one crucial phase of the work—a symbiotic kind of mutual dependency,[16] which he naturally comes to feel toward the patient; his acceptance of a mutual caring which amounts at times to adoration; and his being able to acknowledge the patient's contribution—inevitable, in successful therapy—to his own (the therapist's) personal integration. In the last-mentioned regard, it is of interest that we find literature concerning the importance, for the patient's recovery, of his forming constructive, enduring identifications with the therapist, and the therapist's empathic experiencing of momentary identifications with the patient as a means of his knowing more clearly in what disturbing feeling experience the patient is now immersed; but so far as I know, there is literally no report anywhere of therapists' forming long-range, constructive identifications with various aspects of patients' personalities.

In conclusion, I want to note that the schizophrenic patient responds with great regularity to the therapist's maternal warmth as being a sure indication that the latter is a homosexual or a Lesbian. The younger therapist needs to become quite clear that this is, in actuality, a formidable resistance in the patient against the very kind of loving mother-infant relatedness which offers the patient his only avenue of salvation from his illness. I do not mean that the therapist should depreciate the degree of anxiety, referable to the deep ambivalence of the patient's early relationship with his mother, which is contained within this resistance. I mean that the therapist's deep-seated doubts as to his own sexual identity—and what person is totally free of such doubts?—should not make him lose sight of the fact that the patient's contempt (or revulsion, or what not) is basically a resistance against going ahead and picking up the threads of the loving infant-mother relatedness which were severed long ago.

[15] H. F. Searles, "Dependency Processes in the Psychotherapy of Schizophrenia," *J. Amer. Psychoanal. Assoc.*, 3 (1955), 19-66.
[16] H. F. Searles, "The Effort to Drive the Other Person Crazy—an Element in the Aetiology and Psychotherapy of Schizophrenia," *Brit. J. Med. Psychol.*, 32 (1959), 1-18.

CHAPTER XI

A Client-Centered Approach to Schizophrenia: First Approximation*

John M. Shlien

> The truth shall make ye free—
> but first it shall make ye
> miserable.
>
> —PROVERB

I N THE COMPLEX and challenging field of psychotherapy with the psychoses, client-centered therapy is a relatively new entry. The orientation now known as "client-centered" and formerly by the less accurate term "nondirective" is itself less than two decades old. Unlike most clinical or therapeutic developments, it has grown up in an academic setting, where its rate of growth and degree of influence has increased enormously in the past several years. Where it was once considered a radical view, it is now accepted as a partial technique and a general attitude by many orientations, and much of the power and originality evident twenty years ago is obscured. Its influence has spread into the guidance and counseling fields, education, religion, sociology, and social work, as

* Prepared under a grant from the Ford Foundation (Psychotherapy Research Program) to the Counseling Center, University of Chicago. I am indebted to many for critical and encouraging discussion of this chapter, especially Drs. Eugene Gendlin, Jacob Getzels, Ann Holloway, Richard Jenney, Carl Rogers, Morris Stein, Alice Wagstaff, Mrs. Hellene Sarett, Miss Julie Klorman, and Mr. Bruce Cushna.

well as industrial and clinical psychology; but it has only recently begun to develop in the field of psychiatry. Carl Rogers, central figure in the development of this orientation, is a psychologist; his main experience, and that of his students, has been outside of medical settings. This has limited our contact with the frankly psychotic, who often may need, or be seen as needing, hospitalization. Thus most of the theory and practice has been applied with patients who would be called neurotic. Rogers once held, in fact, that this form of therapy was not applicable to psychotics.

The situation is changing. Therapists have developed in depth and capacity. As more deeply disturbed clients have been seen and helped, further reaches of maladjustment have been explored. Some of these more deeply disturbed clients had been treated elsewhere by physiological or psychotherapeutic means which failed. Some were seen "inadvertently," beginning, for instance, as moderately anxious maladjusted cases[1] which developed much more severe manifestations as defenses peeled off. Also, client-centered therapists have been called upon to demonstrate in VA and state hospitals whatever contributions they might make in work with "psychotics." (This is a word which we do not yet use with conviction or comfort. It is wrong enough to call a person with diabetes—an established disease entity—"a diabetic." That is far from being all he is. He has diabetes; but when his sugar-insulin balance is normal, so is he, in that dimension. Psychosis may simply represent a mode of *fluctuating* adjustment to a realm of experience within everyone, so that while the existence of "a psychotic *state*" is undeniable by definition, the term "*a* psychotic" is very questionable.) One more influence in this trend deserves mention. A growing number of psychiatrists have taken an active interest in client-centered therapy, usually having invented its rudiments independently, often thinking it most appropriate for their own self-directed personal therapy and wanting to learn more of its spirit and formal elaborations. One over-all mark of this trend is the appointment, a few years ago, of Dr. Rogers as joint professor of psychology and psychiatry at the University of Wisconsin.

The main outcome of this trend is that at present we are engaged in the earnest study of treatment of schizophrenia. Although we cannot speak from extensive experience, intensive experience abounds wherever

[1] There is always a risk that therapy will expose deeper levels of disturbance. The topic of diagnosis seems relevant here; it is a probability statement of such risk, but will be dealt with later.

there is therapeutic contact with the schizophrenic condition. It seems certain that this phase of work will bring about modifications of theory and practice, where they are not confirmed, for no one can face the full individual and social impact of psychotic encounters without a "shaking of the foundations."

As Freud said, "Much is won if we succeed in transforming hysterical misery into common unhappiness." In this chapter we seek to understand the schizophrenic psychosis in more literal terms as an extreme form of an all-too-common unhappiness: self-deceit. What follows is (1) theoretical discussion of the nature of psychosis, (2) a general statement of our therapeutic principles, and (3) a case to illustrate the theory and the therapy.

PSYCHOSIS

Some Fundamental Questions   Within this discussion of psychosis, many basic questions need to be asked. The answers will be incomplete and personal, representing no "official" position because there is none, and having no claim to scientific certainty via research. Still, questions of this order must be asked: What *is* psychosis? The psychotic experience? How can psychotherapy help? What is psychotherapy? Are there psychological laws of behavior that apply to this strange, bizarre, confusing world of the deeply disturbed person?

In this area, the words themselves are vague and insecure and our ignorance so great that we tend in desperation to assume meaning where none exists. Let us recognize that the true nature of psychosis is a mystery. (And the nature of the most prevalent convulsive treatment, electroshock, is called "a mystery within a mystery" by the most authoritative book on the subject.[2]) One of our problems, then, is how to deal with a subject consisting of experience which at its worst is indescribable from the inside and incomprehensible from the outside, and this without using words which are themselves confounding. "Psychosis," for instance, has an authoritative, antiseptic sound, but its real sterility lies mainly in its lack of clear meaning. It simply replaces "madness"—now a literary term—and "insanity"—which represents a dated legal concept. Falling into pseudoscientific conventions of language will not help. At the present stage of knowledge the questions are well enough repre-

[2] P. H. Hoch and L. B. Kalinowsky, *Shock Treatments and Other Somatic Procedures in Psychiatry* (New York: Grune, 1946), p. 242.

sented by asking simply: What does it mean to "lose one's mind"? How can a "lost mind" be recovered?[3]

That which we call "a psychosis" is not a disease. It is a learned behavior,[4] exaggerated to a point of no return, i.e., where control is lost and the exaggeration "takes on a life of its own" temporarily. Because this exaggeration is so overwhelming, so much beyond our ordinary capacity to assimilate, it appears to us that we are no longer dealing with, for instance, ordinary suspicion, but something *quite* different—"paranoia." Then it appears that psychosis is not of the same order, not on the same continuum, as "normal" or "neurotic" behavior. But as psychotic behavior becomes more common it is seen as a form of maladjustment similar in kind to lesser degrees of maladjustment, though so much

---

[3] For that matter, how is the mind developed in the first place? It is our assumption throughout this chapter that "mind" develops and exists beyond brain, and following from this, the assumption of social psychological origin of much mental disturbance. It sounds simple, but there is by no means wholehearted agreement in the field on this issue. Current work on molecular structure and the chemistry of schizophrenia, for instance, challenges psychological assumptions. It is possible, of course, that biochemical methods of treatment will develop actual cures for psychotic states, thus outmoding psychotherapy. No less a therapist than Freud thought so in regard to schizophrenia. Also fashionable are experiments with drugs which induce pseudopsychotic states, which suggest to some that if such states can be caused by chemical means, they can also be cured by chemical means, and further that the mechanism of disturbance is fundamentally biochemical.

Undeniably there is always a biochemical basis for behavior of the human organism. But this does not rule out psychological influence, in either the sickening or the healing process. It is certain that anxiety can cause diarrhea. Chemical mechanism? Surely. And a virus or a laxative might cause the same apparent result, but that would not alter the fact that anxiety, a psychological state, can and does cause diarrhea (as surely as a nonchemical stare may cause someone ten feet away to blush). Nor would it mean, more obviously but no more truly, that even though the eventual chemistry, mechanism, and result are the same, two different causes (laxative and anxiety) are therefore the same. Nor would it mean that an antidote for diarrhea is a specific treatment for *either* anxiety *or* a virus, or that a specific for one is of any use for the other. Similarly, a chemically induced psychotic state may not be a true psychosis even though it has the same appearances in terms of hallucinations and like effects. A chemical antidote for the pseudo-psychosis is not necessarily effective for a true psychosis, even though a chemical mechanism exists in either case. Psychological influence is not eradicated by the artificial imitation of its effects. Even though "tranquilizers" will tranquilize, so will a blow on the head, and neither one is equivalent to, or can deny the existence of, "peace of mind."

[4] "Oh, what a tangled web we weave,/When first we practise to deceive!"
                —Shakespeare

greater in quantity that it seems different in *quality* too. There is one sense, unfortunately, in which it *is* different. A boulder balanced on the edge of a precipice can be pressed ounce by measured ounce toward rolling off. Each ounce is just like the last, but when the quantity of pressure totals to the "breaking point," the quality of the *consequences* changes radically. No longer will the relief or counterpressure of one ounce recover the balance. Even if the boulder is not smashed in the fall, an enormous effort is required to restore the original position. It is because of this effort (which so few can make, and so many need) that it is necessary to prevent the "psychotic situation" in life. The "psychotic situation" is a precondition to the psychotic state, which may or may not follow.

Psychotic Stress

What is the "psychotic situation?" To put it briefly, it is that of *having an impossible life to live.* Here is an example of a prototype of impossibility which is not itself psychotic, and may for that reason give a clearer illustration of the meaning of "an impossible life." A normal young woman had a recurring dream.[5] In it she dwelled in a green, filmy, gurgling underwater world, meeting and working with mermaid-like people, her vision wavering and distorted by the current. In discussion she connected this dream, easily and certainly, with an actual experience in which she and a companion had been swimming across a river. The current was too strong for them, and they could not swim to the beach they had set out for. Instead, they were swept to a slippery and steep place on the bank. The companion managed to pull himself up on some of the rocks, and tried to help the young woman crawl out of the water too. It was too slippery and they were too tired. Their fingers were slimy, as were the rocks, and they lost their handclasp. The young woman slid back into the water, fought, gasped, screamed, got her lungs full of water, perhaps fainted from exhaustion, *knew* she was

[5] This is only an illustration, not intended to imply that psychosis is a waking dream, though that idea is not new, nor necessarily wrong. It may be that the psychotic "unreality" which approximates a dream will yet be best influenced by manipulation of the sleep centers of brain areas which control dreaming. Much research is under way in this field. One researcher finds that waking a person just before measured EEG's indicate the beginning of a dream state will produce hallucinations as do other forms of sensory deprivation. The dream is *like* a psychosis in that it is one way in which this person could live her impossible life.

drowning, and sank. People on the bank heard the screams, formed a human chain, pulled her from the water unconscious, and revived her. What had happened? In a word, she drowned. She lost her life. She experienced death as certainly as one can. It is also true that she was revived and was still alive. In her consciousness there were two thoroughly contradictory conceptions: life and death.

Experience, especially an intense one, demands some sense of completion *if* the person is to have a healthy life. The intense experience cannot be brusquely denied to awareness. This young woman was now in the seemingly peculiar position of having two contradictory lives to lead. She died, and she could not put the consciousness of this together immediately with the other fact that she was living. For a while it was necessary for her to have some expression of the life after death, since death was her intense experience and she was still alive, experiencing being. Eventually some process of integration allowed her to know herself as simply, unquestionably alive, someone who drowned but lived through it. Then she could live as a single self, in relation to this issue at least. But for the time it illustrates in a nonpsychotic way the meaning *"having* to live an impossible life." A significant thing is this: she was able to recall, without shame, her impossible life. It was impossible simply because one cannot easily assimilate the experience of being both alive and dead at the same time. But the impossible life in the psychosis is one which may be built on *many* experiences, and they are permeated with the deepest humiliation. They can hardly be recalled without shame. They are impossible in that one cannot bear to live those experiences, yet must in order to be a complete person.

This comes close to the core of the matter—when there is an impossible life, which involves unbearably painful humiliation, a defense (later called self-deception) develops to deny part of consciousness in such a way that isolation follows, and it is this which leads to a psychotic state (later called self-negation). The "impossible life" does not alone precipitate a break with reality, and a lucky thing that is, since contradictions and irreconcilable opposites are within and around us from childhood on. These contradictions are always reflected in individual reactions, some of which are psychotic, some not. I am acquainted with a Negro "passing" for white. It is precarious, and his choice stems from and carries with it considerable feelings of humiliation and discomfort; yet he has not and is not likely to become psychotic as a result because his choice is deliberate and voluntary. He deals as a white man with other Negroes, knowing perfectly well that he too is a Negro as well as white, and he does so with a calculated cynicism which denies nothing.[6]

A more widespread example is the person who is uncertain of sexual identity, not knowing whether male or female is his or her real status. (The more fortunate of these are contented homosexuals.) This complexity, when severe, is more likely to lead to defenses which have a psychotic consequence. Indeed, considerable clinical literature, chiefly psychoanalytic, asserts that paranoid types of schizophrenia always suffer from inadequate sexual identity. Not only is there shame or humiliation attached to this kind of confusion; it is also an *isolating* uncertainty. If it should become, as it often does, the basis for deprivation of any and all sexual contact (excluding masturbation) it is doubly dangerous because sex is of the greatest importance, beyond its intense physical satisfaction, as an antidote—perhaps the best antidote—for the threatening sense of disappearance of self which an isolate experiences. How else can he achieve such intimacy and responsiveness, both of which are prime sources for the reaffirmation of his own being? (I believe that the quest for such affirmation is so desperate in a person who has forebodings of his own disappearing, or loss of self, that it best explains the sadist, who tries to force through pain the responsiveness he needs to bolster his failing sense of selfhood. His urgency makes victims of those from whom he would rather receive love, but he dares not risk rejection since he must have response just to sustain being at all.)

But it is not simply in hidden or esoteric ways that the impossible life is experienced. I asked a nineteen-year-old, remarkably healthy swimming champion where or how he had learned to swim. Of course he had been coached in various strokes, but he had been taught just to stay afloat by his "daddy" (a term widely used in the South, reflecting affection, authority, and close family affiliation). How had he been taught?

> "Well, my daddy threw me over the side of a rowboat. When I started to sink, he said to stand up if I couldn't swim—it wasn't over my head. Yeah, but I didn't know that. Man, I was just a little boy, 'bout five years old. I spluttered and thrashed, and I stayed up for—must have been two or three minutes. Every time I got near the oar he held out to me, he'd draw it back. Man, I hate to even think of it."

[6] "The Negro has the simplest of alternatives: live a life of constant humility or ever threatening danger," says Norman Mailer in his penetrating essay, "The White Negro," *Dissent*, summer, 1957. But again, the point is that simple alternatives are not prepsychotic stress. It is the required complex of both, not the choice of either/or, which creates the impossible life.

"Must have been an awful struggle."

"Yeah, but I don't even remember it."

For two years this boy had nightmares; he lived in a complex relation to his father, composed of love and respect on the one hand and hatred and fear on the other. He still has occasional nightmares, and when his fond "daddy" wakes him up by "roughhousing," he has been "glassy-eyed" and semihallucinating for as long as fifteen minutes—"So my daddy stopped waking me up that way." A part of his experience has never been completed, except in troubled sleep, for he and his father are the "best of buddies." An "impossible" but not uncommon sort of experience, and though a little less raw, made of the same stuff we are accustomed to see in case histories of hospitalized psychotics: "Two years of nearly incessant rape and obscene sexuality initiated by her grandfather, who was also a 'fire and brimstone' preacher who demanded very prim moralistic behavior of her."

One might ask here, who was psychotic? The grandfather? The father who throws his son into the water? The society which pits black against white? (And to some extent pits male against female?) *That depends on the extent to which conscience and defensiveness operate within each individual.* The cynical brute is not in the hospital. He may have other psychological maladjustments, but the hospitals are filled with those most sensitive to oppression and injustice, the would-be moral ones. Artaud, in his essay on Van Gogh, says, "A lunatic is a man who has preferred to become what is socially understood as mad rather than forfeit a certain superior idea of honor." And this seems not far from the truth. The calculating exploiter may not be in the hospital, but the granddaughter mentioned above is there, and she says, in her acute psychotic states, "It never happened." She cannot live all of her experience. Conscience forbids. At best, one self must be denied to awareness, or distortedly perceived.[7] That is a chronic state of maladjustment.

[7] How can there be a "true" or an "original" self *and* a distortedly perceived self? How can there be a denied and a denying experience in the same experiencer, or a known which is its own knower, or *anything* more than one self in one person, really? Metaphysics aside, client-centered theory is a clinical-perceptual theory, and turns to the same kinds of questions in more tangible modes of perception. If one looks through two monocular tubes, separating the vision of each eye, and looks at one color with one eye, a different color with the other eye, one will see first one color, then the other, with quick shifts of the rival eyes and some advantage for the dominant eye. Or with certain colors, one may get a blend giving a binocular yellow, for instance. Or, two separate eyes looking at separate patterns such as crosses and circles may fuse them in a binocular visual field. How can two

The Psychotic State   At worst, the denying self, the self as knower, *also begins to disappear.* At this point a schizophrenic psychosis becomes acute. (And this is really the only point at which I feel sure there is such a thing as a psychotic state.) Denial of part of experience is chosen in self-defense, but the nature of deception is such that the process becomes autonomous.

Then the disturbed person cannot stop it if he wants to. He is "beside himself," out of control. He will doubt his own existence, even try to bash his head against the wall to prove, by pain, his own being. He may not recognize what to us seems "real"—his body, his history, his social image. Normally the self is a realm with powerful known boundaries. That which is "not me" is excluded. Interestingly enough, the normal person will refuse to accept as part of himself what was clearly so before being separated from himself—will not, for instance, willingly drink from a glass saliva which was a moment ago in his mouth, or blood which was in his veins. (Though he will often quickly suck a wound at first, as if to hold onto himself.) But in a psychotic state he will swallow his blood, his urine, perhaps his feces, as if, when not knowing who he is and fearing that he is not at all, he tries in desperation to reincorporate that which he was. The boundaries are gone. He does not know where he begins, ends, or even if he is. Once experienced, this is indescribably frightening, and the acute state leaves him deeply shaken and unsure of himself. Now *he* knows what psychosis is, even though we do not.

Complete loss of self—of all selves—is the ultimate dread faced in the acute psychotic state. The person we call neurotic has an intricate but firm connection with a false self. (In clinical folklore, there is a saying: "A good neurosis is the best insurance against a psychosis.") The acutely psychotic one has no self. His is the essence of fear. Compared with this "experience of nothingness" all other fears—of starvation, ridicule, impotence, castration, or whatever—seem trivial. Even more than existentialist "not-being," the "experience of nothingness" is a confused paradox in its very expression. One cannot doubt it, having been in its presence, but I cannot explain its paradoxical quality better

---

eyes managed by one nervous system in a single skull see things separately, alternating or fusing them? If there is a mechanism for this, there can also be one which enables the personal self to view the world or the experiential self as now one reality, now another, or as a blended confusion. (My thanks to a colleague, Professor Austin Riesen, for personal communication on this problem.)

than to relate the words of a hospitalized patient. In trying to describe part of his hallucination, he put his face in his hands and quaked, "I seen this—this—this *shapeless shape* near me." Shapeless shape is illogical, but that is just the point. This man retains or comes back to concepts, such as shape, and they are all he had when he became detached from the world he has known. Where he now goes, the psychotic reality does not fit even such a broad concept as shape. The mind he had, and was losing, was not equipped to comprehend a world so foreign to experience. In the same way, even "experiencing" itself could not apply, since it was equipment to sense "something." Now it is jolted into primitive terror when it senses "nothing," which the concept of "being" cannot encompass.[8] This is one way in which psychosis is viciously circular. I have asserted that crucial emotional experience must be completed, i.e., integrated, to assure health, and instead we have now the experiencing of that shapeless shape, nothingness, which we are not conceptually prepared to understand, much less integrate. It forms another "impossible life," and the cycle begins again. What is worse, it involves further humiliation, which leads to further defensive denial of the "impossible" psychotic experience. ("It never happened.") Two colleagues have described to me their reaction to a hallucinogenic drug. Both were deeply shaken, both terrified by the sense of "not being," and significantly, both wanted above all to have human contact with a person or persons who *must not leave*. But the relevance of this is mainly to point out that it was far less difficult to pull out of this artificial episode, since there is little felt humiliation. Following the genuine psychotic episode the effect is usually further humiliation and loss of self-esteem ("People will think I'm crazy"). And finally, the result is withdrawal by others and from others. Isolation is increased. Thus a psychosis tends to repeat the three elements which led to it; the "impossible life," the attendant humiliation and denial, and consequent isolation ending in self-negation.

The crux of this line of thought is in the way in which defensive denial ends in undoing rather than becoming—ends in the complete loss of self. Isolation is a mid-point in explanation. There is increasing evidence demonstrating that a major effect of isolation is the hallucination we so readily associate with the psychotic state. Hebb and others

---

[8] With others, we share the view that the phenomenological reality is that which the individual perceives; but I believe that the intense state of psychosis is not the psychotic's "reality." At that point he has none, except nothing.

have experimentally deprived human subjects of external sensory stimulation, blocking eyes, ears, muffling fingers, sometimes suspending the
body in neutral buoyancy and steady temperature, etc. When outside
stimuli are blocked, the void is quickly experienced, with discomfort,
and then filled with "ghosts," sounds, colors, "waking dreams," and a
wide range of images.[9] For days after the experiment ended, the subjects (college students) were fearful of the return of ghosts and other
imaginary phenomena. This effect of isolation is not new, of course. It
has been observed by aviators (Lindbergh reported it in his solo flight
across the Atlantic), submarine crew members, prisoners in solitary
confinement, etc. Nor are such effects caused only by absence of sensory
stimuli; they can also be caused by monotony or too much of one
thing. Any substance—water as well as alcohol—is toxic or intoxicating
in excess. Any stimulus in excess—constant noise as well as constant
silence—produces the effect of isolation, as it excludes all other sensation. The human nervous system needs variety, and has a definite "stimulus hunger." (It is well established, for example, that animals will work
to stimulate portions of the brain by electric shock.[10] This, rather than
destruction of "associative memory pathways," may be the useful function of shock therapy, if it can be justified at all.) Isolation is the next
to final step in the development of the acute psychosis.

SELF-DECEPTION AND SELF-NEGATION

The remaining questions relate to the development and "loss" of the
mind. Particularly crucial is the way in which defensive denial leads to
isolation.

We tend to think of human intelligence, once formed, as an individual capacity. That is mind: our hopes that man will be rational rest
upon it. From the standpoint of psychotherapy, it matters a great deal
whether mind is "given" or "gotten," i.e., biological or social. The ideas
of G. H. Mead[11] are the foundation of a social psychology which has
provided basic assumptions for several schools of psychotherapy.[12] Mead
says, "It is absurd to look at the mind simply from the standpoint of the
individual human organism, for although it has its focus there, it is essentially a social phenomenon. . . . The processes of experience which

[9] W. Heron, "The Pathology of Boredom," *Sci. Amer.*, 196 (1957),
52-56.
[10] J. Olds and P. Milner, *J. Comp. Physiol. Psychol.*, 47 (1954), 419.
[11] G. H. Mead, *Mind, Self, and Society* (Chicago: Univ. Chicago Press,
1934).
[12] H. S. Sullivan is one who explicitly acknowledged this influence.

the human brain makes possible are made possible only for a group of interacting individuals; only for individual organisms which are members of a society; not for individual organisms in isolation from other individual organisms." The mind emerges through a process of communication. This involves social interaction on the basis of what Mead calls "significant symbols" (usually words). A significant symbol is one that is "reflexive," i.e., when it is used it *presupposes another* person, anticipates his response, involves on the user's part some sense of how that other will feel. The bully, for instance, differs from the lion, which roars at the whole jungle, in that the bully participates somewhat in the fright of his victim. He is not trying to frighten himself—quite the opposite (for he is a coward too). But he does. He senses the meaning of his threat and reacts to it, "taking the role of the other." The lion only gestures. The human communicates, and communication means taking into account the other. *Acknowledging the other is essential to the existence of mind,* from beginning to end.

What follows here hinges upon that very point—the existence of the other as a necessary condition for the psychological existence of oneself. That exterior distinction is *paralleled* by an interior but similar duality within each individual consciousness, *where being involves a possibility of not-being.* This view draws upon the social psychology of Sartre, which advances Mead's foundations to a new level. Before offering an interpretation of Sartre's ideas, let me offer the clinical opinion that the psychosis begins with (or stems from) a "lie." [13] This may at first sound like moralizing. Then it may seem immoral, because the lie is seen as the salvation, or at least a resort, of sanity. The mind, which we have been considering as emerged from social experience, is the instrument by which reality is apprehended, and it is founded upon the knowledge of (if not the commitment to) truth. For all the qualifications we can make about "truth," that is what we mean when we speak of "reality contact," for instance (to be without which fairly designates the psychotic state). We think of the lie as treacherous to others, but it is even more treacherous to the liar himself if he falls into self-deceit: he will either be foiled by his consciousness of the truth, or he will find that there is "no one there" within himself to whom he can lie.

---

[13] No single lie, probably, but a series, or perhaps a habit, at first successful. Usually we speak clinically of defenses, distortions, etc., because *lie* carries more threat of reproach. Here the plain word *lie* is used to simplify a complex argument.

Self-deception cannot succeed for long. It will either fail or destroy the self of the deceiver.

It is the nature of human consciousness to be able to doubt, and this includes doubting one's own existence. Children old enough to comprehend the concept of death have also been heard to ask, "How do we know we're really here?" This capacity to doubt is necessary to the capacity to think, and also to believe, with any real conviction. Lose doubt and you lose belief. (The psychotic says of his delusions, "There is no doubt about it," but obversely, "I can't believe any of it.") To be able to doubt is to be able to negate, and to doubt oneself is self-negation—not a desirable end to actualize but a required possibility for belief in being. Self-negation as an actuality, not just a possibility, can derive from self-deception.

Self-deception is not a lie, in the first place. A lie is in conjunction with the truth; self-deception has lost it. Sartre points out, in his careful analysis:

> The essence of the lie implies in fact that the liar is actually in complete possession of the truth which he is hiding. A man does not lie about that which he is ignorant of; he does not lie when he spreads an error of which he is himself the dupe; he does not lie when he is mistaken. The ideal description of a lie would be a cynical consciousness, affirming truth within himself, denying it in his words. . . .[14]

The liar, for one thing, is in possession of the truth. He sees both sides. He intends to deceive, and does not hide his intention from himself. (Later we see that the self-deceiver intends the self-deceit, but he must hide his intention from himself or he could not even attempt to carry it out.) But we are talking now about what Sartre calls the *ideal* lie and this, he says, seldom holds for long. It "happens often enough that the liar is more or less the victim of it, that he half persuades himself of it." There's the rub, there's the treachery of it. The lie ("I could not have done that," "It never happened," etc.) begun in self-defense slips into self-deception.[15] But as long as it is still a lie, it does

[14] Jean-Paul Sartre, "Self-Deception," in W. Kaufmann (ed.), *Existentialism from Dostoevsky to Sartre* (New York: Meridian, 1958).

[15] A famous scene in Tolstoi's *War and Peace* will remind you of the ease with which a lie can slip into self-deception. It can even do so in a group, where it seems so appealing, so protective, that individuals find social reinforcement for their self-deception. Nonetheless, even the social consensus is not the truth. It has its effects as self-deception.

this; it affirms one's consciousness, as something hidden from the other! It presupposes the other! "It presupposes my existence, the existence of the *other*, my existence *for* the other, and the existence of the other *for* me." [ITALICS SARTRE's.] Clearly, the lie fulfills the requisites of communication and social identity which Mead described as fundamental to the emergence and maintenance of the mind and the self; even though it is a falsehood, it relates to the truth and acknowledges two separate communicants.

As the lie slips into self-deception, this fundamental duality of identities is lost. There is no longer a separatedness of deceived and deceiver. Self-deception implies the undifferentiated unity of a single consciousness (not to be mistaken for healthy integrity). It is something one is doing to oneself, yet one cannot. One's consciousness cannot intend, yet hide its intention, nor lie unless it simultaneously knows the truth from which it wants to depart. The very attempt to enter into self-deception will destroy the possibility of a successful lie (defense). If the one who lies is the same as the one to whom the lie is told, then he must know, in his capacity as deceiver, the truth which is hidden from him as the one deceived. Must know it well in order to conceal it, but this requires a duality which has been lost, so he can neither

---

After an undeserved victory, Russian officers are reporting to Prince Bagration:

"The general, whose regiment had been inspected at Braunau, submitted to the prince that as soon as the engagement began, he had fallen back to the copse, mustered the men who were cutting wood, and letting them pass by him, had made a bayonet charge with two battalions and repulsed the French.

" 'As soon as I saw, your excellency, that the first battalion was thrown into confusion, I stood in the road and thought, "I'll let them get through and then open fire on them"; and that's what I did.' "

"The general had so longed to do this, he had so regretted not having succeeded in doing it, that it seemed to him now that this was just what had happened. Indeed might it not actually have been so? Who could make out in such confusion what did and what did not happen?"

Other officers are easily drawn in:

" 'I saw here, your excellency, the attack of the Pavlograd hussars,' Zherkov put in, looking uneasily about him. He had not seen the hussars at all that day, but had only heard about them from an infantry officer.

" 'They broke up two squares, your excellency.'

"When Zherkov began to speak, several officers smiled, as they always did, expecting a joke from him. But as they perceived that what he was saying redounded to the glory of our arms and of the day, they assumed a serious expression, although many were very well aware that what Zherkov was saying was a lie utterly without foundation.

know certainly nor conceal cynically, nor affirm his being by negation of the "other." He ends with only self-negation, which is isolation with all the dangers that entails. One final, somewhat intricate step is this: he denies the one thing he still is—a being in self-deception. It is the nature of existence to be *and* not be what one is. To be courageous, for instance, one must in some sense be a coward also, otherwise one is only "fearless"—(i.e., unaware of danger, unfeeling of fear). Whatever one is, to be meaningful one must also not be. But self-deception is not being what one is, for one is running away from that; neither is it being what one is not, because the deception cannot succeed.[16] So there is *nothing*—no truth, no cynical lie, no belief, no sustaining other, no being oneself or otherwise. Self-deception is the end of sanity, because it leads to self-negation, which is the end of being. That is the final loss of self and the ultimate anxiety. The mind develops through a process of differentiation between self and other and is sustained by a duality in one's own consciousness. It is lost when the boundaries are erased by self-deception.

Psychotherapy offers one road back through the intervention of another consciousness—a person who may re-establish both contact and separate identity; and to whom the lost one can at least lie. The psychotherapist ordinarily hopes to see the client or patient divest himself of all but the clearest perceptions of reality, and throughout, to speak the truth without reservation (whether by the "fundamental rule of free association," trust and confidence, or whatever). That is an ultimate ideal—a combination of freedom and courage which is the healthiest of human conditions. The therapist working with the psychotic can be grateful when the patient can genuinely "lie" again. He has at least restored secrecy, privacy, a separate identity, though shame and conflict will trouble him again.

Of course this is not the final goal of therapy. Self-affirmation

---

[16] In an article which will be relevant later in the chapter, Tausk points out the way in which an infant believes that others know his thoughts, and that a child is surprised when he first learns, quite early, that he can lie, and lie successfully. (That he did have a bowel movement, that he did not take a cookie, etc.) The successful lie puts an end to the infantile stage of "omniscience of thought" and helps to establish ego boundaries. Tausk posits stages in which (1) the outer world does not exist separately; (2) it exists but there is omniscience of thought, joining and controlling the ego with all else; (3) the external world is separate and can be deceived. Thus the lie helps to establish ego boundaries. (Viktor Tausk, "The Influencing Machine," in R. Fliess (ed.), *The Psychoanalytic Reader* [New York: Internat. Univ. Press, 1948.]

through negation is not the end, but the beginning. And there are other means of helping, which include anything that will overcome isolation; or will facilitate complete experiencing of the "impossible life" (i.e., to live with the truth) without unbearable humiliation; or will imply duality and differentiation. There is no virtue in the lie. There is a purpose in understanding it, and its relation to the truth at one pole and to self-deception at the opposite pole; that is, to throw some light on the dynamism of a "defense mechanism" as it leads to self-destruction and essential loss of being—a dimension which will help us to understand the open face of health, the half hidden face of normalcy, the mask of neurosis, and the hollow stare of psychosis, in relation to one another.

PERSONALITY AND PSYCHOTHERAPY

A General Statement Turning to client-centered therapy, this section will briefly review some salient features of our general position. Why "client" instead of "patient"? The negative distinction now seems somewhat picayune and, in hospital work, more embarrassing than useful; but it was intended to avoid the doctor-patient relation, with its implication of "sickness" requiring "treatment" [17] from someone who "understands the patient better than he understands himself." A positive reason is that we really want to think of that person as a person— someone unique with dignity and capacity, worthy of our unreserved respect. If we must have a word for it, "client" seems more expressive of that. Why client-"centered"? This matters much more. Again, the negative purpose is only to distinguish between this and "therapist-centered," "theory-centered," "society-centered," etc. There are such things. The positive meaning is immense. It expresses the major goal of the therapist; to understand and accept the perception and feelings of the client; to share the client's view of reality rather than to impose his own.[18]

It follows then that we rely heavily upon the *growth capacity* of the individual. The therapist is an active and significant person, but he cannot heal—he can only help to create conditions in which the natural regenerative powers take effect. As for *motive*, the drive toward self-actualization is a primary one; every human being would rather be bet-

---

[17] Like the psychoanalyst Szasz, I much prefer the word *influence* to *treatment*, but we all continue to use the latter. See T. Szasz, "The Case of Prisoner 'K,'" in A. Burton (ed.), *Case Studies in Counseling and Psychotherapy* (Englewood Cliffs, N.J.: Prentice-Hall, 1959).

[18] C. R. Rogers, *Client Centered Therapy* (Boston: Houghton Mifflin, 1951).

ter than worse, and strives toward the enhancement of self even though the strivings may often be thwarted and regressive. These assumptions about motive and capacity combine into a general *ethic*, which can simply be called self-determination. Client-centered therapy is founded on the conviction that man should be free, and to this end makes freedom a major means in the therapeutic experience. This is not, as some think,[19] a reflection of political attitudes which supposedly prevail in America. It is a personal psychological conviction that the man who is most free will be most healthy. Freedom means the widest scope of choice and openness to experience, therefore the greatest probability of an adaptive response. For the individual, it seems that the urge to freedom is an urge to health, and precedes, rather than reflects, a political order.

Some Fundamental Propositions   The conduct of therapy is based on propositions developed from a perceptual "field theory" mode of psychological thought. These are detailed elsewhere by Rogers.[20] Many have been experimentally tested. A small but essential portion will be outlined here, and these are so fundamental that we ask ourselves, of necessity, "If this is not true, what is?"

1. Each person is unique. No one else can ever completely know his experience. Some of his experience is consciously symbolized. Some is at lower levels of awareness, beyond the scope of his attention. Beyond joint perceptions of shared experience, the closest approach we have to another's private world is to try to look through his eyes, understand through his interpretations.

2. Behavior is a consequence of perception. The organism reacts to reality as he perceives it. "Objective evidence" notwithstanding, he who thinks the room hot opens the window; who thinks it cold turns up the heat; sees a red light, stops; sees it green, goes; sees an object as good, eats it; the same object as refuse, avoids it. Whatever "it" really is by consensus, physical measurement, or philosophical proof—the way in which "it" is perceived determines behavior toward it. Because perceptions can change, behavior can change. To promote a *stable* alteration in behavior, it is necessary to facilitate a change in perception.

3. Threat is followed by defense. Defense may take many forms, but it is the general and inevitable category of reaction to danger.

[19] R. A. Harper, *Psychoanalysis and Psychotherapy*, 36 *Systems* (Englewood Cliffs, N.J.: Prentice-Hall, 1959), pp. 83-84.
[20] C. R. Rogers, *op. cit.*, Chap. 12.

4. Defense narrows and rigidifies perception. Rigid perception blocks change in behavior. Attacking the defense system is likely to complicate it, causing more of the psychological economy to be devoted to defensiveness, inhibiting change.

5. A portion of the total field of perception becomes differentiated as the self (called here the "self-concept"). The self-concept is an intervening perception which affects outer percepts and determines their values. The self-concept may be one of weakness or of strength, may be of worth or contemptible; lucky or unlucky; lovable or hateful, to name a few dimensions. If one feels thoroughly adequate, no job is too difficult to try; if thoroughly inadequate, no job is easy enough. If strong, one may see a boulder as something to throw into the treads of an armored tank; if weak, the same boulder to hide behind. Experience is evaluated as friendly or dangerous, interesting or boring, possible or impossible, etc., *according to the self-concept* of the experiencer.

6. As experiences occur, they are related to the self-structure, and depending on it, each experience will be (*a*) symbolized accurately, perceived consciously, and organized into the self-structure; (*b*) ignored, because it has no significance to the self; or (*c*) denied or distortedly symbolized because it is threatening to the self.

In short, the self-concept stands between the stimulus and the response. Since self-concept is itself a perception, it can change, so that psychotherapy is possible—not guaranteed, but possible.

Technique   In the framework of these rough statements, the main technique of client-centered therapy may be understood. That technique is "reflection"—particularly reflection of feeling rather than content. At most points in communication where others would interpret, probe, advise, encourage, we reflect. This is the implementation of the attitudes and the propositions expressed above. Reflection can be, in the hands of an imitative novice, a dull, wooden mockery. On paper, it often looks particularly so.[21] Yet it can also be a profound, intimate,

---

[21] I have in mind an example which, if printed, would look like a passive repetition of the patient's statement. Yet to hear it spoken conveys a wealth of feeling and clear assurance of communication. Any interested professional person may obtain this excellent example, on tape recording, of Carl Rogers during an hour with a hospitalized schizophrenic patient. This recording, called "Loretta," contains separate interviews by Drs. Richard Felder and Albert Ellis with the same patient. It may be obtained from the American Academy of Psychotherapists, 30 Fifth Avenue, New York 11, N.Y.

empathically understanding response, requiring great skill and sensitivity and intense involvement.[22]

Technique is certainly subordinate to relationship (though it contributes to it, and is therefore not to be slighted). Currently the emphasis is much more upon relationships out of which new techniques may develop. In his first public paper on schizophrenics,[23] Rogers ignores technique to discuss the conditions—the atmosphere and the relationship—necessary for therapy:

Congruence as a Condition of Therapy

The first condition is that the therapist, within this relationship is internally congruent, or integrated. By this I mean that he is unified in being exactly what he *is* in the relationship. From a more theoretical point of view, it means that his actual experience of himself and the relationship is accurately matched by his awareness of himself and the relationship. Such a condition is the opposite of presenting a façade, a defensive front, to the patient or client. If the therapist is experiencing one thing in the relationship, but is endeavoring to be something else, then the condition I am attempting to define is not met. On the other hand if he is transparently himself, if he is able to be "that which he truly is," as Kierkegaard says, then this condition is met.

I have gradually come to believe that this is the most basic condition of all psychotherapy, and extends to being aspects of ourselves which we regard as non-therapeutic. Thus a therapist experiences a disturbing fear of the deeply suppressed violence which he senses in a psychotic client. Assuming this fear is a persistent one, it is part of my hypothesis that it is more therapeutic for him openly to *be* that fear, even expressing it to the client, than to present a calm and unruffled front in the relationship. To be transparent to the client, to have nothing of one's experience in the relationship which is hidden—that is, I believe, basic to effective psychotherapy.

As I examine my own experience I believe that this holds for

[22] It has always been galling to me to hear client-centered therapy, because of its techniques, referred to as passive or superficial. It is often quite the opposite, though dazzling interpretations and other intriguing esoterics are missing. An Australian colleague with whom I once discussed a particularly deep commitment I felt in a case said, "It's a life for a life." Nothing ever rang more true. This is especially so with psychotics, and I have wondered, as have many other therapists, how many times in my life I will be willing and able to make as deep an investment as seems needed.

[23] Paper given at a symposium on psychotherapy with schizophrenics, at Southeast Louisiana State Hospital, Mandeville, Louisiana, February 20-21, 1958.

working with any individual, but it is especially important in working with the deeply disturbed person, who is so extremely and often accurately sensitive to precisely what is going on in the relationship. Brody, in the 1950 symposium on psychotherapy with schizophrenics, pointed out the sensitivity of the schizophrenic to the unverbalized or partially conscious feelings of the therapist. All therapists have, I am sure, observed this, and the resolution of the difficulty which I am suggesting is that the therapist transparently *be* those feelings. When they are in the open, they cannot interfere with therapy.

What I am saying means that the therapist, by being openly and freely himself, is ready for and is offering the possibility of, an existential encounter between two real persons. The schizophrenic, to be sure, can only rarely and fleetingly and fearfully avail himself of such an encounter, but it is these moments, I believe, which are therapeutic.

Empathic Understanding

A second necessary condition of psychotherapy, as I see it, is the experiencing by the therapist of an accurate and empathic understanding of the client. This means that he senses and comprehends the client's immediate awareness of his own private world. It involves sensing the cognitive, perceptual, and affective components of the client's experiential field, as they exist in the client. Where the therapist is adequately sensitive, it means not only recognizing those aspects of experience which the client has already been able to verbalize, but also those unsymbolized aspects of his experience which have somehow been comprehended through subtle non-verbal clues by the delicate psychological radar of the therapist. The skillful therapist senses the client's world —no matter now hallucinated or bizarre or deluded or chaotic— as if it were his own, but without ever losing the "as if" quality.

I would like especially to note that in dealing with the schizophrenic the therapist, at his best, empathizes with the client's world as it is at that moment and the meanings it has for the client at that moment, whether it is wildly bizarre delusion, a moment of essentially rational self-control, or a chaotic disorganization. It may seem strange to some that I make no distinction as to what the therapist responds to, save that it be whatever aspect of experience is immediately present. This seems to be a sufficiently important matter that I should like to digress to discuss the basis of that point of view, though I shall return again to the topic of empathy.

The Nature of Schizophrenia in Relation to Psychotherapy

I have discussed elsewhere the significant place of the self-concept or self-gestalt—the way the individual perceives himself—in the psychological economy of the individual. *The self is the referent which supplies the "feedback" by which the organism regulates behavior.* It is the criterion as to what is threatening to the individual since only those experiences are threatening which are inconsistent with the self-concept. Those experiences which do threaten, which are inconsistent with the self, are denied to awareness or distorted in awareness, since to symbolize them accurately in awareness would involve a disruption of, a contradiction in, the self-gestalt.

Now in the normal or neurotic individual, and in the paranoid individual as well, the self is intact, and is defended against disruption, either by simple or sometimes by enormously elaborate defenses. The schizophrenic individual however (other than the paranoid) is in my judgement one who has never developed or been permitted to develop a clearly differentiated, strong internally organized self-configuration. In the face of some deeply threatening feelings or circumstances, or with a mounting accumulation of such threats, a wave of previously denied experiences which are incongruent with this weak self sweeps over the individual's awareness. The self-concept is so disrupted that its function as a guide for behavior is surrendered. This is the way I would describe the moment of the psychotic break. Feelings previously denied to awareness are now predominant or regnant, and behavior is consistent with their content. This is the acute stage of the psychosis.[24]

Following the break, confusion and disorganization may reign, or the previously denied or repressed feelings may retain their regnancy, or a badly disrupted self protected by some new pattern of defense may be regnant, or these different conditions may alternate irregularly. If the person is ever again to be whole, all of these real elements of experience must be accepted into a reorganized and more inclusive self-concept which accurately represents more of the total experience of the organism.

Empathic Understanding (continued)

If I have been able to communicate my theoretical views in this brief digression, it will now be clear why, for the therapist, it is immaterial which aspect of the client's personality is momentarily regnant. If he can relate to that aspect with a sensitive empathy and a complete acceptance (of which more later) then this understanding acceptance will enable the client to accept it within himself, and thus eventually to become more of a whole person. Therapy involves the acceptance by the client of the "awful" feelings he has denied to awareness, or the terrifying experience of being chaotic and out of control, and of the elements in his previous self. If he can accept all these as being a part of

[24] An advanced, but not the acute, state as I conceive of it.—J.M.S.

himself, he will gradually assimilate them into a new self-gestalt which includes more of what he is.*

Hence the therapist's sensitive understanding is equally effective with every changing facet which is communicated by the client. Whether he is empathizing with a fantastically strange dream-like expression of a feeling previously denied, or with a self frightened by a sense of its own vulnerability and striving desperately to keep control, or with the chaos produced by a confused regnancy, he is supplying a basic condition of the therapeutic process.

Unconditional Positive Regard

A third condition which is hypothesized as necessary to the establishment of an effective therapeutic relationship is described by the term unconditional positive regard. Let me speak first of positive regard. This means that the therapist is experiencing a warm acceptance of the client, a caring. His feelings are adient—toward the client—rather than abient—away from the client. The word "love" can be used to describe this attitude, providing it is understood as a nonpossessive caring for the client as a separate person, and not a love which primarily gratifies the therapist's own needs.

It is hypothesized that to be most effective this positive regard should be *unconditional*. This means that there are no conditions of acceptance, no feeling of "I like you only *if* you are thus and so." It means that the therapist prizes the negative, defensive, regressive, asocial, mature, positive expressions. He values the client as a total person, and hence values each expression of any facet of that person. I believe that Frieda Fromm-Reichman has frequently shown, in her work with her patients, a very high degree of unconditional positive regard. On the other hand I have listened to recordings of other therapists whose attitude seems to be "I like you, but I feel much more liking and acceptance when you are being rational and 'normal' than when you are being bizarre and regressive." I would hypothesize that these therapists would be less effective.

The Experiencing of These Conditions by the Client

The fourth essential of a therapeutic relationship is that the client experiences, to a minimal degree, the congruence or transparency of the therapist, his empathic understanding, and his unconditional positive regard. These conditions do not exist for the client and hence do not exist effectively, unless they are experienced by him. Here again it is undoubtedly more difficult to

---

* It is evident that I am here sharply in disagreement with the psychoanalytic view as voiced by Redlich when he says "the therapeutic aim must be directed at re-repression rather than at lifting repression." [Rogers' note.]

achieve this in the schizophrenic individual, than with the neurotic or normal. How can the therapist's caring be communicated to a withdrawn and suspicious individual? Some therapists have communicated it by gentle physical contact, some by violent argument in which the schizophrenic is dealt with as an equal, some by the tone of voice.

It seems to me that much of the experimentation in psychotherapy with psychotics comes at this point. If the therapist experiences within himself the conditions of therapy: if he feels "I care: I can sense your experience from your point of view; and what I am and feel in this relationship is completely open to you"; then he will use a variety of personal ways to communicate these attitudes to the client. He will not always be successful, of course. But where the client does experience some degree of these attitudes in the relationship, then the final condition of therapy exists, and the process of therapeutic change will, it is hypothesized, get under way.

OTHER CHARACTERISTICS

There is in client-centered therapy an overall characteristic—an inclination toward the most literal of explanations. There is a deliberate shunning of the arcane, the esoteric (and, some say, the erotic). Empiricism and "commonsense" conjecture typify the research and theory. These lean on and are expressed in terms of learning theory, perception, social psychology, interaction analysis.[25, 26, 27] This characteristic leads to positions which diverge from traditional clinical opinion on many issues. It is possible only to skim over such issues here. Attitudes toward transference, for instance, range from considering it a fiction which protects the therapist from the consequences of his real behavior and effect to viewing it as early stereotypic behavior which will be extinguished in the natural course of events if it is not cultivated. Symbolic analysis plays little role, partly because it is usually content-specific and covered by response to emotion. (I believe the so-called archaic symbols are significant, chiefly because they are cleaner communicants; like new words in a foreign language, they shake loose the multiple complexities of conventional meanings, and say just the elementary things each person means them to say.) The unconscious does not currently figure in client-centered literature. It is considered a reductionistic assump-

[25] J. M. Butler, "Interaction of Client and Therapist," *J. Abnorm. Soc. Psychol.*, 1952.

[26] E. H. Porter, Jr., *An Introduction to Therapeutic Counseling* (Boston: Houghton Mifflin, 1950).

[27] D. Snygg, A. Combs, *Individual Behavior* (New York: Harper, 1959).

tion about phenomona better understood in terms of attention and "levels of awareness."

An ahistorical bias has always been plain among us, and this is one of the currents which moves us to an appreciation of some of the existential writings.[28, 29] Diagnosis is a moot point too, though our departures are not as radical as they once were. We have written elsewhere our views questioning its validity and usefulness.[30] Jung has made a masterful statement with which we agree.[31] For the moment, a statement of Menninger's is one to which I can thoroughly subscribe and which seems especially appropriate in regard to the case you are about to read:

> The word "schizophrenia" becomes a damning designation. To have it once applied to a young man can be to ruin a career, despite all evidence of subsequent healthiness. A name implies a concept; and if this concept is unsound, the diagnosis can ruin treatment; the very naming it can damage the patient whom we essay to help. Nathaniel Hawthorne in *The House of Seven Gables* told us what we psychiatrists should well know:

> "The sick in mind . . . are rendered more darkly and hopelessly so by the manifold reflection of their disease, mirrored back from all quarters in the deportment of those about them; they are compelled to inhale the poison of their own breath, in infinite repetition."

> It is not that we decry classification as such; we recognize it as a useful scientific tool. But it is dangerous when it leads to reification of terms.[32]

TREATMENT OF A CASE

One Who "Needed Help Bad"   Few things are more difficult for a therapist than presenting "a case." It was a living, breathing, sometimes

[28] Jean-Paul Sartre, *Existential Psychoanalysis* (New York: Philosophical Library, 1953).

[29] L. Binswanger, "Existential Analysis and Psychotherapy," in F. Fromm-Reichmann, J. L. Moreno (eds.), *Progress in Psychotherapy* (New York: Grune, 1956), Vol. I.

[30] J. Shlien, in M. Lewis, C. Rogers, J. Shlien, "Time-Limited, Client-Centered Psychotherapy: Two Cases," in A. Burton (ed.), *Case Studies in Counseling and Psychotherapy* (Englewood, N.J.: Prentice-Hall, 1959).

[31] C. G. Jung, "The Practice of Psychotherapy," *Collected Works* 16, Bollingen Series 20 (New York: Pantheon, 1954), pp. 85-86.

[32] K. Menninger *et al.*, "The Unitary Concept of Mental Illness," *Bull. Menn. Clinic*, 22 (1958).

gasping, sweating experience. I seriously doubt that we can really picture each other's work this way. I know we cannot do it justice. Also, there is a natural reluctance to make public what was private, even though it is disguised. (I have always admired Freud's forbearance, waiting until "Anna O." was dead before writing about her.) How to present the material? The raw data are verbatim dialogues, but that would fill a book, a sometimes tedious book. Subtleties of gestures, unspoken thoughts, analyses, would fill a shelf. They play a part. Worse still, we are conditioned to look for journalistic answers—who did it, what was wrong, where are the points of insight and the hidden keys uncovered by the detective-therapist? It doesn't happen that way. Therapy is bigger—a whole atmosphere—and smaller—moments of internal experience—than can be conveyed by the synopses we can offer.

Michael K. was twenty-eight years old when I first saw him. He had been committed by his family, and was sitting beside the examining psychiatrist at a "diagnostic staff" in a state hospital. He said he "needed help bad" and spoke of the "machine on his head." My reaction: sympathy, fascination, and challenge. I liked this boy. I wished I could help him. The timer rang indicating an allotted five minutes had passed (the hospital has 8,000 patients), and he was gently dismissed by the overworked psychiatrist. Diagnosis (no question): paranoid schizophrenia. Recommended treatment: electroshock.

Two weeks later, cardiograms and other records completed, his treatment was about to start. I had a vacancy in my schedule and asked that shock be canceled and he be assigned to psychotherapy. During sleepless nights in some of the tense nine months ahead, I often wished I had not gone to the hospital that day.

Michael served as a navy frogman during the Korean war; tough, but scared; was "trigger-happy" on landing parties, shooting at the dark. After discharge he worked as a carpenter until auditory hallucinations became so distracting that power saws endangered him. His family put him in a private sanitarium. There he received electroshock for three weeks, insulin for seven. He once escaped by climbing over a seven-foot wall on a midwinter night. While there he was given "truth serum," and on becoming conscious saw his father standing at the foot of the bed while the white-coated attendant wrote down answers to questions. He confessed to some childhood sexual incidents which caused him great shame. Discharged with no improvement, he stayed at home. He visited a sick friend, who died the next day. Mike wondered if the cigarette he gave his sick friend had poisoned him. He went to a veterans' hospital for outpatient treatment. To the psychiatrist there he seemed "outwardly friendly and cooperative, but unwilling to talk about himself because these were 'personal' problems." Mike had the typical attitude of his socioeconomic class toward "talkin' doctors."

His mother, who later came to see me a few times, said that "Mickey" had always been a good boy, loyal to his family, always told her the truth—"would never lie to me"(!). She first noticed "something wrong" after Korea. "He began to wolf down his food when it was so hot it would burn." During the next few years she was his confidante when he was confined to his house. She would listen to him for "as long as I could stand it, then I'd have to leave the room. I tried to tell him not to talk about those things [whorehouses, etc.]—just to forget it." She mentioned his need to have more relaxed relations with girls, nice girls, and her distaste was evident when she recalled a time she had cleaned him up with medicinal soap after a visit with other boys to a prostitute.

The father was a first-generation immigrant, a cabinetmaker, in poor health and irascible with his sons, though meek and polite with authorities. There were three sons in their twenties and one older married daughter.

Early Phase Mike came from his locked ward to see me at my request. I told him I would visit the hospital twice a week and would be there to talk with him as part of his treatment. He plunged into a description of the "machine on his brain." [33] He thought "on," and it went on, broadcasting his thoughts over radio and television; he thought "off" and the broadcast stopped, but his thoughts continued to repeat in his brain. "Off" caused less shame than the broadcast, but more confusion and loss of sleep. He had "nothing to hide—a clean record from Washington on down." The thoughts changed in voice—maybe an old man, a woman, or a little boy. He had been to the F.B.I. to complain. They had laughed, and he laughed as he told of it, but said it hurt him at the time. His mood shifted from friendly affable amusement at being a source of entertainment to feeling extremely angry and resentful at being exposed. For some of his thoughts were "rotten," expressed in obscenities which "shouldn't be broadcast—what if children are listening, for gosh' sake."

[33] The influencing machine is described in its classical forms by Tausk, *op. cit.*

It frightened him to think that nothing in his past could be hidden (he had indeed been grievously exposed at many points), but he reassured himself that he had done nothing wrong—"a couple of *mistakes,* yes."

"They" had screamed at him this morning that he "has a fruity voice" and he'll "have to suck dick" to get out of here. "Telling me I'm a fairy—I'm a *man.* I been a man since I was nine." Whether there was real homosexuality or not, Mike at least expressed a defiantly false sureness of his manliness, his independence and power to cope with the world.

In the next two weeks we began to talk to one another. Mike felt relieved. The voices subsided in volume, talking instead of screaming. He asserted complete innocence—except for a few mistakes, such as blaming the Masonic temple for his problems. He struggled to face himself. "It's pretty hard for a guy to tell a doc what's really wrong with him." As he moved closer to this effort, he moved farther away defensively. Now he bore no responsibility for his thoughts, much less their broadcast; everything was put into his mind. "They can even shove images right into your head. Maybe it's Hollywood. Maybe it's the F.B.I." Now his moods switched around to the theme, "Why me?" reflecting his vacillating self-concept.

> "I'm nobody. Why pick on me? I'm just an ordinary guy, a worker, I don't make any trouble or had much education—just an ordinary guy. [Brightly.] I'm the only one in the U.S. it's done to. It's something for me to find out for everybody. They tell me I'm a movie star. I'll go down in history. [Suddenly deflated.] I'll go down in history—yeah. I couldn't make a pimple on a movie star's ass."
>
> I say, "Mike, sometimes you feel worthless, and sometimes great, don't you?"
>
> "Yeah—I dunno. I—what am I? I don't know. Just nobody, I guess."

During the next weeks he began to challenge me: I was like everyone else, knew everything, would not tell him about it. He didn't want to hurt my feelings, but did not hide his anger and disgust. We were still friends.

He wondered what his "mistake" really was. For he too was "journalistically conditioned"—to find the guilty culprit, to track down the fatal flaw. Maybe it was picking up a blond girl in his car, thinking she was a movie actress, then spending weeks trying to find her again. Then he left the city, alone for the first time, feeling isolated. Some fragments of the interview of this period illustrate typical interaction:

MIKE: I drove up past the Great Lakes Naval base—the electronics station there, and I thought—maybe that's where it's done. It all seemed so strange. I was all shook up. I felt so, so— ill at ease—so ill at ease. I got to a little town, got a room. Then I started to cry.

THERAPIST: I guess you mean you were trying to get away, and it wasn't making you feel any better—you still felt strange and scared.

M.: Yeah—I felt so strange—I went— Can you please tell me where to find a Lutheran preacher? They told me, and I went to church and prayed, "Jesus Christ, please help me now," and I tried—I wanted to talk to someone—to ask 'em if it was all recorded, and that I didn't do it. And I said a lot of foolish things, blamed a lot of people.

T.: Wanted someone to know. Someone to understand.

M.: Oh they *all* know. You know, Doc—everyone knows, but no one will tell me. Maybe I'll have to pull the silver out of my teeth, but that won't help—my dad caught some of it, and he has false teeth. I've got a right to live a normal life, Doc. Why don't people understand? A man makes a mistake, you don't have to murder him, drive him out of my mind. [Strikes match ferociously.]

T.: [Could respond to the admission of error and resentment of punishment, but impressed by match.] Makes you *mad*.

M.: Hell, yes. [Glares.] Then I heard these two guys at the plant say, "We can't turn 'im off yet, we got a sum of money invested in 'im." Now, why don't they tell me what it's all about? [34]

T.: Why won't *some*body level with you?

M.: That's right. Why won't—I've had a hell of a time, Doc. I'd hate to see anybody go through this. Seemed like if I tried to explain this to somebody, they'd think I was nuts. Why won't someone believe me? They laughed, the F.B.I. I guess they got a charge out of it.

T.: Makes you feel there's nobody on your side, nobody who sees it your way.

M.: They don't seem to. I been to a lot of places. Doc Millman, I told him, and he said, "I don't see no wires on you, Mike." Yeah, don't see 'em—well, I don't know how it's done, it's electronic or what. Anyway, I know I'm personally not to blame, but they can't help me.

[34] Probably distortion; the men are in a woodworking machine plant, and it takes only a little twist to misunderstand *them* (the machines) as *him*.

T.:   How about me, Mike?

M.:   I don't know about you. [Pause.] If you could go through it, maybe a week, maybe a few days—but I'd hate to see anybody else go through this. But if you could, just for a couple of days—they can illusify your mind, like I seen [movie actress] and she called me over, waved, like this, and she was so real, you could reach out, shake hands, dance, do anything you want—

T.:   So real, so vivid—it's an amazing and marvelous thing. I guess you're telling me maybe I ought to experience it too, but—[Mike looks startled]—what's the matter?

M.:   They just said, "What a son of a bitch you turned out to be." Screaming it at me. I never done anything. I never killed, raped, or crippled. People put thoughts in my mind. I'm all confused. Everybody must know I'm not a bad guy. [Begins to sob.]

T.:   Hurts so much.

M.:   If somebody was in my shoes, they couldn't tell nobody. I told my fiancée. She says, "See a doctor." I told the minister. He says, "Mike, better see a doctor." What's the use? I ain't got a chance. Not a chance in hell.

T.:   I guess you're feeling, "I've tried, and nobody understands. Nobody shares with me—I'm just all alone with it."

M.:   All alone, Doc, that's it. What's the use? [Pause.] Can I bum one of your cigarettes?

At the next session, Mike said he had received shock treatment that morning (to my dismay!) and had "forgotten a lot of things." He was meek, submissive, watchful for cues as to what his behavior should be, anxious to please, and showed temporary amnesia for recent events. The administration of shock was by accidental order, and was discontinued, but it was a breach of trust which affected our relation in ways I can never appraise.

Middle Phase   Mike was very morose. He thought his behavior had undermined his family's confidence in him. He felt very helpless now—caged, imprisoned, victimized—and said he got himself in this jam by blaming others (the Masonic temple, etc.). He remembered being given "truth serum," strapped in bed and struggling not to tell the answers to questions put to him. It was on this occasion that his father heard him confess his childhood experience of fellatio, for one thing. When he was taken home from the sanitarium, he thought he ought to tell his mother about it, but she was "not too pleased." At about this time Mike began to develop and/or hint at long-standing feelings toward psychiatrists as the punishers, the probers, the exposers, the unhelpful villains in his experience.

Some of this developed in the next interview. Mike was talking about his observations of a woman patient at a dance.

> M.: I was trying to figure it out. Everything I thought, I saw her lips repeating. She was in the same sort of shape I'm in. She repeated every word that ran through my head. Then I thought—maybe it was the patients who were mentally ill, it might be good to use this machine on those people. It might help them. Now, it might be the psychiatrists who are doing this. Who else would want to know the function of the mind? *I* don't. It's a wearying thing to me. I'm pretty tired of it.
>
> T.: Maybe this would help some other people, but it's not helping me—I'm tired of it.
>
> M.: Yeah. Well, I studied it, up in my mind, I thought about it. I was given truth serum, and I wondered how the inventor did it, and what I worried about was *whether the inventor is responsible.*
>
> T.: I don't understand that, Mike. What do you mean?
>
> M.: I read books on it, and studied on it. And maybe when I told about this during truth serum, maybe that's when they heard of it. I don't know if I had anything to do with it. I can't figure it out. It's too impossible. You can't see anything. All you can do is hear—and you can see hallucinations.

He went on to speculate that he invented it, but they (the psychiatrists) perfected it, wanting to test his strength.

> M.: Let 'em experiment with somebody else. The mind is a delicate thing. I'd hate to see anybody else go through this shit. It's not funny. I know I didn't invent this thing, and if I did, I'd like to burn it. It's like taking your fucking life away from you. I don't go around pulling switches and throwing the juice in people. [Probably a reference to shock therapy.] Now the guy at the foot of the bed—he wrote everything down, and maybe they got the idea from me. Whoever invented this fucking thing oughta be shot—then I'm thinking, oh oh, maybe I'm partly to blame for this.
>
> T.: Seems as if somebody else ought to be punished, but then you think, "God, maybe I thought of this—I wish I hadn't."
>
> M.: That's right. I think I kind of invented it but the psychiatrists perfected it.

As Mike began to assume some responsibility (symbolically), he defensively moved farther away from ultimate blame and further into self-deception. He finished the interview in a rage at being deceived, the butt of jokes, dishonesty, experimentation.

In the ensuing week, he told the ward physician to "please cut my brains out before I kill somebody." This referred to me, for I had become the enemy of enemies. Nor was this simply transference. I *do* represent hospital, professional people who treat and mistreat, I *do* refuse to "tell him all about it" (couldn't), I do frustrate, misunderstand, and disappoint. Mike became violent in the ward, for which he was sent to "security" or given sedation. Often he refused to see me. When he would come, his "oceanic rage" was more than I could bear with equanimity—I became afraid, and often wished I did not have to see him. During this period, attendants sometimes waited outside the closed door.

Looking back, the most interesting thing is the advice given at this time. What Rogers says in this chapter, "It is more therapeutic for him openly to *be* that fear, even expressing it to the client, than to present a calm and unruffled front," was probably written with me in mind. I regret that I did not test his hypothesis. Rather, I took the "liontamer's" advice of the ward physician who said, "Never let them know you're afraid.[35] It frightens them." The clinical director, a wise and experienced therapist, felt that there were really safeguards in Mike, and that I need not be afraid, but if I was—"You have to live with it while it lasts." So I presented a calm front while I worked through my fears and Mike worked out his rage. The end of this period (which lasted three months) was marked by my suggesting that we walk outside on the grounds for the hour. We trusted each other to do this, and the most significant moments of therapy took place thereafter while sitting on a bench or on the grass.

Later Phase   Mike asked for and obtained a grounds pass—freedom to leave the ward. He was given permission for home visits.[36] His family said he was "fine." Does that mean he had solved the riddle of the influencing machine? Or that it was gone? Neither, completely. He was much less affected by it. For one thing, he recognized *some* of the images as recollections of his own past experience. This was an advance over acknowledging the possible invention of the machine—it acknowledged the content of his experience. Second, he began to deny, to his mother (and less to me) that he heard any voices. He took the view (a realistic one) that if he told us, it would delay his release from the hospital and that *if he did not tell us, we would not know.* His privacy

[35] Really laughable, since no one was fooled, and we knew it.
[36] These and all administrative decisions were made by the ward physician.

was restored! He might say, with a grin, "I don't want to talk about it," or soberly, "I can live with it," or just "No, not any more." If his privacy was restored by human contact, what sort of contact was there in those hours on the lawn? Sometimes silence. Sometimes talk of the same sort already reported. Sometimes he began to cry softly, saying, "They talk about needing love and affection. I know what *that* means. The only good thing I ever had [his engagement to a girl] taken away from me, broken up." He blew his nose, dropped his handkerchief, and as he picked it up, glanced at me. He saw tears in my eyes. He offered me the handkerchief, then drew it back because he knew he had just wiped his nose on it and could feel the wetness on his hand. We both knew this, each knew the other knew it; we both understood the feel and the meaning of the handkerchief (the stickiness and texture, the sympathy of the offering and the embarrassment of the withdrawal) and we acknowledged each other and the interplay of each one's significance to the other. It is not the tears, but the exquisite awareness of dual experience that restores consciousness of self. A self *being,* the self-concept can change.

Six months earlier, there had been an interchange like this:

> M.:   Can I bum one, Doc?
> T.:   Does it make you feel like a bum, Mike, to take my cigarettes?
> M.:   Yeah. I—it's a way I feel. I hate to have to ask for anything. At home, when I'm not working, I hate to see Mom put the food on the table.
> T.:   Hurts your pride?
> M.:   I hate to feel like a bum. I guess I am a bum.

Having a grounds pass, Mike could buy his own cigarettes (but not carry matches), and he offered me one, or bought me a Coke, as often as I did him. These were important ways in which he restored his feeling of equality and self-respect. More often, he did not want to talk about himself, was sometimes surly, wanted to discontinue therapy, insisted he was ready to go home. No one felt he was "cured," but he made it look good enough on the outside and was so much better on the inside that the hospital was not helping any longer. His parents took him home. He told them that legally they could, because they were the ones who "signed him in." At one time this was "impossible" to him; his parents could *only* love and want him, *never* would commit him.

Where is Mike now? Happy ending? No—this is really a fragment, a fragment of therapy and of his life. Mike does not come to see me. Where he lives, "A person has to be goofy to go to a psychiatrist." After four months at home, he is working again at his carpenter's trade, trying to make a life for himself. He said on the telephone that he is "pretty *good.*" His mother said, "*pretty* good." Shall the curtain of privacy be drawn against the inquiry of science? I think so. My mind goes back to a scene on the lawn of the hospital. Mike said, "I went to church yesterday, Doc, and I said a prayer that I could go home and this would never happen again. I said a little prayer for you, too—that you could help me and always be well yourself." I was moved, and said, "Thank you." Right now, in my way, Mike, I say a little prayer for you. For all of us.

CHAPTER XII

The Monad, the Dyad, and the Family Therapy of Schizophrenics*

Don D. Jackson

ONJOINT FAMILY PSYCHOTHERAPY has become an important research tool, especially in investigating schizophrenia. Its value as a treatment method, however, remains unknown because its origin is so recent. In this chapter I shall discuss family therapy using as an example the treatment of a thirty-year-old catatonic woman.

THEORETICAL FRAMEWORK OF FAMILY THERAPY

Until the 1930's reports of psychotherapy of schizophrenics were largely conceived within a monadic framework. The patient was studied in terms of his thinking difficulties and the imbalance between the structural aspects of his psyche—the id, superego, and ego. From the written reports available in the literature, which are few in number, it appears that the patient was taught that his anxiety was anachronistic and his projections not related to reality. His unusual experiences and expressions were related to the primary process much as dreams are discussed in terms of manifest and latent content. Support for the ego was emphasized in order to stem the flood of instinctual impulses. Federn

* From the Mental Research Institute and the Department of Psychiatry, Palo Alto Medical Clinic. The ideas expressed in this paper are the responsibility of the author but have been arrived at in collaboration with Gregory Bateson and the research staff.

and others stressed the need for therapy's taking place within the confines of the positive transference.

During the thirties, the mother of the schizophrenic appeared on the horizon and continued to loom ever larger during the next decade. It is not immediately apparent what changes this new figure created in actual psychotherapeutic work but some change must have resulted from a now *dyadic concept* of the schizophrenic's problem. The patient, his relationship to his mother, and the subsequent manifestations of the transference to the therapist actually provided two dyads. This meant that an infinite time span had been created for the patient—from birth to his present therapy sessions. The therapist was now a more sure guide than he had been in previous years in traversing the eras of living because he thought and felt more in terms of the patient's *actual* experiences.

There was another important change in introducing the dyad to the therapy of the schizophrenic and that was the increasing focus on countertransference. Perhaps because the therapist had a mother himself he could identify with the almost unverbalizable horrors that stemmed from the schizophrenic's longing, despair, and hate. When a therapist became a part of these feelings he was more able to become aware of his own responses since it was unlikely that any mortal could sit inscrutable amidst these emotional barrages.

Next there was an important extension of the recognition of transference, and of the fact that it did not develop over a period of time as with neurotics; rather, the patient came wearing it on his lapel. His ordinary day was filled with people to hate and fear, often with good cause, so his transference distortions continually were revivified. By experiencing how the patient distorted their relationship, the therapist was able to recognize the reaction the patient created in others. Sullivan, perhaps more than most experts, recognized that the patient was no mere victim but constantly recreated his own doom. These processes had to be interfered with, and clarified for the patient, and the therapist had to be freer to interject himself into the patient's life from the first meeting. During the forties the school of "active" therapists came to the fore and helped dispel any residual notions about the schizophrenic's relation to a delicate violet.

Despite this broadening of conceptualization and technique there were still major lacks. The patient's productions continued to be treated as "slightly unreal," since they were considered the productions of a grown child who was no longer faced with the same situation that he once had experienced. Understanding the patient's productions in terms of their unconscious meaning was emphasized. That the patient really was misunderstood because his current reality problems were minimized was not seriously considered.

Second, it was not clear *how* the patient managed to make every problem the original problem. The therapist explained schizophrenic behavior in terms of affects and dynamic structures, but these were difficult to translate into techniques of dealing with people. Further, it was puzzling to many therapists why the patient could do well in his session in the hospital setting but apparently would quickly relapse once he went home. Although Sullivan recognized the importance of the acts of "significant others" he did not have sufficient personal experience with the schizophrenic's family to give him the needed data. As early as 1927, Sullivan made an important observation when he stated that he did not believe in "split affect" but thought there was a difference in what the schizophrenic thought and what he felt called upon to say. This cryptic remark apparently refers to "those others" that the schizophrenic feels he must accommodate. Since specific data were lacking, in all probability this remark merely puzzled his colleagues.

Administrative considerations contributed to the therapist's lack of knowledge about the patient's relatives. The notion of the privacy of therapy and the experience of noting that patients did most poorly with their own family encouraged therapists to stay as far away from relatives as possible and to encourage boarding houses rather than home when the patient was first trying out his wings. A recent report by G. W. Brown from the Maudsley Hospital in London confirms the validity of this thinking. He demonstrated that the final therapeutic results for chronic schizophrenic patients after leaving the hospital depended on whether they returned to parents, spouse, or were able to live in a lodging or with siblings. The failure rate was high for those patients returning to the parents or spouse and was not related to their coming from a clinically sicker group. On the other hand, if a married patient was able to return to his spouse and remain outside of the hospital he achieved a higher level of social adjustment than did any other group.

As the psychotherapy of schizophrenics became commonplace more ambulatory patients were treated in the office setting and a situation was created that required dealing with spouses and relatives. Initially the emphasis was on collaborative therapy, but under the stimulus of Ackerman, Bell, Mittlefort, and others conjoint interviews were attempted. Interest in group therapy, and interest of social scientists in research on the family spurred such attempts. In order to study the family, it was necessary to have the members in therapy, and there was an additional economic appeal to this practice. Collaborative therapy is like a chain in that it is dependent on its weakest link. It also poses manpower problems and sometimes flounders on the status problem between workers in the psychiatric field. Thus, if one therapist could effectively treat a family, many advantages would be obtained. The question is not answerable at present. Instead the method can merely be described in terms of some obvious advantages and disadvantages.

SOME ADVANTAGES OF CONJOINT PSYCHOTHERAPY

Occasionally a psychotherapist has written a paper espousing the efficacy of having the patient face his real parents and discuss his feelings with them. The general tenor of such papers is that this real-life action is important and more meaningful than verbal shadowboxing. Perhaps the most important aspect of family psychotherapy is that the patient has to see his parents as real people; he has a preceptorship under the therapist who is dealing with his parents; and he is at least partially defeated in his usual attempt to protect his parents by treating outsiders as if they were all similar to the parents. In family therapy he has to (1) note the difference between the therapist and the parents (ideally assuming there is one); (2) note the differences between his parents rather than blend them into a somewhat meaningless "they"; (3) see the parents as patients, because they become involved with the therapist just as he is. These points are illustrated in the following incidents:

> The identified patient was a thirty-year-old divorced, catatonic, schizophrenic woman with an eighteen-month-old daughter for whom she had never accepted responsibility. The patient had been hospitalized a total of five years and had entered family therapy because she had moved from a distant city to live with her parents. The plan was for the grandmother (the patient's mother) to return to the patient's previous home and retrieve the child when the patient and parents had adjusted to each other. When first seen the patient was mute and the parents were considering rehospitalizing her. I urged them to put off the decision until we had had a few conjoint meetings.
>
> Discussion of how the baby was to be handled when she arrived became an issue from the start. The parents joined together in reassuring the patient that there would be no problem, everybody would pitch in, etc., and succeeded in making her appear to be even more hesitant, confused, and recalcitrant. However, the

therapist, having left the interview for a few minutes to observe the family through a one-way screen, noted that the father looked discontented when the mother remarked with breathy reassurance, "Oh, daddy will be glad to baby-sit when you and I want to go shopping or to the movies." Upon confrontation the father admitted that he was very unsure of his like for or ability at baby sitting and that he had never taken care of his own children.

Following this interview the mother telephoned the therapist to state that the daughter was quite upset, excited, and confused. The therapist spoke to her on the phone and the gist of the conversation was that she didn't know where the baby could sleep, whether they could handle her, etc. The therapist assumed the response was in relation to the parents' indecision and told her that the baby could sleep anywhere, even in the bathtub, and that the important thing was their feeling about having her. Following the conversation the patient calmed down and appeared in much better shape at the next interview.

The father was out of town at this time so the mother and daughter came alone. During the interview the mother said that her husband was nervous and had periods when he was unable to go to work and when she took care of him. She also described how the patient's younger brother had had a similar spell just before leaving for Korea during the conflict there. The therapist asked the mother: since her husband as well as her son and daughter had had breakdowns, was she ever able to allow herself to let down or did she always have to be the strong one? The mother looked very confused, blushed, and finally stated, "It's all over and there's no sense in going into it," and "It was just silly. It is past history." Despite the therapist's telling her that with this attitude she could not possibly understand her daughter, furthermore that it was unfair to treat herself this way, she still denied that her own "breakdown" was of any importance and would not go into the matter. The therapist turned quickly to the daughter and asked her what her understanding of this was, and she replied promptly, though in a whisper, that her mother could understand other people when they had troubles but seemed unable to admit that she had any of her own. The mother then launched into a long apology for having left her daughter so much when she was an infant and became tearful and admitted the extent of her difficulties with her husband in the early days of their marriage. The patient listened interestedly and upon questioning remarked that she had not been told of this before. She nodded, however, when the therapist stated that she must have had some inkling of it.

The afternoon following this session the patient called and stated that she wanted to fly back to fetch her daughter. She came into the therapist's office that afternoon to pick up a letter from him assuring the foster home that he felt she could take the child to her parents' home. The mother was trailing her daughter in the manner of a sheep dog, obviously reflecting her helplessness. When she appealed to the therapist: "What are we going to do about the ticket? I don't have enough money on me," the patient reassured her that she had already called the travel service and that they would accept a check. She returned with the child and for two weeks was in a surprisingly good state. During this period the parents broke out in a rash of quarrels, and the father for the first time in his marriage was impotent.

Unlike collaborative therapy, the patient is not able in conjoint therapy to line up the therapist and parents and withdraw from all of them. The parents and therapist interact and the patient cannot help but notice the interaction. Should either parent become anxious or should either one join the therapist in a temporary coalition, there will be a response on the part of the patient. Further, if the therapist expresses toward the parents thoughts or feelings the patient has also had, but not expressed, he may create for the patient the feeling that "I am not the only one"; or even more important, "My impressions were right after all." The parents' competition for the therapist and mutual buckpassing in their guilt over who made the patient sick splits them and reveals the basic differences between them. This is usually true even though initially they give the appearance of being united in a gluelike structure. As the parents relate to the therapist they identify more with the patient in a sense that they discover aspects of themselves which are patientlike. Needless to say, the patient is watching this process and understands more clearly their unspoken feeling towards him and is able to see them as more human.

> The mother of the schizophrenic patient described above came into a session looking particularly jittery and unstrung. She stated that she "felt like the patient today," whereupon the schizophrenic daughter promptly replied, "Well why not? I thought this family therapy was for all of us." Characteristically, both the mother and patient were able to make such statements because the father was absent.

The conscious deception and lies on the part of the parents seem rather frequent in these families and appear to be a preliminary to expressing their more hidden feelings. Although the patient may be shocked and angry by such disclosures, either at the parents or at the therapist for showing up the parents, he is also relieved because his own guilt is lessened and often he hears confirmed what he has already suspected. Of course, after the patient hears the family deceive the therapist, or withhold information from him, he recognizes *mutatis mutandi* that they have done the same thing to him.

The understanding of schizophrenic communication is a unique advantage of conjoint therapy when the therapist is confronted with a remark in "schizophrenese" which he finds puzzling in content and in timing. He is present at the birth of the schizophrenic's message and can more easily understand its meaning as well as its intent. I used to assume that the language of a schizophrenic was the result of a thinking disorder. Then I became an advocate of the "he doesn't know what he's saying so interpret for him" school; and, finally, under the influence of Fromm-Reichmann, I came to realize the schizophrenic often had a much better notion of what he meant than I did. However, not until family therapy did I realize the bombshell aspect of these often terse and poetic utterances. The patient disqualifies his own messages in such a way that the parents can easily ignore them as being crazy, incorrect, or nonunderstandable. The presence of the therapist, however, changes his technique and encourages the patient to liven up the conversation with a small bomb burst from time to time.

> The parents of Mrs. B. were discussing how they met. At the time both were recovering from a broken romance and rather quickly took to each other. The therapist remarked that considering their respective emotional states at their first meeting, their expectations of each other must have been of a rather high order. This remark caused some discomfort on both parents' part since they preferred to think of their meeting as the splendid serendipity of their broken hearts. The patient, suddenly looking very troubled, spoke out: "I'm worried about having been premature. I don't think premature babies are normal." The father replied that the patient was often concerned about time; things were either "too early" or "too late," etc. The mother joined in to state that the patient had been reassured many times that prematurity was not connected with abnormality and stated that the therapist's reassurance might help. When the therapist started to reassure the patient that prematurity was not connected with her difficulties the patient spoke up again stating: "I have a feeling I was born too early." Despite the parents' active protestations I woke up and took up the question, "Was the patient born too early in the marriage?" No premarital conception was hinted at, but the parents were able to state that the mother's becoming pregnant the first week of marriage necessitated drastic changes in their plans for their respective careers.

The advantage for both therapist and patient of direct experience with family members was most vividly shown in the case of Mrs. B. by her brother's joining the family sessions. This brother, three years her junior, was obviously the parents' favorite and was constantly used as a "white" against the patient's "black." It was as if the parents rested their case for an organic etiology of schizophrenia on their ability to have produced such a *wunderkind*. On one such visit he stayed with his parents about ten days, during which we had three family sessions. In the first session the brother carefully disidentified himself from his sister and her misfortune and she remained quiet and glum. Toward the end of this session, however, I was able to elicit the fact that he had limited a promised visit of three weeks to ten days, and that the mother was deeply hurt by this. The father, though openly fond of his son, appeared relieved that the visit was cut short. Differences between the son and his mother increased during the next session when it was revealed that he resented his parents, especially his mother's interference in his two attempts to get married, and that he had quit college in a rage and enlisted for four years in the Army. The patient had not been present during most of these crises between the parents and brother, and became an avid listener as the material developed. By the third session she was looking somewhat bouncy and commented spontaneously that she had not heard most of this material before. The brother remarked that he was sorry that he was going to be present for such a limited time since he would like more opportunity to discuss his personal difficulties. He indicated now that he was far from happy in his work, a fact which the parents had never acknowledged. It was also revealed that his wife was the dominant partner and she had cut the visit with his parents short in order to have more time with her relatives.

Following the brother's visit the patient achieved an assurance and freedom of speech which she has maintained to date. The superficial explanation appears to be that she was able, for the first time, to compare herself less unfavorably with her brother and to realize that she had been the victim of certain distortions. In addition, she was aided by the fact that her parents genuinely were surprised by, and partially accepted, their new view of their relationship to the favored son.

As a final point about the advantages of family therapy, I want to mention the kind of revelation about the meaning of delusions and other communication distortions that can occur within a few minutes during a conjoint family session.

Mrs. B's father announced during a meeting that he had received a job offer in Washington and was seriously considering taking it. He had a wry smile which I took to be an expression of his delight in getting away from me and family therapy. His wife expressed herself rather clearly, after stating that anything was all right with her, to the effect that the possible disruption of the family sessions were a threat to her "just when we were getting someplace." The father denied any wish to leave, although he admitted he had always liked to travel. His wife attempted to point out to him that the new job involved just the kind of administrative responsibility he did not like, but he was effective in parrying these thrusts. As the room grew a little warmer, the patient, with a pained expression on her face suddenly announced she might not want to move to Washington. Something about her presentation made me treat her remark lightly, and I leaned toward her and in a mock stage whisper asked, "Why not?" "Because the F.B.I. is there" she promptly replied. I leaned closer and whispered, "Really? Come off it." Whereupon she broke into the first belly laugh that had occurred during therapy. This relinquishing of a delusional position occurred just as her father was stating: "Oh, there we go. She's always worrying about somebody being after her." A few minutes later the patient was comfortable enough to make the observation that "We just can't seem to stand closeness. As soon as things get better somebody has to break it up."

DISADVANTAGES

Perhaps the chief disadvantage of family therapy is the danger of creating severe, even explosive, family disharmony. Alcoholic episodes, psychosomatic disorders, separation, or divorce are all possibilities in the face of therapeutic mismanagement. Furthermore, the aftermath of an explosion may be a coalition against the patient, which may mean incarceration for a patient who has been living at home, or increased inaccessibility for an already hospitalized patient. Should the patient be the one who acts out in relation to therapy the family may quickly decide that schizophrenia is not a family problem.

A relative disadvantage is the lack of conventional psychodynamic operations as compared to individual psychotherapy. The therapist is confronted with too many people in the room to explore associations and personal history to the extent that he might wish, and the chances of achieving an "ah-ha" effect in a group that has spent a lifetime disagreeing is infinitesimal. The therapist has to learn to phrase interpretations so that the usual disagreement among family members can aid him in his cause.

At the end of a session I announced to Mrs. B's parents that I had made a great discovery. They were allowed to be curious about this until the next session. At this time I spoke directly to the father and stated that it appeared that he and his wife had a need to be apart and to reserve a good bit of time for themselves. The father, as was expected, immediately disagreed; however, the mother disagreed with her husband, as usual, and felt that the therapist had made a creditable point. She provided some new factual data on the fantastic ability they had in keeping their paths from crossing. This episode was followed by the kind of repercussion that if not a disadvantage is at least an unfortunate by-product of family therapy. If the therapist succeeds in elucidating some of the marital schism the patient becomes more anxious and may attempt to break up therapy. Following the session described above, Mrs. B. became loud and fearful. She shouted that the therapist was running a divorce court and warned her mother that there was a plot to kill her engineered by the father and the therapist. She calmed down after I talked to her on the telephone in a response to an SOS from the mother. I told her that she had endangered her own health by being protective of her parents and that I saw little chance of their breaking up after thirty-odd years of shared dissatisfaction.

Family therapy is technically complicated and most of the complications have countertransference possibilities. One of these complications is the therapist's tendency to identify with the patient and to become critical of the mother. Frequent supervision is often necessary to guard against this difficulty and to help the therapist to see all three people in the room as patients. There is a further difficulty in knowing whom to support in any one moment and for how long. Obviously if the patient is supported, the parents may feel criticized and they may pull the family out of therapy. Another technical problem is that the patient may intervene just at that point where an issue is becoming well defined. The intervention may consist of making himself the butt of an attack, an object for contempt or pity, or he may simply withdraw, hallucinate, and so on and thus attract the most attention. This may pose a problem for the therapist, who can become angry at the patient for "messing things up" at a crucial point. On the other hand, when the patient is in the position of becoming clearer on an issue or of making an improvement, the mother or less frequently the father may intervene.

Mrs. B. had been under pressure from her parents for some time to get a driver's license. At the beginning of a session, the mother excitedly told the therapist the good news. The patient was going to take a driver's test. As I expressed congratulations to the patient, who was looking quite pleased, the mother indicated that there were some secrets that needed to come out. With almost corny histrionics she explained that the patient had told a lie on the driver's test when it asked the question, "Did you ever suffer a nervous breakdown?" The therapist explained to the patient that a letter from him could take care of this point. The mother was continually talking, in such phrases as "Little white lies, where will they stop? You tell one and what will it lead to?" Later in the session the mother was explaining that her daughter was so negativistic it was necessary for the mother to tell her the opposite of what she meant in order to receive her cooperation. When the therapist asked her about the integrity involved in this philosophy she saw no connection with her previous concern about the patient lying. Although this was a good point, for me to have made, there was nevertheless an element of punishment against the mother in bringing it up.

It is difficult to study transference and countertransference situations in family therapy because there are so many moving, shifting coalitions. An observer is usually able to point to many events that the therapist was unable to notice. The tolerance of ambiguity on the part of the therapist has to be fairly great. He cannot, as in individual therapy, explore all the avenues that may be appealing.

A final disadvantage to family therapy exists in attempting to relate therapy to theory. Our language for small-group interaction is inadequate and conventional dyadic frames of reference do not suffice. When one is dealing with present and past, the hopes and expectations, the verbal and nonverbal behavior, and the immediate ongoing interactions of at least four people, it seems doubtful that it can ever be encased within a framework smaller than a circus tent. Several complementary descriptive systems may be the best we can achieve in describing family interaction.

SUMMARY

In this brief description of conjoint family therapy I have tried to show that this method of approach requires a new conceptual framework which is a logical extension of earlier monadic and dyadic constructions. Some advantages and disadvantages are described which render a final decision as to the effectiveness of conjoint family therapy out of the question at present. As in all psychotherapy, transference and countertransference problems and the therapist's ability to grasp the data being fed him are central issues.

CHAPTER XIII

Individual Therapy of Schizophrenic Patients and Hospital Structure*

Helm Stierlin

MAN IS AN ANIMAL who can be complexly confused. Other higher animals can also be confused, either experimentally or in the course of their natural life experience, by becoming subject to conflicting drives or interdictions. So-called artificially induced animal neuroses are one example; another example is the naturally occurring displacement activities[1] described by Tinbergen,[2] Lorenz,[3] Kortlandt,[4] and others. But

* Assistance in preparing this article for publication was given by the Chestnut Lodge Research Institute under its grant from the Ford Foundation.

[1] Displacement activities were discovered at about the same time by Kortlandt and Tinbergen. Such displacement activities in animals occur in situations of so-called drive conflict: a certain drive has been strongly activated but cannot be discharged through its usual channels. This happens mostly when (1) two strongly activated drives are competing with each other, or (2) an outer situation is not sufficient enough to lead to the consummatory action of the strongly activated drive (mostly the sexual drive). The stickleback, for example, who is in a strong fighting mood but prevented from discharging his aggressive energies, will dig holes in the sand; that is, he will carry out an activity that belongs in the realm of the nesting instinct. For an excellent study of displacement activities in the human see H. Lincke, "Bemerkungen zur Triebpsychologie der Ersatzbefriedigung und Sublimierung," *Psyche*, 7 (1953), 501-520; E. Weigert, "Human Ego Functions in the Light of Animal Behavior," *Psychiatry*, 19 (1956), 325-332.

[2] N. Tinbergen, "Die Übersprungbewegung," *Ztschr. Tierpsychol.*, 4

the confusion into which man can be thrown is much deeper and more complex than what occurs in these instances. In animals there exists no comparable equivalent to human schizophrenia.

Two basic facts account for man's extreme susceptibility to confusion: first, his comparatively prolonged dependence on a mothering person[5]; and second, facilitated by this dependence, his growing exposure to, and participation in, a communicative interplay with other people, committing him to the use of certain expressive movements, symbols, and finally a language—which have meaning only within given relationships and cultures. This long dependency and the learning and manipulation of symbols harbor the potential for seemingly extreme and contrary developments: they make possible the miracle of man's acculturation, of an astonishingly complex and creative self-realization within a world upon which he can impose his meanings and images; but also, at the same time, they prepare the ground for a degree of possible confusion, of loneliness, of an emotional starvation amidst plenty which appear to be equally uniquely human. These opposite developments must therefore be viewed as the two sides of one coin. They are two possible outgrowths from man's prolonged dependency and his interactions with others via expressive movements and symbols.

In further elucidating these basic conditions of man's existence we have come in recent years to focus our attention on that phase of human life in which the young child, still being embedded in a symbiotic dependence on the mother, makes his first decisive steps toward greater independence and separateness. These steps occur at a time when he, by the very fact of his great dependency, is still most susceptible to many influences communicated to him in more or less subtle ways. In the fortunate case these influences may contribute to the child's growth toward greater independence, creativity, and to a rich and meaningful

---

(1940), 1-40; *The Study of Instinct* (Oxford: Oxford Univ. Press, 1951).

[3] K. Lorenz, "Über angeborene Instinktformeln beim Menschen," *Deutsche Med. Wochenschrift.*, 77 (1953), 1566-1569, 1600-1604.

[4] A. Kortlandt, "Aspects and Prospects of the Concept of Instinct," *Arch. Neer. Zool.*, 11 (1955), 155-284.

[5] A most interesting comparative biological study on the unique role and meaning of man's unusually prolonged dependency has been made in Adolf Portmann, *Biologische Fragmente zu einer Lehre vom Menschen* (Basel: Benno Schwabe, 1944); *Zoologie und das neue Bild vom Menschen* (Hamburg: Rowohlt, 1956). For other interesting studies of this problem made from a biological and anthropological point of view, see: G. Bally, *Vom Ursprung und den Grenzen der Freiheit* (Basel: Benno Schwabe, 1945); F. J. J. Buytendijk, *Mensch und Tier* (Hamburg: Rowohlt, 1958).

exchange with the people and the world around him. In the unfortunate case, however, they may lead to a kind of crippling enslavement which we have much reason to suspect lies behind the manifestations of one of the most tragic and puzzling human conditions known to us—schizophrenia.

Much light has been thrown on this crucial developmental stage by some observations and comments by René Spitz.[6] Spitz, in line with other investigators such as Therese Benedek,[7] Harold Lincke,[8] Lewis B. Hill,[9] has pointed out that there exists between the mother and the newborn infant an almost instinctive interlocking of needs, an immediate symbiotic fusion. This fusion only gradually loosens, to the degree in which the child develops and differentiates his various motoric, perceptive, and communicative tools. As this process continues, the symbiotic fusion must, to use Spitz's words, be replaced by emotional ties. In other words, the separation that is forced upon the child as a consequence of his growing bodily and mental differentiation necessitates a new bond—a new type of relatedness. This new relatedness is characterized by the inhibition, or at least selective inhibition, of those drives and needs in the child which would previously tend to seek their fulfillment in a kind of symbiotic short cut taking the availability of the other person for granted. In the new goal-inhibited relatedness, however, the partner emerges as a person with characteristic needs and peculiarities of his own. The very blockage of these primitive, fusion-oriented drives, as manifested in the child's wish to be cuddled, fed, etc., provides the energy for the exploration and development of new modes of closeness which correspond to the child's advanced differentiation. It is a closeness which is now experienced in an increasingly complex matrix of stimulations and frustrations, of challenges and responses, of tolerable ambivalence. It can be described as a kind of dialectical closeness whose very strength is evidenced by a great range of expressiveness within the relationship but without harboring a threat to the relationship.

I would like to consider the process from another angle. The ability

[6] R. Spitz, *Die Entstehung der ersten Objektbeziehungen* (Stuttgart: Klett, 1957); *No and Yes* (New York: Internat. Univ. Press, 1957).

[7] T. Benedek, "Contributions to the Libido Theory: Parenthood as a Developmental Phase." Presented March 8, 1957, at the meeting of the Washington Psychoanalytic Society.

[8] H. Lincke, *Zur Genese der Identifikation und des Überichs* (in press).

[9] L. B. Hill, *Psychotherapeutic Intervention in Schizophrenia* (Chicago: Univ. Chicago Press, 1955).

to tolerate and express intensely ambivalent feelings within one relationship is, we have reason to believe, a unique human achievement. For example, the mating of the stickleback fish, according to Lorenz and Tinbergen, inevitably ends with the destruction of one partner if there is no rival at hand on whom the male stickleback can unload his accumulated aggressive energies. The marriage, on the other hand, is bound to be harmonious when such a rival is available. The enemy is needed, so to speak, for the sake of marital peace. This very simple example may serve as the prototype of a restricted expressiveness within one relationship: the very closeness and dependence of the two partners on each other makes the expression of a wide range of conflicting and ambivalent feelings equivalent to self-destruction.

The available evidence suggests that the higher an animal is on the ladder of phylogenetic development, the greater his potential for enduring ambivalence within one relationship. In man the ability to express and tolerate ambivalence within one relationship—to endure it without having to dissociate or project feelings, particularly the negative feelings—appears to be closely linked to his ability to differentiate and introspectively clarify his own feelings. In a complex modern society this seems to be one of the most essential characteristics of mental health.

With these remarks in mind, I would like to focus again on the above-mentioned stage of the child's development during which, still strongly dependent on his parents and particularly his mother, he makes his first ventures against the person on whom he is dependent. His increasing self-awareness and mastery over his body, the growth of his differentiation and expansion, are factors driving him toward such action. According to René Spitz, the child's ventures at greater self-expression and self-assertion are frequently bound to occur in crisislike dramatic accentuations corresponding to the maturation of new body functions and the acquisition of new skills. The child's acquisition of sphincter control, for example, making possible the willful elimination or withholding of feces now very pointedly permits him to become nonconforming and negativistic; that is, it allows him to say "No."

Yet whether he can dare to say "No"—and this is an important point—is highly dependent on factors which are outside his control. This depends, above all, on the desire and the ability of his parents to permit such assertiveness. This ability, it may be added, also includes firmness in preventing the little child from becoming a tyrant. The parent rather provides a fine balance consisting of controls from without, where none exist yet within, as well as a free range for self-assertiveness, this balance being sensitively geared to the child's age, needs, and capacities.

There is required, therefore, a parent-child relationship in which the child can be dependent and protected, but at the same time can feel trust that his separateness will be tolerated. He must experience himself as being different and antagonistic, but need not, because of this, fear that he will be unrelated.

What specifically constitutes this ability of the parents that facilitates such a relatedness in the child?

It is characterized, it seems to me, by two essential but seemingly paradoxical elements: on the one side, by a great deal of freedom and spontaneity in the parents' own interaction with their child, and on the other, by an element of detachment. The parents' own naturalness and ease in expressing a wide range of feelings will encourage the child to act similarly and will foster an interpersonal climate of lively mutual stimulation and responsiveness, of a meaningful reciprocity. This then is the very matrix of emotional ties and of relatedness once the oneness of the original symbiotic fusion between mother and child has ceased to be tenable. The detachment, on the other hand, is the basis of an attitude of caring and responsibility, of the ability to see the child in his own right and to be particularly aware of his great impressiveness and vulnerability. It represents the capacity to step out, so to speak, of one's own spontaneous and often blind reactivity, thereby enabling one to take a look at the other person apart from one's own needs. This detached look will take into account the other person's different personality, his past and his future, and particularly it will allow a recognition of his necessary growth toward greater separateness and relative autonomy. The natural spontaneous responsiveness toward the child must thus be rooted in a kind of intransitive watchfulness. It appears then that only a combination of these two basic and seemingly contradictory elements, freedom of expression and a detached considerateness, will guarantee that the relationship in question will not foster the child's exploitation and that it will further instead of prevent his growth. In contrast to a symbiotic relationship which is growth-crippling, I would like to call such a growth-permitting relationship one of *nonexploiting solidarity*.

This nonexploiting relationship represents, in my opinion, the structural nucleus for all truly therapeutic relationships and particularly for the psychotherapeutic relationships with schizophrenic patients. Many modifications and degrees of complexity—necessitated by traditions, the structure of society and of the medical profession, etc.—later come into play, but the essential elements of this structure, it appears to me, usually can readily be recognized. I propose to examine some ramifications and consequences of this viewpoint which seem to have particular relevance for the treatment of severely psychotic patients, dealing at first with some aspects of the structure of classical analysis.

The principle of nonexploiting solidarity is clearly evidenced in the therapeutic framework of psychoanalysis as developed by Freud. For this relationship is essentially structured around a solidarity between the therapist and his patient designed to facilitate the expression—and thereby better understanding and integration into the latter's character— of those aspects of his personality which he had to dissociate from his awareness at an early age because of frightening sanctions. Yet in this relationship, which typically mobilizes highly charged emotions, there exists also, characteristically, a great deal of structured distance between the therapist and his patient. This distance is maintained and reinforced by the various elements of the professional setup in which the therapeutic process takes place. It appears to me that many details of the classical psychoanalytic situation—for example, the therapist's sitting behind the patient, the routine of appointments, the extolling of a screenlike passivity of the therapist, etc.—serve primarily as some sort of institutionalized safeguards designed to maintain a professional, attentive detachment in the therapist. They are basically auxiliary devices needed to counterbalance the great pressures from the patient which tend to draw the doctor into a strong emotional involvement with the patient. This detachment of the physician, institutionally reinforced, serves, in other words, as an essential element in structuring his relationship to the patient as one of nonexploiting solidarity.

In delineating this characteristic therapeutic solidarity Freud structured a situation in which it was possible for therapist and patient to suspend, at least temporarily, many of society's conventional values which are usually unquestioningly accepted by its members. Highly censored sexual taboos and wishes, religious blasphemies, embarrassing infantile cravings, etc., could be expressed in this framework; the therapeutic hour provided a temporary sanctuary within the world of conventional values. In this situation both therapist and patient found each other in a certain sense beyond the conventional "good and evil" and this further facilitated the patient's self-expression and subsequent self-understanding.

If we now consider, in the light of the foregoing, the ideal structure for the psychotherapy of psychotic, and particularly schizophrenic patients, several points become apparent. Fundamentally, the therapeutic relationship must be one of nonexploiting solidarity as outlined in the examples of the early parent-child and analyst-patient relationship. But due to the extent of the patient's sickness, several characteristic modifications have to take place. For, unlike the usual neurotic patient, who is strong and integrated enough to enter into an analytic relationship while his everyday life is going on, and who is thus able to find his sanctuary for greater self-expression and self-exploration amidst the agitations of daily life, the average psychotic patient has neither the strength nor the motivation to do so. The psychotic patient, as a rule, does not actively and straightforwardly seek help. If he asks for help, he does it indirectly in ambivalent and often cryptic ways. And often he is so withdrawn in his despair and hopelessness, so encrusted in a paranoid wall, or so openly assaultive and obnoxious that he discourages with great persistency and success those who are trying to help him. Consequently, a very major part of the psychotherapeutic work with schizophrenic patients consists in frequently groping and intuitive endeavors on the part of the therapist to establish any relationship at all.

The vicissitudes and problems inherent in such endeavors are well known; often only great persistence and patience can kindle hope where hope has long been given up. The encounter between therapist and patient not infrequently occurs on a level of primitive feelings and needs, often corresponding to a developmental stage where inner experiences cannot yet be verbalized or conceptualized and where the felt anxiety, ungraspable and undefinable as it often is, is bound to become tremendous. And this anxiety is not unfounded. It reflects the ever present danger that even the last defensive remnants of the patient—self-crippling as they are, but needed to provide the minimum feeling of boundedness, security, and self-esteem—will give way to a state of complete nothingness and fragmentation, a threat that appears only too real in the light of many observable states of extreme dilapidation.

These factors, the unusually long therapeutic effort required and the frequent vagueness as well as intensity of the feelings and anxieties aroused, necessitate a softening or even abolition of many aspects of the therapeutic structure of classical analysis. Instead, the psychotherapy of schizophrenic patients often has to proceed in a climate where the therapist can feel free to make full use of his total personality, and where he is relatively unhampered by many of the more conventional views as to how a doctor should treat a patient.

But further, as a direct result of the lessened rigidity of the therapeutic setup and the high degree of therapeutic investment required, there will often be a much greater involvement of the therapist with his patient than is the case in the average analytic relationship. For it is only natural that the often primitive feelings and needs that have been kindled in this relationship will tend to seek satisfaction within this relationship. Thus forces operate within it which tend to re-enact—that is, drive the therapist into—a similarly deep and symbiotic entanglement, potentially both extremely frightening as well as intriguingly pleasurable, that seems to be characteristic of the schizophrenic's early relationship to his "schizophrenogenic" mother.[10] Yet instead of merely re-enacting such a symbiotic *folie à deux* it becomes the task of the therapist to direct his involvement with the patient into constructive channels; that is, to make it useful for the patient in his strides toward greater growth and relative autonomy.

This, then, forces us to take a new look at the essential requirements for the establishment of a relationship of nonexploiting solidarity with the schizophrenic. This rather unusual treatment situation, in my opinion, requires that the therapist of schizophrenic patients have in his own personality at least part of those controlling and detaching forces which the analyst of neurotic patients finds, so to speak, ready made for him in the classical structure of psychoanalysis. It also makes desirable, in my opinion, a hospital structure which optimally reinforces and facilitates the therapist's contribution toward a relationship of nonexploiting solidarity as described previously.

In the following I want, therefore, to deal with the personality of the therapist and with the structure of the mental hospital insofar as both are relevant to the establishment of a relationship of nonexploiting solidarity and to the facilitating of optimal self-expressiveness in the patient.

PERSONALITY OF THE THERAPIST

Frieda Fromm-Reichmann is reported to have said once that any schizophrenic patient could be helped if one could only find the right mother for him. What, then, are the main characteristics of such a good mother? In thinking about this crucial question and in surveying the literature for an answer, I found a hint in a passage written by Lewis B. Hill.[11]

---

[10] H. Stierlin, "The Adaptation to the 'Stronger' Person's Reality," *Psychiatry*, 22 (1959), 143-152.

[11] L. B. Hill, *Psychotherapeutic Intervention in Schizophrenia*, pp. 38-39.

In the course of time, pondering over the quality of the attitude of the physician toward the sick schizophrenic which is most useful I have come to think that the requisite human interest, concern, curiosity, and warmth and helpfulness are all most safely and satisfactorily expressed in what can be called an "intransitive" mood. The patient needs to feel the presence of these qualities in the doctor but must be protected from any sense of their being imposed upon him or of their making any demand that he cannot meet. It goes without saying that the doctor, being human, notes in himself erotic interests, anger, amusement, weariness, and so on. But these also must be intransitive—that is, not aimed at the patient.

In these sentences Hill conveys the paradoxical combination of attitudes of a parent who is able to structure for his child a growth-permitting relationship of nonexploiting solidarity. Sullivan,[12] it appears to me, had in mind a similar combination of attitudes when he characterized the optimal psychiatric attitude as one of "participant observer," thus also stressing the crucial mixture of empathic solidarity and observant detachedness so strongly required for successful psychotherapy with these patients. It is my personal impression that the therapists at Chestnut Lodge who find a particular challenge and interest in the psychotherapeutic work with schizophrenic patients have, in spite of seemingly great outward divergence of character and temperament, this basic personality trait in common.

Bipolarity of the Hospital Structure

It is my opinion that this bipolarity of the forces of participation and observation necessary for the successful therapist's dealings with the schizophrenic patient must be reflected and paralleled in a corresponding bipolarity of the total hospital. I have developed this aspect in a previous paper.[13] In this context let it suffice to point out that in an institution like Chestnut Lodge a structure has crystallized which makes possible and reinforces an ongoing, equally intense involvement and deinvolvement of the individual therapist with his psychotic patient. I have called these ever present, strongly institutionalized, and seemingly contradictory forces the *tendencies for sensitization* and *tendencies for stabilization*. At Chestnut Lodge there are several factors which are

[12] H. S. Sullivan, in Helen Swick Perry and Mary Ladd Gawel (eds.), *The Interpersonal Theory of Psychiatry* (New York: Norton, 1953).
[13] Stierlin, "The Adaptation to the 'Stronger' Person's Reality."

tendencies for stabilization: the selection of a group of "schizophre-nophile" therapists, the small number of patients making up one doc-tor's caseload, and the prevailing general conviction that schizophrenic patients can be helped by intensive psychotherapy. All these factors tend to promote an active, sensitive involvement of the therapist with his schizophrenic patient. Also, there is the amount of supervision given by older therapists to less experienced ones, and the compulsory training analyses at the nearby psychoanalytic institute which provide the ful-crum for this involvement. Further, the strong prevailing emphasis on discussion and research is an additional factor in promoting detachment and fostering an objective clarification of the relationship in question. They all belong to the factors for stabilization. It appears therefore to be just the counterplay of these two forces, operating on an individual as well as on an institutional level, which tends to create the optimal framework for the development of a nonexploiting and growth-permit-ting relationship in the treatment of very sick psychotic patients.

THE HOSPITAL'S FUNCTION IN SELF-EXPRESSION

The mental hospital, in matching and reinforcing the sensitivity as well as the stability of the therapist, supports him in establishing a personal relationship of nonexploiting solidarity with his patient. But that is not its only contribution to the psychotherapy of schizophrenic patients. For, if we follow further the line of thought taken in this study, the hospital can be viewed, because of its peculiar organization and place in society, as a unique therapeutic structure harboring the elements that foster maximal expressiveness and growth explored in the parent-child and analyst-patient relationships.

Life in a mental hospital has been repeatedly described, particularly in the writings of Erikson,[14] as a moratorium. The very fact that it removes the patient from the pressures of his everyday environment and provides him with a kind of protected emotional breathing space is considered to be most helpful; the absence of pressures, the lessened need to make immediate, anxiety-laden, and sometimes irreversible decisions will enable the patient to gain a perspective, to see his own situation in a different light, to become aware of new sources of strength within himself, and thereby to grow.

On a general level this statement appears to be correct. Yet it throws little light on the question which is of foremost interest in the present

[14] E. H. Erikson, *Ego Identity and the Life Cycle: Psychological Issues* (New York: Internat. Univ. Press, 1959).

context: How can the mental hospital by its very structure, apart from providing a breathing space, facilitate for the deeply psychotic person a kind of insightful self-expressiveness?

In order to explore this problem I would like again to compare some aspects of the traditional analytic treatment situation designed for the neurotic with that which has become established for the psychotic patient.

The expressiveness engendered and maintained in the analytic situation, it must be remembered, is still a highly controlled expressiveness. The expression of emotionally charged and previously censored wishes, fantasies, and feelings is kept in bounds, so to speak, by the mutual recognition of the situation in which this expression occurs. Both patient and doctor never altogether lose sight of the fact that all this is part of the therapeutic process and that, at the end of the hour, the patient must and will be able to carry on his activities in the outside world. There is still functioning, in other words, an observant part of the patient's personality that will enable him to keep his problems in a kind of workable semisuspension that makes it possible to ponder about them without becoming too incapacitated by the anxiety stirred up in this process. There exists a manageable optimum of anxiety and feeling intensity—not so strong as to become too disruptive and threatening to therapist and patient, and not so weak as to be lacking in the production of the emotional fuel necessary for a successful "working through" of the patient's problems and for the subsequent achievement of lasting personality changes.

In contrast to this, there does not exist such a manageability in the case of the more deeply disturbed schizophrenic patient. That minimum of reality-orientedness which keeps the realistic aspects of the treatment situation in the neurotic patient's awareness is frequently lacking in the schizophrenic; his feelings for his therapist therefore often have a quality of terrible, unmitigated realness. They are, so to speak, unbuffered by any consideration of the allegedly "therapeutic" or "contract" nature of the ordeal he is going through. It is for this reason that it often appears to be unjustified to compare this form of "transference"—the patient's intense focusing of subjectively real feelings onto the therapist—with the usually much milder emergence of resistances, fantasized material, etc., which is characteristic of the therapeutic process in classical psychoanalysis. For the schizophrenic this "transference" is an intensely real experience with feelings which, despite the fact that they usually represent the not-yet-understood re-enactments of past experiences, are intended to be exclusively personal and which are therefore bound to be experienced by the therapist, at least momentarily, as extremely personal, too.

From this follows the need for an important function of the mental hospital. It must take upon itself a great deal of the burden of the patient's needs for an intense and often frighteningly unconventional expressiveness. At least it partly relieves the therapist from becoming the sole target of the patient's intense and often ambivalent strivings, experienced by the latter with such strong subjective realness. It becomes a kind of an institutionalized punching bag which, in its totality, can take beatings from the patient which normally neither the therapist alone nor the people of the patient's usual environment would be able or willing to endure. It provides, in other words, an enclave in which the patient, in a somewhat different sense from that outlined previously, can dare tentatively to live out, with a feeling of subjective realness, those tendencies and needs which when expressed in the outside world would immediately evoke heavy sanctions of one sort or another and would be too disruptive to be tolerated in an outpatient relationship. The hospital thus represents an island within the world of conventional reality. The whole hospital is, in a certain sense, placed beyond the "good or evil" concepts of society; it is a place where many of society's sanctions for the enforcement of its values are suspended.

Yet the mental hospital must also be viewed as an institutional "anomie," as a kind of special social safety valve established by society to take care of certain devious but nevertheless ineradicable and potentially explosive needs and trends. Left unchecked, these needs would become a threat to many conventional values; for instance, to the ethics of marriage, professional conduct, etc., which more or less clearly have come to be considered as essential for the functioning of society as a whole.[15]

Yet this line of thinking reveals the unique problem a mental hospital is bound to encounter, which is the need to reconcile its service as a custodial receptacle for society's troublemakers with its goal of providing an island which facilitates therapeutic self-expressiveness. It must be expected that this very fundamental conflict of interests will deeply affect and distract the hospital from functioning as a truly

---

[15] Another example for such institutionalized safety valves are gambling places like Las Vegas where, with official semi-approval, society's usual taboos against gambling are suspended under certain exceptional and controlled conditions. See T. Parsons, *The Social System* (Glencoe: Free Press, 1951).

therapeutic institution and it is with some basic aspects of this dilemma, those which have a particular impact on the treatment of schizophrenic patients, that I want to deal now.

The mental hospital, although it is an island within conventional reality, must nevertheless be staffed with the very members of this society who share, wittingly or unwittingly, many of society's conventions and beliefs. In a certain sense, then, the typical hospital nurse or aide is a citizen with two nationalities. For example, within the hospital he often is expected to be unusually permissive in situations in which he would unquestionably condemn permissiveness in his outside life. But further, unlike the therapist, who normally sees his psychotic patient only one hour a day or less, the aide's daily contacts with this patient frequently extend over many hours. He is, therefore, often much more strongly exposed to the patient's unconventional behavior, his excessive demands, his hostility, and also to a frequently tempting interaction of symbiotic mothering with him. All this will tend to draw him into a deep involvement with a particular patient. This means that the aide, in order to make his contact with the patient therapeutic, must also find his own balance of sensitivity and stability in his dealings with the patient. Yet unlike the therapist, the typical aide has often little chance to achieve an intellectual clarification of his position. He is not trained to do so nor has he the ready access to a comparable amount of supervision, discussion with colleagues, etc., which are main factors in maintaining and reinforcing an independent detachment and stability in the therapist.

The following excerpts from the case of a girl treated at Chestnut Lodge for her schizophrenic psychosis are intended to illustrate further some of the therapeutic problems inherent in the hospital's unique and problematical position of being outside and, at the same time, inside the conventional world.

Joan, a twenty-four-year-old single college graduate, was admitted to Chestnut Lodge in an almost mute, catatonic conditon. It was her second schizophrenic break. The first had occurred about a year ago necessitating a hospitalization of six months. This first hospitalization ended with the patient's running away from the hospital. Joan appeared at that time outwardly improved, but was unable to hold a job and continued to be troubled by suicidal impulses and many strange ideas and paranoid notions. Evidently her attempts to redissociate the threatening psychotic material were only partially successful.

At Chestnut Lodge, where I became her therapist, Joan remained for several months in a state of practically mute, anguished, and apprehensive frozenness. Only slowly and gradually did she open up and communicate more. She impressed others as being a very overapologetic, overpolite, and shy girl, afraid of imposing on others and of revealing a more aggressive and self-assertive side of herself. While in this condition she elicited from the personnel, but hardly responded to, much rather warm and seemingly benevolent encouragement to express herself more straightforwardly, to show a little more healthy aggressiveness, and so on.

This repressed aggressive part of herself finally became manifest. Coinciding with a very anxiety-laden visit home it suddenly broke through with explosive vehemence. Now the patient presented almost the very opposite of her catatonic frozenness. She was excited, restless, and hyperactive. She turned into a defiant, sarcastic, and contemptuous person, upbraiding other patients, snobbishly ridiculing the ward personnel and expressing most unflattering opinions about the values of mutual helpfulness, solidarity, and so forth. Also, in a rather provocative and flaunting manner, she carried on a relationship with a male patient and showed little outward concern about the possibility of a pregnancy.

In this situation the attitude of the ward personnel, previously characterized by a good deal of encouraging warmth and desire to help, became very disapproving. Joan, sensing that she had become for many of the personnel a disliked and even hated troublemaker, in a kind of desperate abandon lived up to the role of the "bad girl" by increasing her flaunting and openly sarcastic behavior. She got the publicity of an *enfant terrible*. This focusing of attention on her, negative though it was, had further disturbing consequences. The other patients living on Joan's ward responded to this "negative favoritism" by themselves developing more attention-provoking regressed and disorganized behavior—like self-neglect and messiness, impulsive assaultiveness, etc. —thereby increasing the general ill feeling toward the root of all this evil, the patient. Finally there was a fog of agitation around her. She succeeded also in involving her parents who, already feeling most ambivalent about the patient's progress, received fuel for their negative and distrustful feelings toward the hospital and particularly toward the physicians treating Joan. All these developments accelerated a crisis which almost led to the patient's removal from the hospital and thus to the discontinuation of her psychotherapy. The crisis was resolved, instead, by the patient's being transferred to another administrative service.

This outline is necessarily oversimplified. Many data which have a possible bearing on the problems discussed in this study had to be left out. Nevertheless, it is sufficient to throw light on some ever present, covert and overt curbs squelching the patient's optimal expressiveness. These curbs have their basis in the needs of the personnel and the structure of the hospital.

The Need for Success

There was much concern and apprehension in what appeared to be a setback for Joan. Her manic, excited, and sarcastic behavior was seen as a reversal of her improvement, so far gradual but continuous. This was conveyed to Joan but not directly. She in turn felt even more anxious about what she was experiencing and doing. But being unable to control her behavior, she was even more anxiously driven in the direction of explosive agitation.

Joan's behavior thus conflicted with the strong need, shared by practically all members of the hospital community, to see improvement and therapeutic success. This need is very understandable, but awareness of it is required. It is based on and reinforced by many factors—personal, institutional, and cultural. For example, the great financial burden often placed on the relatives of these patients tends to promote guilt feelings in the therapist as well as in all other hospital staff if "nothing is moving." Further, the fact that the intensive psychotherapy of psychotic patients is still generally viewed with a great deal of disbelief or competitive distrust (the more so since it can presently be afforded only by a relatively rich few) can provide for a hospital climate in which success is badly needed for everybody's self-esteem. But this need, it appears to me, becomes particularly activated when a certain patient initially shows great promise but then, for one reason or another, threatens to get stuck. And this seemed to have been the case with Joan.

The need on the part of the personnel and the therapist to see improvement and therapeutic success thus interferes with the patient's need to use the hospital as a protected experimental ground for greater self-expressiveness. To put it briefly: instead of daring to express some of his more strange, disturbing, unpleasant, and often openly psychotic tendencies, the patient, under the pressure of these hospital needs, will continue to "cover up." In line with his previous life experience, he will be pressured into conforming to some conventional stereotype of so-called normal or healthy behavior instead of benefiting from the unique chance to face, and thereby to learn more about his alleged or real "craziness." In other words, where there exists great pressure to see improvement the fact tends to become overlooked that some outward disintegration is frequently prerequisite for the development of a more wholesomely integrated state. Such concepts as "re-progression," [16] "re-gression in the service of the ego," *"reculer pour mieux sauter,"* etc., all convey this fact. For example, many states of chaos and turmoil which occur during psychoanalysis and adolescence must often be viewed as the manifestations of an unavoidable break-up of more limited and unworkable personality patterns in order that a more workable integration may emerge. Yet the psychiatrist, educator, or nurse who is unable to see the total Gestalt and the necessity of this process will automatically call pathology any greater disintegration, upset, or "acting out" and thereby tend to treat the symptoms instead of the disease; that is, he will again keep the patient from optimal self-expression.[17]

At precisely this point it is crucial for the treatment of the patient whether the hospital maintains a permissive and growth-oriented ideology of its own or whether it remains identified with the conventional ideas and stereotypes about mental health maintained by the remainder of society. If the hospital varies little from society, that is, if a particular hospital community is strongly identified with conventional ideas and values about health, social usefulness, etc., it can be expected that the members of this hospital community see their main therapeutic goal in bringing the patient back into line with these conventional standards, by the easiest and fastest means at its disposal. Electroshock, lobotomy, and the heavy use of tranquilizing drugs, all geared to bringing the patient quickly "back into shape" are under these circumstances the logical means for the treatment of psychotic patients. On the other hand, when a long-range permissive viewpoint can be held even under pressures such as those described above, the patient's chances for persistent and constructive personality change will increase.

The Need to Feel Competent This need of the personnel is related to the need to succeed, but it is not quite the same. It is the need to find

---

[16] Kortlandt, "Aspects and Prospects of the Concept of Instinct."

[17] The extreme of a crippling personality structure which is strongly fixated and rigidly defended is probably the so-called paranoid state. In applying the above considerations one might ask whether any personality change in such a patient can be achieved without some period of increased outward disturbance, which may manifest itself, for example, in a more catatonic condition. However, data with which to answer this question are as yet lacking.

self-acceptance and self-esteem in having achievements and personality traits which are positively valued and respected by the surrounding society. In a hospital this more general need tends to become crystallized in the need to feel professionally competent and respected.

In the case of Joan, the personnel reacted with particular sensitivity to any of her behavior that threatened their belief in their own importance and professional competence. It appears to me to be a characteristic that even very deeply regressive, masturbatory, and messy behavior of patients can often be tolerated relatively easily by the personnel as long as it seems to be, so to speak, wrapped up in a whole bundle of helpless dependency and craziness. It can then be accepted and pardoned as constituting a part of the patient's "sickness." But this tolerance rapidly diminishes when a patient like Joan uses her superior intelligence in order very pointedly and snobbishly to call attention to the nurses' inferior social position and to their lack of education, or when she seems to trample on such commonly accepted values as respect for others, sympathy, mutual helpfulness, and so on. Surely, it is one of our implicit therapeutic goals to make these values meaningful for a patient. But it makes a decisive difference whether these values are dogmatically enforced upon a dependent person, thus necessitating the dissociation of a hated bad part of the self, or whether they emerge as a result of the acceptance of the "good" as well as the "bad" in oneself. It seems to me that Joan, in encountering a strong and disapproving resistance from aides and nurses, was again prematurely pressured into "goodness." Again, as in her earlier relationships, she was not given a chance to express, and thereby to understand and integrate, a very essential side of her personality.

The Need to Belong   Before and during the period of "crisis" Joan expressed great dissatisfaction with the ward on which she was living. She tended to praise the administrators and nurses of other wards while abusing and derogating the members of her own ward—patients as well as nurses and aides. In other words, she refused to be a member of the group to which she had been assigned. Also, this attitude was bound to elicit resentment and disapproval from the persons thus rebuked, and this resentment was very apparent. Again, it has to be kept in mind that the resentment was complexly determined, but the threat to in-group solidarity which Joan's behavior implied was a strong contributing factor to the resentment.

The great need for an in-group solidarity is, at least partly, a direct outgrowth of the fact that the hospital is an "island in itself" within the surrounding society. For the more the hospital, in at least some of its prevailing attitudes and values, is set apart from the remainder of the culture, and the less this apartness is understood and based on the individual's convictions, the greater will be the pressure to form a strong *esprit de corps* which provides a sense of security through a strong feeling of belongingness. It is the same phenomenon that drives the young rebel, at odds with the values of bourgeois society, into the arms of the Communist movement, the beatnik group, or teen-age rebel gang; the more he feels threatened as an outsider, the more he will find himself feeling pressured to become a faithful and unquestioning insider of the deviant subculture. The greater the need of the personnel to lean on each other for support—expressed, for example, in such euphemisms as "we are one great family," "we stand all for each other," etc.—the less the chance of the individual group member to express attitudes and feelings which are actually or potentially group-disruptive.

This tendency toward strong in-group formation in the hospital is, apart from the personalities involved, reinforced by several trends: one operating on a more general cultural level, the other more specifically related to the present training of psychiatric personnel but particularly to that of psychiatric nurses. I have in mind what David Riesman[18] has described as a general trend toward "other-directedness"; namely, the increasingly clear emergence of a personality structure that tends to find its sense of security and identity less on the basis of having rigidly internalized a certain set of values and more on a flexible, change-oriented adaptation to what is expected. There seems to be now, very much in line with this general development, a tendency to make the young psychiatric nurse "relationship-conscious"; that is, not to instill in her so much a set of clear-cut doctrines and formulas about mental illness but rather to give her a feeling for the intricacies of interpersonal relationships. Also, the new psychiatric values of "naturalness" and "spontaneous emotional responsiveness" are emphasized and make her previous indoctrination with the more conventional, organic orientation appear as a professional handicap.[19] Yet the greater the changes in orientation expected from a particular nurse and the less the rationale for these changes is thought out and clearly understood, the more this nurse

---

[18] D. Riesman, *The Lonely Crowd* (New Haven: Yale Univ. Press, 1950).
[19] See Morris Parloff's study made at Chestnut Lodge in 1956: "A Comparison of Psychiatric and Medical Nurses' Training," read at a meeting of the medical staff of Chestnut Lodge.

will tend to "feel out" what is expected from her; but also the greater will be her need to conform and to find approval as an accepted member of the given hospital in-group.

In a mental hospital whose very *raison d'être* is to help patients, it can be expected that considerable attempts will be made to include the patients in the in-group; in fact, to make in-group belongingness a therapeutic goal in itself. But there are also great difficulties in doing this. For the very essence of in-group formation is the requirement for a more or less hated out-group. The hate for and the hostile projections onto this out-group provide, so to speak, the cement by which one's own feelings of solidarity and belongingness are fortified. (For this reason we all need, in a greater or lesser degree, our Communists, Southerners, Catholics, etc.) In the case of a hospital ward, such needed out-groups are, for example, other rivalrous wards, a particular hospital department, "those higher up," the psychiatrically unenlightened outside world, and so on.

Yet it remains a fact that the out-group which is closest at hand and which is realistically most often threatening and troublemaking is the patient group. But this group, for reasons given above, must be most exempt from such hostile projection.

Nevertheless, as I have shown in an earlier work,[20] such a projection in the service of solidarity directed against the patients as a group often occurs, particularly in the greater and badly understaffed mental institutions. It is, however, much more likely that not the total patient population but a limited subgroup, labeled as "criminal psychopaths," "actor-outers," etc., will become the target of a more undisguised projection. But even in a small hospital geared to the intensive psychotherapy of psychotic patients we must assume that there exists a readiness to single out certain patients as potential targets for such projections. And this readiness will be the greater the higher the stake each group member has in group belongingness. When Joan, in the above example, demonstrated her own strong antigroupism in launching her defiant and rebellious protest against the ward and the hospital, this interlocked with the group's need and readiness to have a hated outsider. Joan, by realistically threatening group solidarity, offered herself very handily as a needed object for the group's projections, promoting the group's solidarity. And the more the general anxiety about the patient's "acting out" increased, the more this vicious circle of mutually reinforcing "to-

[20] H. Stierlin, *Der Gewalttätige Patient* (Basel and New York: Karger, 1956).

getherness" and hated "outsiderdom" became intensified and prolonged. Again, this was far away from permitting a true therapeutic expressiveness to the patient.

These examples must suffice. They were meant to show some of the unique therapeutic opportunities and problems inherent in a structure like the mental hospital: a protective testing ground for greater self-expressiveness, set apart from society yet at the same time required to function and to justify its existence within this society. I do not know how this basic antinomy is solvable. And yet we cannot avoid feeling everywhere its impact on the treatment of psychotic patients.

Man, as shown in the beginning of this chapter, is an animal who can be complexly confused. But he has also the unique chance to extricate himself from this confusion, to shape his own destiny and to understand—and thereby to create—the conditions of a productive relatedness to other men and to the world around him.

I have tried to describe what I believe to be some essential characteristics of the conditions under which man, with the help of others, can extricate himself from confusion. These conditions represent the structure of all psychotherapy. I believe the nucleus of this structure resides in the early parent-child relationship in which the parents provide a sensitive balance of lively participation and caring detachment. This provides the optimal basis for the child's growth. In applying this idea to the investigation of the optimal treatment conditions for psychotic patients, the picture becomes increasingly complex. More problems entered into it than I had anticipated. But still I believe the basic considerations remain valid despite the fact that I could not find the Archimedean point from which to give a satisfying answer to questions arising in the process of this study.

CHAPTER XIV

The Psychotherapy of the Affective Psychoses

Edith Weigert

MANIC-DEPRESSIVE PSYCHOSES have been approached by psychotherapists with a certain reluctance. The ambulatory treatment of
manic-depressive patients implies a considerable risk of suicide, or of the
deleterious effects of acting out. But beyond that, we find a widespread
pessimism as to the therapeutic results in their treatment. The pyknic
body scheme, the frequency of this psychosis in the same family, the
regularity of the cycles, all contribute to the fortification of the assumption that the manic-depressive psychoses are psychotherapeutically inaccessible. Psychodynamically oriented psychiatrists like Sullivan,[1] who
showed an inspiring hopefulness and skill in work with schizophrenic
patients, were rather hopeless about the manic-depressive. Though the
prognosis of a single manic or depressive phase is not bad, the hope of
the psychotherapist to change the character basis of the psychosis, and
to prevent the recurrence of pathological cycles, is dim. The recommen-
dation of pharmacological, sleep, or shock treatment of manic-depressive
patients is more frequent than in any other psychopathological disorder.
Karl Abraham,[2] who first applied psychoanalytic techniques to the treatment of circular psychoses, recommended psychoanalytic treatment not
in the acute phases of the psychosis, but in the free interval where the
patient, according to Abraham, behaves, and is analytically accessible,

[1] H. S. Sullivan, *The Interpersonal Theory of Psychiatry* (New York:
Norton, 1953), p. 284.
[2] K. Abraham, *Selected Papers on Psychoanalysis* (New York: Basic,
1953).

like an obsessional neurotic. In the psychoanalytic literature, theories about the psychodynamics of manic-depressive psychoses prevail over case presentations, and some manic-depressive case histories presented by Helene Deutsch,[3] George Gerö,[4] and Edith Jacobson[5] are partially atypical, since hysteric, obsessional, schizophrenic, and paranoid features complicated the pictures of the treated illnesses. Edward Bibring[6] described the depressive syndrome in various organic as well as psychogenic illnesses, in depersonalization as well as states of boredom, and Bert Lewin[7] has concentrated his investigation on the syndrome of elation. However, the idea that manic-depressive syndromes present a unity has not been dropped by these psychoanalysts. In a Washington study group[8] twelve cases of this psychosis have been studied and certain common character features of them have been elaborated. These criteria, which characterize family background and early life experience of the patients, have been submitted to a statistical comparative study by R. W. Gibson.[9]

In these studies the dynamics of the character structure of the manic-depressive patients have been spelled out in the patterns of their interpersonal relations. The families of these patients occupied an isolated, exceptional role in the community; they were concerned with gaining and maintaining a position of prestige or success, and the patients were from childhood on destined to remedy the failures under which the family suffered. The parents were at war with each other. One parent was weak and unable to achieve success, and the more aggressively striving parent, frequently the mother, blamed the partner for the family's plight. The tensions in the family were often increased by sibling rivalry, and the patient, in a favorite position, was exposed to envy and inclined to undersell himself and to hide his qualifications. The lack of consistent parental authority led to weakness in the consolidation of the

[3] H. Deutsch, "Zur Psychologie der Manisch-depressiven Zustande, insbesondere der chronischen Hypomanie," Internat. Ztschr. f. Psa., 19 (1933).

[4] G. Gerö, "The Construction of Depression," Internat. J. Psycho-anal., 17 (1936), 423-461.

[5] E. Jacobson, "Depression: the Oedipus Complex in the Development of Depressive Mechanisms," Psychiat. Quart., 12 (1943), 541-560.

[6] E. Bibring, "Das Problem der Depression," Psyche (Stuttgart), 5 (1952), 81-101.

[7] B. Lewin, The Psychoanalysis of Elation (New York: Norton, 1950).

[8] M. B. Cohen, G. Baker, R. A. Cohen, F. Fromm-Reichmann, and E. Weigert, "An Intensive Study of Twelve Cases of Manic-depressive Psychosis," Psychiat., 2 (1954), 103-137.

[9] R. W. Gibson, "The Family Background and Early Life Experience of the Manic-depressive Patient," Psychiat., 1 (1958), 71-100.

patient's ego and superego and made him dependent on the anonymous, vacillating authority of the conventionalities of public opinion. The crucial disturbance of the ego formation could be traced to the early infantile phase of identification with the mother. Due to anxieties in this early closeness, the person of the child and that of the parent are not clearly crystallized; the splitting into a good and bad object, as well as a good and bad subject, maintains the ambivalence so characteristic for the manic-depressive patient.

PHENOMENOLOGY OF THE MANIC-DEPRESSIVE PERSONALITY

I want to continue this study by consolidating the features that the manic-depressive patients that I was able to observe have in common, and compare them with the characteristics that have been elaborated in the former studies.

When we look at the patient between episodes of his illness, we are startled by the change in his external behavior; he vanishes into the background of a given environment with a pseudonymity that reminds one of the mimicry of animals that take on the protective coloring of their surroundings. The patient says what he is expected to say, and he smiles when he is supposed to smile. He takes his clues from his encounters, in superficial imitation obviously intended to please and not to hurt. But this imitation does not give him opportunity to explore what is going on in the other person or in himself. He does not lose time and energy in introspection, since he seems to be preoccupied with the superficial impression he makes on his surroundings. His self-esteem seems to walk on a tightrope and the conventional amiability has to guarantee that he has no enemies, that he does not fall into disgrace. He can play different roles, but this role-playing is geared to applause and it remains unconvincingly artificial. Since it does not reveal the real person, it lacks the subtleties that characterize a person's uniqueness. The manic-depressive patient carries to excess the features of the other-directed individual (Riesman), of the unauthentic "man" in a mass society (Heidegger), who imitates everybody and anybody, is directed by rumor and gossip, by waves of public opinion, without the experience of personal, responsible decisions and direction toward goals of his own.

Nevertheless, the manic-depressive patient remains very vulnerable. His sensitivities are reflected in his changing mood swings, his tendency to be emotionally contaminated, irresistibly weeping with those who are sad and laughing in abandon with the cheering crowd. But the manic-depressive patient is a victim of the emotions which he conceals behind his conventional façade,[10] and which scarcely enter his cognitive sphere, though the patient has a more than average degree of intelligence at his disposal. His emotions and mood swings remain enigmatic to him; they overwhelm him and sweep him off his feet. When the façade of conventional adaptation breaks down under emotional pressure, the patient becomes a captive of a monotonously grinding depression or a runaway, flighty elation. In the manic mood he still hangs on to spurious pride, an illusionary arrogance; in the melancholic episode the self-esteem is lost in a delusion of inferiority. This loss of self-esteem presents a serious danger to survival, for it undermines "the instinct which compels every living thing to cling to life." [11]

THE PSYCHOTIC ATTACK

Freud has compared the outbreak of an acute melancholia to the normal process of mourning. The phenomenology of both processes does show great similarities, with the exception, says Freud, that the disturbance of self-regard is absent in mourning. "In mourning it is the world which has become poor and empty, in melancholia it is the ego itself." [12] The melancholic attack is sometimes preceded by a loss of a beloved person, but at other times it is hard to discover the loss which the patient has suffered.

One patient became depressed just when he had reached the summit of success, a highly responsible and independent position, but he had no superiors from whom he could secure advice and guidance; he was left to his own devices, and was exposed to demands, criticisms, and envy. He felt deeply unsure whether he could live up to the expectations of others. He suddenly felt isolated and became depressed.

Another patient became depressed at the time when he became engaged to be married. As long as he strove toward this goal he was elated, carried by hopes and images of future fulfillment. He struggled tirelessly to conquer the doubts of his beloved woman and the resistance of her parents. But when he had reached his goal, his hopes suddenly collapsed and he became beset by doubts: Could he live up to the realistic commitment? Was his love strong enough to endure the monotony and tribulations of daily adjustment? He suddenly became aware of flaws and

[10] J. Smith, "A Formulation of Unconventionality in Manic-Depressive Communication," *Psychiatry* (in press).

[11] *Ibid.*

[12] S. Freud, "Mourning and Melancholia," in *The Standard Edition* (London: Hogarth, 1957), Vol. XIV, 243-258, 249.

shortcomings in his previously idealized partner. Would not disappointments, fault-finding, resentment, and hatred creep up and mar the image of perfect marital bliss by which his former drive had been carried?

The ego of the depressed patient is impoverished by the loss of hope. But not only is the ego impoverished, his world becomes poor and empty too; it appears dark and colorless, tedious and estranged when the light of hope and trust in love is extinguished. The contours of his scene of living become the walls of a prison. The closeness to the partner becomes suffocating while he clings to her. The windows into the future are closed by blinds. The patient and his world are both impoverished. What Heidegger calls "being-in-the-world" becomes meaningless. The contrast becomes particularly poignant when the depressive mood has been preceded by ecstatic hopes and ideal expectations which carried the stamp of illusionary wish fulfillment. The all-embracing hope for perfect bliss changes into the bleak despair of nothingness. Entering into a depression is like entering into Dante's Inferno, *Lasciate ogni speranza voi ch'entrate*. The proverbial saying "While there is life, there is hope" could be turned around for the melancholic patient: "While there is hope, there is life."

The vital functions of the melancholic patient are deeply disturbed, since he has no hope. His appetite is low; there is no taste in his food; less frequently he gorges his food as if he could fill an inner emptiness. He does not sleep, or his sleep is fitful, unrefreshing, as if the fear of annihilation kept him alerted and when he awakens from a restless sleep he faces another day of hopelessness. He struggles through the agitations of despair and may find some relief in evening hours from sheer exhaustion. The agitation and anxieties indicate agitation against the tragedy of his fate. In a retarded depression he succumbs to mute despair. The agitated patient's self-expression is reduced to monotonous whining and wailing, resembling the crying of a deserted child. But the tragedy is that the cry for help remains frustrated; the comfort that is offered does not bring relief and may even increase the despair. The patient clings to the doctor or the nurse, follows him or her around with a sticky insistence on being relieved, but there is no comfort in the tender touch either.

The melancholic patient, unlike the paranoid patient, seldom accuses his helper, and mostly accuses himself of his hopeless condition. Freud [13] has pointed out that the self-accusations of the melancholic patient

[13] *Ibid.*

are insincere and imply a more or less veiled blame of the object by
whom the patient feels deserted. The patient's anger, rage, hatred, resentment, and vindictiveness that have been repressed return out of repression, and torture not only the patient, who is sensitive to these painful emotions but also his immediate environment, which cannot offer
any relief. The insistence on being frustrated is interpreted as a turning
of the patient's hostilities against himself and as an attempt at expiation
of guilt. Edward Bibring[14] has warned against applying this formula
automatically to the understanding of the depressed patient's predica-
ment.

I see an even closer similarity between the depressed patient and
the mourning person. In his bereavement the mourner is deprived of
hope. He has not so much to eradicate his memories of the past—these
memories may become in the long run a blessing—but he has to shift
the goal of his hopes for the future and that is a painful process. There
is no love relation so free from possessiveness and ambivalence that the
loss of the beloved partner would not leave the bereaved person with a
bleak look into the future, with some resentment against the desertion,
and some indignant protest against fate. As to the past, the bereaved
person is mortified that the passed love relation has not been deeper or
more fulfilling. The higher the ideals of blissful union, the deeper is the
pang of remorse. For the bereaved person cannot turn his accusations
against the lost partner who is now more than ever idealized—*de mor-
tuis nil nisi bene.*

The labor of mourning is therefore also a work of repentance, implying the wish for a deeper capacity for love and dedication. It is not only
the sober acceptance of reality—that the dead person is definitely lost—
which lifts the mourner gradually out of his state of painful bereavement. Neither is it the magical belief of expiating his guilt by suffering
that liberates him from his grief. When the mourner gradually gives up
his bid for omnipotence and his raging against fate, it is the awakening
of hope and trust in his creative ability to love and dedicate himself
which rises out of the humiliating, yet clarifying and cleansing, experience of mourning and repentance. In the labor of mourning a sublimation takes place, a resignation as to immediate gratification and a shift
of hope toward new, sometimes more removed goals. When the bereaved
person outgrows the selfishness of his egocentric clinging possessiveness,
his attachment to the memory of the departed as well as to the world

[14] E. Bibring, *op. cit.,* 81-101.

that is still left to him may rise to a level of less demanding and more promising spiritual integration.

The melancholic patient is seriously handicapped in the labor of mourning as well as in the work of repentance. He has been so much infatuated with the image of his goodness, his perfection, and with the power of being successful that he is entrenched in a position of all-or-nothing-demands identical with his ideals. There is no distance between him and his ideals, as there is no distance between him and the object of his personal attachment. He has lived in illusions about his realistic limitations. His hopes were directed toward an unreachable goal, as if it were immediately reachable, and his striving lacked a realistic humility. If a person is intoxicated by the ideal to be Caesar or nihil, he may find himself sooner or later in the abyss of the nihil, the despair of nothingness. His hopes lose their meaning, but he is not yet capable of going through the process of renunciation and reorientation which would give his hopes new directions.

Thomas French[15] has pointed out how important the goal-direction of hope is for the integration of the total personality. Hope provides the experience of subjective freedom of choice, since the libidinal and aggressive instinctual energies are collected and converge toward a goal that has the ego's confirmation. Therewith the erotic drives are in the lead over the aggressive drives. In the despair of melancholia this directive, organizing function of hope is lost, the complete disorganization of a psychosis threatens, or the patient is compulsively driven into suicide, since life has lost its positive values for him. But the pains of melancholia can become the birth pains of renewal, liberating the potentialities. Immediate gratifications are relinquished in the labor of mourning. In this very renunciation, a redirection toward new goals prepares the reintegration of the personality. Every creative process of sublimation is initiated by some labor of mourning.

Another pathological way out of the depression is the flight into a manic state of defense which represents a caricature of hope, a distortion of trust into gullibility, an illusory self-definition in which the patient loses the distance from his ideals. There remain sufficient residues of doubt to interfere with the patient's sense of security. He changes the images of his aspired identity, his plans, his foresights, so rapidly and so abruptly that the observer is alarmed by the process of

[15] T. M. French, *The Integration of Behavior* (Chicago: Univ. Chicago Press, 1952), Vol. 1.

accelerated movement, of disregard for boundaries and interpersonal considerations. The patient is fleeing from his anxiety of disintegration; he puts little trust in his hopes, his aggressive impulses win out over the impulses of eros, a diffusion of instinctual impulses explodes the collectedness and goal-directedness of the personality. His interpersonal contacts become attenuated, spurious, and transient, directed only toward a momentary exploitation of ego-support by outsiders. Mourning and remorse are more or less completely repressed. In the transition from a depression to the sudden activation and expansion of a manic attack the danger of suicide is most intense; the prison walls break down, but as yet there is no trust in a hopeful rebirth of a widened and fortified personality.

Childhood History

The outstanding features of a lack of hope and trust lead us back into the childhood history although the outbreak of a typical manic-depressive psychosis does not occur until after puberty. Psychoanalytic literature has stressed the oral phase of libido development and the accompanying incorporative tendencies which may determine the development of a later affective psychosis. Melanie Klein has described the "depressive position," [16] the struggle of the infant to accept the good and the bad mother as a total person, incorporating enough of the good mother to endure the frustrations of the bad one. René Spitz[17] and Margaret Ribble[18] have described the anaclitic depression. The loss of the mother's tender care in the period of oral, nutritive dependency leads at first to an agitated, anxious protest, then to a waning of vitality that, without the return of the mothering relation, leads to death. We may see in the anaclitic depression a precursor of later melancholia, but there are many stages of possible recuperation and solidification between this early deprivation and the outbreak of an illness in adulthood.

The oral deprivation is certainly an important factor in the history of manic-depressives, but it has perhaps been overemphasized in psychoanalytic literature. Bowlby,[19] under the influence of ethological

[16] M. Klein, *Contributions to Psychoanalysis* (London: Hogarth, 1950), p. 291.
[17] R. Spitz, "Anaclitic Depression," in *The Psychoanalytic Study of the Child* (New York: Internat. Univ. Press, 1946), Vol. 2.
[18] M. Ribble, *The Rights of Infants* (New York: Columbia Univ. Press, 1943).
[19] J. Bowlby, "The Nature of the Child's Tie to His Mother," *Internat. J. Psychoanal.*, 39 (1958), 1-24.

literature, has pointed to other primary factors in the infant's tie to the mother, the crying, the clinging, the responsive smiling, and the following. And distortions of these primary functions appear in the melancholic attack—the crying, clinging, and following—while the smiling seems completely extinguished.

The predisposition for a manic-depressive illness is influenced by the total parent-infant relation in all its emotional aspects and their further development in childhood. Therese Benedek[20] describes the total "depressive constellation" in childhood. She distinguishes three types of mother-child relations. The first, which gives the child the most secure preparation for life, is that of the discerning, responsive mother who trusts her own instinctive motherliness as well as the growing potentialities and self-sufficiency in the child; she lets him use his imagination and allows him playfully to experiment with new discoveries without exposing him to unnecessarily discouraging frustrations.

The second relation is loaded with frustration, anger, and rejection. The mother either did not welcome the child in the first place, or she trusts him and her motherliness so little that she misinterprets his cries for help or his clinging, as signs of her own failures. She throws her hands up in angry despair and the child finds himself forsaken, rejected, and he reacts to his mother's anger with defiant withdrawal, anger, or hatred. When the child survives the frustrations of this constellation, he may develop a distrustful toughness, a determination not to be fooled, and to shift for himself. He seemingly resigns himself to frustration, convinced that he has a bad parent, but his brittle self-sufficiency may break down under stress and strain, if no trustworthy experiences come to his rescue later.

The third type of relation, according to Benedek, represents the depressive constellation: it is that of the anxious, oversolicitous and overprotective mother who does not trust her child's growing abilities, nor her own adequate response; she remains at the beck and call of his wishes, and she tries to protect him anxiously against inevitable frustrations, she keeps him captivated in the primary symbiotic unity which should be gradually superseded by a mutual encounter between an "I" and a "You" as two unities gradually becoming independent.

In the depressive constellation there is a lack of trust—that basic trust which Erikson[21] called the matrix of all wholesome development.

[20] T. F. Benedek, "Toward the Biology of the Depressive Constellation," *J. Amer. Psychoanal. Assoc.*, 3 (1956), 389-427.
[21] E. H. Erikson, *Childhood and Society* (New York: Norton, 1950).

This basic trust provides for the future of the growing child the unshakable security that he is not alone; that there is hope also in times of frustration; that somebody is there to understand and meet his needs. The concept of basic trust describes the mutual responsiveness and gratification between mother and infant better than the concept of primary narcissism which makes of the dependent infant a self-centered tyrant. But when the basic trust is defective, we observe the development of a secondary, defensive narcissism growing out of the anxiously disturbed mother-infant relation. In the depressive constellation the original symbiosis fails in due time to be replaced by an encounter of an "I" and a "You" who define their needs to each other, experience pleasure and pain, joy, and angry protest, yet arrive ever again at the harmony of mutual understanding and gratification. In the depressive constellation the symbiotic identification persists. The anxious, overprotective mother clings to the child. She is not able to hope wholeheartedly for his growing independence and she worries and clings to him for solace as he clings to her. The child is seduced to exploit her solicitous submission to his unlimited wishes for his defensive narcissism, yet he feels insecure about the lack of defined boundaries in his field of action. The mother feels guilty for any frustration to which the child has to be exposed and the child shares the mother's anxiety, grief, and despair first on the preverbal level where the wordless emotional contamination becomes a powerful, overwhelming experience.

Later the child becomes the parent's confidant on the level of verbal communication, when the symbiotic identification still partially persists. The emotional contamination outweighs the rational understanding; the child cannot digest the communications and is swept off his feet by the parent's worrisome complaints or stunned by the adult's self-defeat. The child's imagination is overstimulated by the waves of intense contaminating emotions. He cannot yet sufficiently distinguish between imagination and reality, and the progress from the primary to the secondary process of thinking is delayed. The child remains more an onlooker than an actor. When his own wishes and impulses urge him to act, to defiantly declare his independence, to protest against the imposition of social rules and regulations, like cleanliness, sphincter control, and later forms of disciplined behavior, he encounters parental distress: "How can you do this to me!" The child's aggressiveness is unacceptable to the parent, for it disrupts the symbiotic identification violently and the child shrinks away from his explosions of anger and rage. He does not learn to tame them in experimental play and fighting-encounters that settle the differences between the "I" and the "You" in reasonable and creative integration. The persistent identification does not permit a clear definition of boundaries between the "I" and the "You." The child's aggressiveness appears uncanny and dangerous to him and becomes even more intimidating when it explodes in temper tantrums and uncontrollable scenes of mutual aggravation and spiraling exasperation.

Since the child is handicapped in changing his world to suit his wishes by techniques of alloplastic action, he withdraws more and more into the world of autoplastic imagination. The aggression that is not channelized into the skills of self-defense and self-assertion builds up air castles of victorious grandiosity. These omnipotential fantasies of a secondary narcissism are further nourished by a position of favoritism in relation to one or the other parent who seeks his or her vicarious gratification in close identification with this child; the symbiotic identification may shift from mother and child to a similarly close identification between father and child. The parent plans the child's future from his egocentric point of view. A daughter has to be trained for the artistic career that the mother missed because of her marriage. A son has to make up for the disappointments his father suffered when he had to sacrifice an academic career to make a living for an economically hard pressed family. A child has to replace a deceased sibling, and to live up to the idealization that glorified the image of the dead child in the eyes of the parents.

Sullivan[22] has impressively described the havoc created in a child's development by the contamination of parental anxieties. Freud has mentioned "borrowed guilt feelings" in the childhood history of melancholic patients.[23] We frequently find depressions and pathologic mourning processes in the family to which the patient has been exposed in his childhood. Heredity may be an important factor contributing to the development of a later affective psychosis. But in addition, the favorite child of a depressed parent is exposed to contamination by intense anxieties, depressive and desperate emotions which stunt his development. Some sketchy examples may illustrate this thesis.

A child who was born soon after her father's suicide had to share the mother's nagging guilt feelings and despondency from the early days of her existence. She lacked the zest for living and maintained a persistent pessimism, a chronically depressive outlook on her chances of sur-

[22] H. S. Sullivan, *op. cit.*
[23] S. Freud, "Das Ich und das Es," *Gesammelte Schriften* (6 vols.; Leipzig, Wien, Zurich, n.d.), p. 395 n.

vival. Where the depressed parent in his own despondency leans heavily on his favorite child as a redeemer and savior, the child is seduced to believe in his omnipotent, messianic role, but on the other hand he finds himself again and again impotent to stave off the parental despair. The child's vital need for admiration and emulation of a vitally strong parent is frustrated. He dreams of heroic and demonic roles, but he cannot try them out and fit them to his real size because his aggressive impulses elicit the weak parent's sorried wailings. When he tries to shake off the dependency and overidentification with the depressed parent, such acts because of shame and defiance engender new guilt feelings and insecurities about his identity.

A manic-depressive patient spent the first six years of his life alone with a depressed mother while the father tried to build up a new economic existence in a far-removed country. When mother and son joined the father in a completely strange environment, the son was bewildered about his identity. He became ashamed of his mother and yet guilty for deserting her in her depressions. He did not want to be a sissy and shifted his clinging dependency to his contemporaries outside the family. He now imitated the big boys in his environment. His rage exploded in minor delinquencies; his explosive aggressiveness was unskilled, fumbling, and enigmatic to him and others. In adolescence he became a joiner restlessly preoccupied with failure and success. He was compelled to prove his magic power in a constant gamble with the risks of fate. He could not relax in his pursuit of dazzling success, for he had never given up the omnipotent position in early childhood. His bravado was unconvincing because it remained intensely vulnerable to failure. When a person of prestige did not greet him, when his schedule was not filled with appointments, when his appeal for popularity fell flat, he sank into a feeling of worthlessness and complete defeat. As an adult he was still clinging to the compensatory pseudosecurity of his bid for omnipotence. He was late wherever he went, as if he could magically overcome the barriers of time and space and gain pretentious prestige from keeping people waiting for him. Whenever he could afford it, he let his temper fly in boisterous anger, as if his noisy indignation would have a magic power over his fellow men. But an accumulation of failures threw him into the nothingness of melancholic despair.

A woman patient had as a teenager succeeded by her managerial talents to separate the parents who were embroiled in a sado-masochistic interdependence. This separation saved her father from alcoholism and her mother from a depression. The daughter sank into a depression when her heroic efforts became dispensable and the parents could again take care of themselves. She felt hopeless since she now missed the justification for her existence and ruminated in an agitated depression about the meaninglessness of life, insisting stubbornly that only a convincing supernatural knowledge about man's fate after death could give her peace. Hidden in her impetuous, obsessive ruminations lay the nostalgic longing for basic trust and hope for a new lease on life.

The disturbed emotional development of the patient who sooner or later becomes the victim of an affective psychosis precludes ever reaching the level of the Oedipus conflict. The prolonged symbiotic identification with a weak, possessive, and exploitative parent has provided the patient with a position of favoritism and ill-defined ego boundaries, so that his self-esteem vacillates between over- and underestimation of his real potentialities. In his arrogant imagination he considers himself at times the victor in the family battle centered around the Oedipus conflict. Parental overindulgence and overprotection have not confronted his impetuous bid for omnipotence with realistic limitations and necessary renunciations. He has missed a strong parent whom he could admire and emulate; his compassion for a helpless, weak parent turns sooner or later into impotent rebellion, shame, and contempt; and his borrowed guilt feelings, the residues of persisting identifications with the parent, elicit self-doubt and self-contempt. Libidinal and aggressive impulses have remained partially diffused. These impulses remain untamed and unskilled, explosive, and poorly controlled. There is a nostalgic yearning for basic trust, but his hopes reach only the fleet products of his imagination. There is no consolidated "I" able to encounter a "You" and to respect the mutual boundaries. The weakness of the ego elicits a constant defensive selfish concern and need for narcissistic supplies. If a partner does not lend himself as a means of support, there is not enough trust to prevent the anxiety of annihilation. The lack of ego consolidation corresponds to a lack of definition of the superego. Freud called the superego the heir of the Oedipus conflict; but when the Oedipus conflict remains unsolved the superego is more a super id, deeply anchored in the archaic desires for emotional omnipotent mastery, but buffeted by the waves of approval and disapproval by external authority without a rudder of his own. Instead of the rationally consolidated superego we find a multiplicity of ego ideals, images of absolute perfection and grandiosity. The ideal of being the parents' redeemer is one of the most exalted ideals, but its realization is doomed to failure.

The poet-philosopher Sören Kierkegaard, the father of modern existentialism, suffered from severe melancholic attacks and elated mood swings. His childhood was overshadowed by his father's melancholy. The father felt that the curse of God was weighing heavily on his family and his marriage was unhappy. Five of his seven children had died before him. His youngest son Sören was his favorite and he shared with him images of an abundant fantasy life, religious and philosophical argumentation as well as his wordless gloomy brooding. In their common daydreams they visited foreign countries and imaginary people on their long walks through the rooms of their home. The father saw in the son's outstanding endowment a hope for his own redemption. But the son expected an early death; the borrowed guilt feelings had paralyzed the hopes for his own existence. In his early writings, with their thinly veiled autobiographical character, we find the picture of a primal scene which illustrates the bitter disappointment of a son in his father. It is a Biblical scene in which the young Solomon sneaks into David's, his royal father's, bedroom at night and finds the old hero prostrate in despair accusing himself of his sinful sexual greed. "And Solomon became wise but he did not become a hero," wrote Kierkegaard. "What is the torment of sympathy, if not the fact that you have to be ashamed of the father whom you have loved above all." [24]

ADULTHOOD

Erikson has masterfully described the identity crises of another religious genius who suffered from manic and depressive mood swings: "young man Luther." [25] The lack of ego cohesion makes for a prolonged adolescence; the young person needs a moratorium from society to find himself and the goal toward which he is striving. The dependence on conventionality and external approval is only a protective shield hiding the deep insecurity in the young person's self-realization. He has a great versatility in imitation and role-playing, he vacillates between active and passive, masculine and feminine roles, his fantasy may roam like that of Kierkegaard through the vast realm of historical and mythological ancestry to find a suitable image for identification and emulation. Far beyond biological adolescence the modern manic-depressive patient visualizes himself in most contradictory roles, e.g., as successful capitalist and businessman on the one hand, and as a socialistic pacifist on the other hand. The manic-depressive woman patient visualizes her future

[24] S. Kierkegaard, *Studien auf dem Lebensweg* (Jena: Eugen Diederichs Verlag, 1922), p. 225.
[25] E. H. Erikson, *Young Man Luther* (New York: Norton, 1958).

as that of a dedicated wife and mother and, at other times, as that of an ambitious career woman. Introjected into the ego is the image of the defeated, despondent parent from whom he has not dared to emancipate himself in healthy aggressiveness. He has not gone through the resignation of the Oedipus conflict and has not accepted the boundaries of his ego. The projection of fantastic omnipotent ego ideals militates against the introjected despondency. The shifting ego ideals carry the hope for perfection and redemption. If his hope collapses the ego is left in a state of hopeless, helpless impotence. The nostalgic yearning for the original symbiotic closeness to the parent is reflected in the religious wish to lose himself in an all-embracing cause, in an all-consuming passion that threatens to devour the ego; but the very threat of annihilation is so loaded with anxieties that the patient clings to self-confirming supplies from the outside and submits to conventional behavior patterns to secure his survival. But in the midst of success the fear of defeat creeps up on him in enigmatic mood swings. A passage in Kierkegaard describes this abrupt alteration of mood: "I have just returned from a party of which I was the life and soul; wit poured from my lips, everyone laughed and admired me—but I went away—and the dash should be as long as the Earth's orbit————————and wanted to shoot myself." [26]

Under the biological pressure of instincts and the social pressure for cultural adaptation the individual strives for self-realization, or authentic selfhood, which transcends the limits of his biological and social functions in the vision of an integrated self-image projected into the future. This self-image has a supreme value for the human being because it gives meaning to individual existence. The existential philosophers, with the exception of Sartre, who considers human existence as meaningless and absurd, have pointed out that the individual by his capacity of self-awareness struggles to maintain his authentic selfhood and his spiritual uniqueness, even to the point of sacrifice of his own life in defense against internal and external pressures. In the manic-depressive patient this spiritual uniqueness and vision of authentic selfhood is tragically threatened by the nostalgic yearning for the archaic symbiotic union of the self with the other, the defective use of aggressiveness for self-assertion and self-definition, and the leaning on conventional adaptation for the sake of social confirmation that has to make

[26] S. Kierkegaard, *The Journals* (ed. and trans. by A. Dru; New York: Oxford Univ. Press, 1938 [1836]). Reproduced by permission of the Oxford University Press.

up for incomplete self-definition. The ill-defined ego boundaries or lack of cohesiveness of the ego are reflected in "phenomena of depersonalization in which the individual is aware of his body without being aware that it is his." [27] Phenomena of depersonalization, of self-alienation, are very frightening experiences; they are accompanied by a subjective feeling of loss of freedom and self-determination. Milder forms of self-alienation are boredom and a feeling of inner emptiness.

Side by side with the compulsive submission to conventionality we find in the manic-depressive patient symptoms of rebellion, a search for freedom from the chains of unauthentic conventionality. There are a number of artists among the manic-depressives who struggle for self-expression. Ernst Kris has described the artist's regression in the service of the ego.[28] As long as the artist is creative he is relatively free from depressions; in sterile episodes he often sinks back into self-contempt and despair. Like Kierkegaard, the artist tries to free himself from the "sickness unto death," from the paradox of desperately wanting to be himself and desperately not wanting to be himself; the artist creates himself and simultaneously loses himself, in a creation that encompasses his world and recreates the archaic symbiotic unity between the self and the other.

The search for selfhood enters into a critical phase when the manic-depressive patient is confronted with an experience of love. Insofar as the manic-depressive patient is tied by the chains of conventionality, the erotic experience remains superficially determined by the dependence on success or failure. The erotic conquest provides a triumph, a powerful confirmation which silences the doubts about his worth. The sexual competence is not necessarily weakened by the inability to solve the Oedipus conflict in childhood. Among the patients that I have treated there were persons who demonstrated a considerable prowess in sexual performance but an excessive anxiety in view of any commitment. The manic-depressive patient is frequently intensely attracted by a person on whom he projects the fantasy-image of goodness and perfection, and the attachment seems to promise complete bliss and happiness. But a commitment awakens his anxiety, the anxiety of inner disintegration due to the awakening of his repressed aggressive-destructive impulses which might destroy the love object and/or himself. We frequently find a tendency towards Don Juanism in the manic-depressive patient; he escapes

[27] H. Elkin, "On the Origin of the Self," *Psychoanal. & Psychoanal. Rev.*, 45 (1958-1959), 57-76, 61.
[28] E. Kris, *Psychoanalytic Explorations in Art* (New York: Internat. Univ. Press, 1952).

from one love object to another with the ever-renewed illusory hope that a new love relation might bring redemption from the evil within him. The sexual prowess does not suffice to convince the manic-depressive of his goodness and wholeness. "Where the persecution-anxiety for the ego is in the ascendant, a full and stable identification with another object, in the sense of looking at it and understanding it as it really is, and a full capacity for love, are not possible." [29] Since the cohesion of the "I" is not established, the patient is not able to experience the full, real "You"; the projections of his wishes and fantasies stand between the "I" and the "You." An intense yearning arises for full identification, for the oceanic feeling of perfect union, the bliss of the primordial symbiosis, but the demonic images of anxiety to be possessed, exploited, annihilated or to possess, exploit, annihilate the other drive him into flight. A classical example of such a flight is Kierkegaard's engagement to Regine Olsen: as soon as he committed himself, he became aware of the death of his love and after a year of torturous conflicts and ruminations he dissolved the engagement. He experienced a deep despair; the words that Dostoevski put in the mouth of the Staretz Sossima describe the state of mind that Kierkegaard went through: "What is hell? I think it is the pain that one is no more able to love." [30]

The marital relations of manic-depressive patients are burdened with severe tensions of ambivalence. The manic-depressive patient frequently has the illusion of being a good lover, since his hostilities have been repressed since early childhood days and he may take his need to depend on the partner, or to make the partner depend upon him, as an expression of his ability for warmth and affection. But there is a lack of distance, of respect for the boundaries of the "I" and the "You" which acts as a constant irritant infringement on the partners' need for self-assertion. The enthusiasm that wipes out the boundaries and fills the partners with momentary joy and bliss wears off in daily frictions when a consensus or a balance of interests cannot be reached. The manic-depressive patient expects not only himself but also the partner to live up to standards of perfection. Any departure from the ideal of a perfect union gives rise to the specter of ambivalence which is insufficiently neutralized in the fusion of identification. The manic-depressive patient is, as I have described before, intensely vulnerable to disappointment and even minimal slights or indications of the possibility of desertion; these give rise to feelings of resentment and hostility to which the manic-de-

[29] M. Klein, *op. cit.*
[30] F. Dostoevski, *Die Brüder Karamasoff* (Munich: Piper Verlag, 1916).

pressive is sensitive. The divergences cannot be argued out in free communication since mobilized hatred cannot be endured. Withdrawal intensifies the inner conflict, "the shadow of the deserted object falls on the subject," [31] and the manic-depressive is tormented by self-reproaches which may initiate the sliding into depression.

I have mentioned before the lack of sincerity in melancholic self-reproaches. Genuine repentance and true humility would imply an acknowledgment of resentment, envy, and hatred, of all those negative emotions which are mobilized by the closeness of the "I" and the "You." Such acknowledgment would broaden the boundaries of the "I," not in the sense of boundless ecstasy but in the sense of a more realistic definition of his self which permits also an acceptance of the "You" in a loving respect for the boundaries. The marital relation of the manic-depressive patient rarely leads to such resigned awareness of the limiting defensive selfishness and to an experience of a genuine encounter of the "I" and the "You." The intimate relation of the manic-depressive patient returns in most cases to that of ambivalent dependency, to denial of competition, castration anxiety and penis envy, to denial of inner loneliness, since the tragic human uniqueness and loneliness remains unbearable for him. A more or less superficial peace can be maintained; since the patient is an excellent manipulator, he manages a tolerable adjustment, using the partner as a provider of narcissistic supplies and generously providing for the partner. He masters the interpersonal situation by domination or submission, and in this using and being used, exploiting and being exploited, there may be enough instinctual gratification, mutual companionship, and tender care transmitted to keep the marital relations mutually satisfying and pacified. But serious conflicts which might lead to a deeper awareness of the "I" and the "You" are avoided.

The extroverted manic-depressive frequently turns to the outside for confirmation of his worth, driven by the gnawing doubts of his inferiority feelings and by his anxieties about being deserted. He pursues a gambler's race for success; he gambles for prestige, for wealth, for popularity, but he gambles always for more than he needs. His friendships are characterized by buddy-buddy familiarity; but familiarity breeds contempt, and negative emotions are unbearable. Ruthless opportunism also does not fit into the high standards of the manic-depressive and yet a certain degree of opportunism is necessary for the pursuit

[31] S. Freud, "Mourning and Melancholia."

of success. Failure mobilizes anxieties and thus the manic-depressive maintains a high speed in his daily activities, a speed that does not permit relaxation or a patient dedication to a task that does not provide quick results. The restlessness of external activities deprives friendship and family life of depth and intensity, and sooner or later the patient loses the hope and the courage of continuing the struggle for escape from his anxieties.

Further crises of his sense of identity arise at the turning point of biological development after the birth of a child. The upheaval in the instinctual and emotional equilibrium at the time of delivery threatens the person who is disposed to develop an affective psychosis. A new horizon opens up and self-doubts crop up as to whether the young mother can meet the challenge. Also, an unstable father might become oppressed at the sight of new responsibilities. The unresolved identification of the young mother with her own mother reproduces an opportunity to re-establish a similar identification with the newborn child. There is the same lack of trust in the patient's mothering abilities and in the adequate response to the infant's vital needs; instead she compensates by oversolicitude and overprotection for the hateful riddance reactions that may painfully break into conscious awareness and cause guilt feelings, self-blame, and self-defeat or flight into manic self-expansion and vagueness. But the post partum affective psychosis has largely a favorable prognosis and an equilibrium may be soon re-established— which does not exclude the possibility that the tradition of symbiotic identification may be carried over into the next generation.

The time of involution is another critical period in which the patient has to change his ego ideals and redefine his identity. This change implies restriction of goals, limitations of expansive ambitions, loss of partners and friends, separation from children who are now living their own lives, all of which requires renunciation and a turning inward of hopes, for which the extroverted manic-depressive personality is ill prepared. His dependence on success and external applause suffers painful defeats. His hopes shrink when he cannot transform his needs for immediate gratifications into investments in sublimated interests. The narcissistic loss of physical beauty and body strength elicits protest in form of hypochondriacal preoccupation. The reduction of opportunities for expansion produces unrealistic worries about the impending doom of impoverishment. Lack of hope and trust, and limitations in the ability for serious dedication make the reintegration of the manic-depressive

personality in the involutional period particularly strenuous. If his being-in-the-world loses its meaning, he may succumb to psychotic despair or suicidal defeat.

PSYCHOTHERAPY

The treatment of an affective psychosis confronts the psychotherapist
with paradoxical difficulties. The patient urgently demands help and yet
he desperately refuses it. Freud thought that schizophrenia and the
manic-depressive psychosis, the narcissistic neuroses, in contrast to
the transference neuroses, were not suitable for psychoanalytic therapy. Modifications of classical psychoanalytic techniques are certainly
necessary; but it has been found that the functional psychoses too develop intense transference phenomena during treatment. The psychotherapist may be able gradually to melt the armor of distrustful withdrawal and seemingly resigned hopelessness in his long and arduous
work with the schizophrenic patient. But the manic-depressive patient
is frequently carried away by spurious hopes and gullibility. He demands
narcissistic supplies and ego support, but he is easily discouraged when
his desires for magical help cannot be met with a quick successful relief.

It is therefore necessary that the psychotherapist does not offer false
promises and cheap comfort, but examines the emotional situation thoroughly and fathoms the depth of the depression and the dangers of
manic escape. It is inevitable for the therapist to enter into close contact
with the patient's relatives when the patient suffers from a manic-
depressive illness. He explains to the patient that this contact is a precondition for treatment and does not violate the patient's confidential
communications. The illness is frequently enigmatic to his relatives and
the patient's despondency puts a heavy burden on their shoulders. This
burden can, to a certain degree, be eased by the psychological understanding that the therapist can provide. And this understanding also
diminishes the patient's guilt feelings in relation to his family. The therapist explains to the patient as well as to the family that the patient is in
a process of mourning; the loss he has suffered may not be so obvious
but can be gradually discovered. It can also be made understandable
that the patient cannot yet accept the loss and that he is like a mourning person who rages inwardly against fate. And since the patient is related to whomever or whatever he has lost by a tenaciously close, possessive identification, he also partially lost himself, i.e., his sense of identity; he is a kind of penitent and though his self-accusations are fantastic, sometimes outrageously unrealistic, it is no use trying to talk

him out of them. Deeper investigations will gradually put them into a more realistic perspective.

Since the manic-depressive patient is in a crisis of lost identity, he needs a moratorium, protection against self-damage or suicide; he is transiently unable to take care of his self-preservation and, if the family is not able to provide the protection of a moratorium, suitable hospital care has to be provided. It is important that the therapist convey to the patient the fact that his extremely painful emotions are not useless; that they represent a self-healing process comparable to the fever of a contaminated organism. Even though the patient cannot as yet consciously participate in his therapy, the process of mourning and penitence goes on in his unconscious mind, and he will gradually learn to participate. The serene, firm security of the therapist calms the anxious agitation of the patient and his relatives.

If external security measures cannot be provided, the therapist, the patient, and his family take a considerable risk. The therapist may ask the patient to call on him at any time of day or night, when the compulsion to damage or kill himself becomes overwhelming. If the patient is already able to establish some positive attachment to the therapist, this attachment is in itself the best safety that can be offered. But the therapist's readiness to be at the patient's disposal at any emergency call can seduce the patient to test his power when his attachment to the therapist is highly ambivalent, and the therapist may become contaminated by his patient's anxieties. A similar unfortunate involvement may result from the dispensation of sedatives, tranquilizers, or electroshock treatment. It is preferable that the relation between the patient and his psychotherapist be kept free from all nonpsychotherapeutic measures and that these be delegated to a cooperating administrator. If the patient is in a very desperate condition, around-the-clock nursing service has to be established.

In a manic episode the patient is no less in need of a protective moratorium to regain his sense of identity. He may gradually learn to see that his overactivity and restlessness represent a flight from very painful emotions and that it is to his advantage to face and endure the pains of an inner rebirth. Some modern obstetricians recommend that the pains of delivery be not avoided, so that the patient can rally all his energies to join in the natural process. I mentioned before that it is the tragedy of the manic-depressive that he is not able to mourn or to repent sincerely. In melancholia he flees into an orgy of self-torture unconsciously aimed at a magic expiation of guilt feelings; in the manic state he escapes into extraverted distraction from the inward battle and into illusions of expansion.

It is true that the manic-depressive defenses are directed against insight, but that does not mean that the patient lacks the ability of introspection. He can be gradually won over to an attitude of meditation, for an exploratory look into himself, when the therapist conveys to him his conviction that there is a meaning in the process of his illness and that his spastic defenses against the pains only increase them and postpone the solution. Where therapist and patient can settle down for a lengthy exploration into the unconscious causes of the illness, as well as into the unconscious aims of the inner process, this very endeavor kindles some light of hope; and I have pointed out before the organizing and integrating power of hope. It is an uphill struggle because of the patient's flighty defense of extraversion. He cannot be forced to stick to the job, and only the trust in the therapist's serious dedication can prevent the patient's rebellious escape.

It is important to sort out the fantastic guilt feelings and the patient's realistic failure, his lack of authenticity. The patient, due to a persistent archaic relation of identification, suffers from borrowed guilt feelings. He has protested against this identification with a depressed and clinging parent; he may now hate and despise him and deny the identification that unconsciously persists. It is painful to discover how similar he is to his object of contempt. Only a deepened understanding of the parent's tragedy may free the patient from his prejudices, his black-or-white morality, the all-or-none ambivalence in the relation of identification. Forgiveness due to deepened understanding of the object of identification enables him to accept himself too.

The patient's guilt feelings are not so much linked up with his erotic, incestuous wishes. In psychoanalytic terms, the libidinal development of the manic-depressive patient has not reached the level of the Oedipus conflict. Eros is the integrating force of life. The creative experience of love is the great healing agent and it remains healing even in the process of mourning in which the possession of the love object has to be relinquished. The patient feels guilty about his sexual intentions due to the admixture of pregenital possessiveness and exploitativeness that tends to devour or to be devoured, to cling and be captivated. The addiction of identification deprives the partners of their freedom and mobilizes the counterforces of aggression and destruction, rage, resentment, and hatred. The manic-depressive patient is afraid of love, because his freedom is threatened by any commitment—a commitment to an individual as well as to an ideal. Not having reached ego cohesion and a consolidated superego he pursues his ego ideals with the same all-or-none possessiveness as his love objects and loses distance from them. When he loses the faith that he can appropriate his ideal in complete identification he faces the horror of nothingness. The manic-depressive patient is afraid of his self-assertive aggression and of his unskilled destructive impulses. Their positive meaning has to be reinterpreted to the patient as stemming from his healthy fight for freedom and constructive self-love. The tragic tension in human existence between being and not-being, death and rebirth, the tension between yearning for union and the need for uniqueness, can be transcended when the individual ceases to cling to the pseudosecurity of symbiotic identification or does not escape into an isolating, defensive narcissism. The manic-depressive patient shies away from this human tragedy; but it is a relief when he can understand that his fight, the upsurge of rage and hatred, is not a perversity, a pathological absurdity, but an accentuation of the human condition itself.

In the self-cure to which Kierkegaard[32] submitted his melancholia he illustrates the process of mourning and renunciation by the Biblical legend of Abraham willing to sacrifice his only and beloved son Isaac. Kierkegaard suffered himself from the possessive overidentification with a melancholic father. In Kierkegaard's interpretation of the Biblical story, Abraham achieves in his most personal, not socially sanctioned, understanding of the will of God the "infinite movement of renunciation," the leap into nothingness, because his sacrifice extinguishes his rational hopes for the future, but in achieving this renunciation he reaches a higher level of love *sub specie aeternitatis*. In the infinite movement of faith the son is given back to him, not as a reward for obedience, not in a life after death, but here and now in a new, more meaningful relation that opens the deep sources of trust. The *credo quia absurdum*, the "leap into faith," represent more than a resigned mourning about the hardships of a rationally interpreted reality. The new hope in living springs from the basic trust through which man does not only passively submit to fate, but embraces destiny in a new dedication which unites him with the ground of existence.[33]

[32] S. Kierkegaard, *Furcht und Zittern* (Jena: Eugen Diederichs Verlag, 1923).
[33] It is significant that Kierkegaard chose the legend of Abraham and Isaac to illustrate the double movement of resignation and renewal of faith in the human process of mourning and repentance. The transfer of guilt from father to son gave rise in the Christian dogmatic development to the

The manic-depressive patient in psychotherapy does not have to go through the labor of mourning alone. He goes through the phases of repetition together with the therapist. The transference represents repetition and resistance against change and transformation. In the psychoanalytic treatment of neurosis the development of a transference neurosis is encouraged; it is the core of the treatment, for the transference neurosis recapitulates the emotional development under the observation of a relatively intact ego able to relax in free associations and assisted by the interpretations of the analyst. Conversely, the manic-depressive patient has a less intact ego. He is mostly too anxious to relax in free associations. He has too little distance from himself and from the participant observer to engage in much observing and he is anxious to identify himself with the therapist and anxious to escape from close identification. There is little of the object relation that allows a full encounter of an "I" and a "You." The patient projects the images of positive and negative identification on the therapist; he sees in him a savior, a magic helper, a demon, or a useless bystander. The psychotherapist therefore cannot passively wait for the development of a transference neurosis and he cannot hide in an unreachable neutrality. He has to be there with his personality fully present, asking pertinent questions to elucidate the patient's past and present situation. He tries to penetrate the patient's armor of conventionality. He does not avoid the question "guilty-not guilty" about which the patient ruminates monotonously, but he questions the competence of the court of justice before which the patient argues this question. The patient's court of justice is a sick conscience, sickened by the precocious assumption of an omnipotent parental role in childhood. The therapist accompanies the patient through the painful process of re-evaluation of values. But the therapist is not the judge, nor does he stem the patient's repressed rage of accusations against whoever or whatever the patient has lost. He understands his rage against fate, but he does not lose time in sentimental sympathy; he demonstrates the repetition in the patient's significant relations and the repetition that takes place here and now in

---

concept of "original or hereditary sin" and the concept of expiation of sin through the son's sacrifice (crucifixion). The Jewish Covenant between God and man, which originated in the legend of Isaac's sacrifice, introduced the rite of circumcision, the symbol of submission of sexual desire and of human selfish desire in general to the broader aspects of procreation. The spirit of procreation in the literal and sublimated sense gives the repentant mourner hopes and meaningful goals to live for, after he has given up the narrow self-seeking goals in the labor of mourning and repentance.

•

the relation to the therapist, the lack of distance, the exalted expectations which cannot stand the test of reality, and his horror of desertion from which he recoils. He also shows the patient how he provokes this desertion again and again.

There is some degree of identification taking place in every transference, particularly in that of a deeply regressed melancholic patient; he uses the therapist transiently as a "parasitic superego." But the psychotherapist of a depressed patient does not foster this transference; he interprets the transference, wherever it shows up, he works toward the goal of making himself superfluous, encouraging the patient to use his own judgment, to find his own values, and to recognize where his narcissistic defenses, his overweaning arrogance, hidden behind hypocritical humility, make him truly guilty. This arrogance reveals itself blatantly in manic episodes. The therapist does not become impatient with the patient's repeated relapses into infantilism and clinging dependency; the child in man is after all his most promising asset. The patient has to run backwards to gather momentum for a better leap. What Kierkegaard called the "leap into faith" frees the individual from the addiction to security and opens the potentialities of a self-transcending, creative encounter. The patient's trust in himself can only be gained through a better understanding of himself, of his struggle for freedom and authenticity. This trust in himself goes hand in hand with a trust in mutuality: an acceptance of the boundaries of the "I" and the "You," and an ability to grant each other the freedom of spontaneity.

The working through the transference represents a long struggle, until the manic-depressive patient rediscovers the sources of basic trust. The psychotherapist should have all the qualities of an unanxious, responsive mother who gives her child as much protection as he needs and enough freedom to experiment and develop his potentialities. That implies that the psychotherapist should be able to trust his patient's trend toward recovery. This trust is put to a hard test. The patient's tendency to give up, to let himself die, his escape from facing his loss, his true guilt, his horror of desertion sometimes elicit the countertransference of discouragement in the therapist. When the therapist becomes discouraged, there is no use denying it for the sensitive patient will feel it. The therapist is exposed to a barrage of contaminating anxieties. This holds particularly true for states of involutional melancholia, when the patient has lost the hope for a meaningful future. When the therapist accepts the responsibilities of treating a manic-depressive patient, he asks himself whether he is able to accept the risks of the work. If his self-esteem is dependent on proving his therapeutic success, he had better refuse the job and save the patient from a repetition of his desolate experience of being deserted. He himself must have had a good insight into the despair which surrounds a human existence with the horror of nothingness. But he should also be removed from the fashionable wallowing in false, masochistic despair which has become a defensive habit among the generation of beatniks and "angry young men" who avoid the real despair in the atomic age in literary productions of gloom. Since the manic-depressive patient is the victim of self-deception and illusions in his interpersonal relations, the psychotherapist should be able to encounter him with simple, straightforward honesty. He has to watch the pulse of his countertransference, being alerted to the tendency to become identified with the patient, or defensive against his clinging dependency.

Some psychotherapists[34] have recommended provoking the depressed patient into outbreaks of anger and rage to stave off the dangers of self-punishment by which the patient turns the rage against himself. Outbreaks of rage may become inevitable and the therapist, being human, cannot help at times being provoked into anger himself. Such clashes are not fatal, they may even clear the air. But an artificial provocation does not seem necessary to me, because it interferes with the immediate honesty of the emotional exchange. When an explosion of anger occurs, it is only useful if the therapist keeps his head sufficiently above water to explore and interpret the emotional exchange thoroughly from the angle of both transference and countertransference.

The psychoanalyst should on the whole remain receptive, listening, and observing with wide-open attention, not with the narrowly focused attention of a policeman who is on the trigger to jump at the next danger signal. The patient's own narrow, defensive attention is contagious; he is alerted and tends to alert the partner to his own forecasts of gloom. The analyst's hovering, wide-open attention does not recoil from facing and discussing all potential dangers that the patient's imagination brings up with horror. These dangers touch on murderous impulses, death, annihilation, all forms of nonbeing which the patient tries desperately to avoid. The calmness, even a mild sense of humor, with which the therapist meditates with the patient about these tragic aspects of living help also to widen the passive attention of the patient

[34] S. Rado, "Psychosomatics of Depression from the Etiological Point of View," *Psychosom. Med.*, 13 (1951), 51-55.

and shift his active energies from emotional protests and upheavals to a more practical rational scrutiny of the evil which he fears to encounter and tries to deny. But the calmness of the therapist has to be genuine, otherwise it carries no conviction. Since emulation plays an important role in the treatment of the manic-depressive patient, it is desirable that the therapist be free from defensive egocentricity and from prejudice against the heightened egocentricity in the patient. The therapist meets the patient's intense need for close symbiotic identification with generous detachment. It becomes clear in the treatment that maintaining distance and perspective allows an encounter that is free from ambivalence, from exaggerated hopes and fears, and provides the emotionally overstimulated patient with a clear, fresh air to breathe—an atmosphere in which there is a good chance to find himself, his own identity. It is important that the therapist is free to express his own identity in which there is a harmonious collaboration of active and passive, masculine and feminine potentialities, but this harmony cannot be preached. It is enough that the patient be exposed to the nonverbal self-expression of the therapist's personality. The most important factors of the therapeutic process cannot be put into the rational terms of a teachable technique, for they depend on the total personality of the therapist, on his ability to understand clearly the patient's total personality, on his realistic visualization of the patient's past as well as his future and his capacity to discover the patient's repressed resources that open up a new hopeful meaning of his existence.

SUMMARY

This study has pursued the psychogenetic origins of manic-depressive illness to a loss of basic trust and its replacement by a prolonged symbiotic identification with a parent who has been depressed and distrustful of his parental function and who clings to the favored child for vicarious gratification or salvation from his own frustration. The patient has not reached the ego strength able to endure and transcend frustration. His interpersonal relations as well as the relation to his shifting ego ideals lack the respect of distance; they are characterized by the all-or-none demands of a defensive narcissism and by the bid for illusory omnipotence. The patient succumbs periodically to the hopelessness of defeat or flight from facing his despair. His episodes of sickness indicate the need for a moratorium to overcome the deceptive dependency on external approval, to work through the labor of mourning which is simultaneously a labor of repentance. Psychotherapy can help the patient in providing such a moratorium for him in a more realistic re-evaluation of values, sorting out the false guilt feelings that result from overweaning self-idealization. In accepting his boundaries and his real losses the patient may become able to turn from despair of meaninglessness to a renewal of basic trust in his authentic existence.

INDEX

M

McGhie, A., 235n.
Mailer, Norman, 291n.
manic-depressive psychosis, 146, 147, 349-376
marasmus, 19
Masserman, J., 239n.
maternal deprivation; *see* deprivation
May, R., 197n.
Mead, G. H., 295, 296, 298
mechanisms; *see* dynamic mechanisms; formal mechanisms
mechanistic theory, 12
melancholia, 124, 144, 145, 146, 147, 352, 353-355, 356, 359, 369, 373
Meng, H., 237n.
Menninger, K., 308
Menninger, K., and W. C., 4
"mental image," 50, 52, 53, 64-65
Meth, J., 83n.
methodology, 149
Miller, S., 230n.
Milner, P., 295n.
mind-bind concept, 202-204
Minkowski, E., 5
monadic framework, 318
Moreno, J., 239n., 308n.
mother(s)
   role of, 4
   of schizophrenics, 152-160, 319
mother complex, 94, 96-97, 101, 107-112
mother image, 109-112
mother problem, 100-101
mother symbolism, 113
mother transference, 256-284
motherliness, 79
mourning, 352, 354-355, 359, 371, 372
multiple therapy, 11
Murray, H. A., 75n.
mute clinical phase, 64

N

Nacht, S., 254n.
"nadir," 51, 52, 53, 54, 55-56, 57, 64, 65
narcissism, 358, 375
narcissistic neuroses, 368
naturalness, 346
need symbols, 150
negativism, 30, 35
Neumann, E., 99n., 100n., 111n.
neurotic(s), 8
nonexploiting solidarity, 333-337, 338
nonverbal acts, 75
nonverbal communication, 34
normal behavior, 44
Nothingness, 177-178, 185, 197, 198, 199, 206, 207
nothingness, experience of, 293-294

O

obsessional behavior, 29
obsessional preoccupations, 27, 28
obsessional substitutions, 30
obsessive-compulsive behavior, 49
obsessive-compulsive psychoneurosis, 45, 47
Oedipal dynamics, 159, 160, 162
Oedipal tendencies, 135
Oedipus complex, 113-114
Oedipus conflict, 361, 363, 364, 370
Olds, J., 295n.
omnipotence, 179, 361, 375
ontology, 5
oral frustration, 145
organization, levels of, 50, 53, 57, 58, 63, 65
orientation, 61
other-directedness, 346

P

paleologic thinking, 83
panic, 10, 21, 23, 30, 31, 72-74